All the best wishes

Adrianne Roy x.

Do You Know Who I Am?

Adrianne Roy

Hiren

Hiren Publishing 2010

ISBN 978-0-9567245-0-2

Typeset by Ben Cracknell Studios
Printed and bound in Great Britain
by TJ International, Padstow, Cornwall.

Hiren Publishing
Rorkes Drift
Bulls Cross Ride
Hertfordshire
EN7 5HS

Dedication

To my Mum who is my inspiration.
One in a million.

To my Dad who would have been so proud – RIP

To my son Chris, my Hero. I love you.

Acknowledgements

Many people were involved in the production of this book and deserve a massive Thank you;

Zelia Hagisavva, for typing up my scribbled notes from my illegible writing, and for all her constructive comments. Paul Yiannoullou, for taking time out from his busy schedule to graphically design the village and for putting up with my indecisiveness. Yolanda Deferranti, for her talent and invaluable time in designing the cover. Gary Wood, for his fabulous comic illustration. Leila Barbaro for taking such an amazing photograph and Negin Erfani for making me up to look so good. Flore Yiannoullou, for her Greek translation, *Efharisto*, (Thank you). My editor, Lorna Read, for her valuable advice and comments. My amazing copy editor, Dawn Booth for the most tedious part of the process full stop exclamation mark. My proof readers who read the manuscript at various stages and gave me constructive comments and encouragement; Sandra Yiannoullou, Helen Yiannoullou, Anna Papa, Penny Tomazou and especially my final proof reader, Lesley Dickinson for turning my manuscript into a finished product.

To my uncle Anastasis, Aunty Theognosia and Aunty Maria for providing me with the unforgettable stories of the early years.

Particular thanks go to my publishing consultant, Ian Sherratt who guided me through the process and made everything happen.

Thank you to my dear friends and family, who I have neglected somewhat throughout this process, for your encouragement and support – you know who you are.

And finally a huge Thank you to my Mum and Dad for struggling so hard to get me where I am today.

CHAPTER 1

The Village

"I told you, I am Greek and I'm built that way and there is not a damn thing I can do about it," said Annie.

"Why don't you, just for once, stop being argumentative and let me do my job," said Doctor Michael.

"Okay, okay, keep your hair on."

"Right. As I said to you earlier, for an individual to know who they are in life, they must first go back to their roots to see where they came from, because it is the experiences that they gain in life, and the influences of the people that come into their lives that determine who they become. So please, can we start again from the beginning?" said Doctor Michael.

"All right. Well, I suppose my roots start with my mother Kika, who was born in 1931 in a small, mountainous village in Cyprus called Eptakomi. Legend has it that a dragon once lived in the mountain there and so the mountain was named "Thrakontas" after the dragon. My mother was the youngest of six children, three boys and three girls and so I guess, that's where the story begins …"

During a victorious card game in the village *kafeneion* (café), and after a few glasses of *zivania* (Raki), Vasili said to his best friend Savva: "What do you think about us marrying off our eldest children to each other so that we can *simpetherepsoumen* (become in-laws)?"

"What a great idea my friend," said Savva. They shook hands to congratulate each other for their children's betrothal and toasted the contract with another shot of *zivania* before they rushed to their respective homes to break the news to the unsuspecting Stavros and Kaliopi.

"Stavros, I have some good news. You are marrying Kaliopi," Vasili said to his eldest son.

"What? But Dad, I'm only eighteen," said Stavros.

"Exactly. It is time for you to get married and have a family of your own. I had two children by the time I was your age."

In those days, it was understood that the parents picked the marriage partners for their offspring, whether they liked it or not, and this marriage arrangement was called *proxenia.*

A wedding was a happy and exciting occasion, not only for the respective families but also for the whole village, as it was a rare opportunity for the villagers to let their hair down and celebrate with music, dancing and drinking. Apart from the obligatory Sunday church service, or the occasional *panayiri* (religious festival), at Christmas and Easter, a wedding was the only social event for the villagers and Vasili's youngest son Nicholas couldn't wait to spread the news.

"There's going to be a wedding! There's going to be a wedding!" shouted young Nicholas, as he charged through the village on the donkey.

The village church plaza was the venue for the wedding reception and the whole village attended as guests.

The sound of traditional Greek folk songs played by the village fiddler bellowed through the village as the guests danced on tables with glasses on their heads, smashed plates and got drunk. Kaliopi was paraded through the plaza on a mattress covered in rose petals to symbolise her purity, while the groom was slapped on the back by the *koumparous* (best men) to symbolise the new burden of responsibility he had taken on.

The mischievous ten-year-old Nicholas, with his equally mischievous eight-year-old sister, Marika, got drunk on Cyprus brandy which they had secretly hidden under one of the tables and were sent home by their mother, Maria, to sleep it off before Vasili got a whiff of their intoxication. The wedding went on into the early hours of the morning, until the last remaining drunken guests went home.

As the sun rose over Thrakontas mountain, the village woke to the sound of the cockerel and, with the excitement of the wedding over, the village chores resumed again.

Vasili and Maria were poor farmers. Maria came from a wealthy family of landowners but she fell in love with Vasili who was a *mistarkos* (poor slave boy) and her family disowned her when they eloped and married against her parents' wishes. Together with their six children they lived in a small clay house built with Vasili's bare hands and which he painted white to reflect the hot summer sun.

It only had two rooms: a living room where everyone lived and a separate bedroom where they all slept. There was one bed for the parents, one bed for the boys and one for the girls. Being the youngest and smallest child, Kika always got pushed off the bed and ended up sleeping on the stone floor with only a folded tea-towel as a pillow.

There was no bathroom, just a *mastrapan* (tin can) which was used for bathing and an outside hut with a hole in the ground used as a toilet, with another *mastrapan* filled with water for flushing. Water was scarce in the scorching summer months, so flushing was a luxury, as was toilet paper, so they had to use whatever was handy to wipe their bottoms: leaves, hay, sometimes even large stones. Suffice to say, a clothes peg for the nose and Sudacrem for the bum would not have gone amiss!

Vasili was a large, strong man built like an ox, with a violent temper to go with it. He had a huge moustache which he curled up at the corners and wore a traditional *vraka* costume – a large black piece of material wrapped around the lower regions between the legs and tied on the hip, rather like a saggy nappy. The whole village feared Vasili when he was annoyed and if they heard him coming, they ran into their houses and closed the shutters to avoid incurring his wrath. He did not tolerate injustice and was a bull in a china shop if he felt aggrieved and didn't care who got in his way. But deep down he was a gentle giant who protected his family and the village.

Maria, on the other hand, was a very petite, quietly spoken, placid lady. She wore traditional Cypriot costume of long floral tunic hiding her body, a white apron and a *mandili* (head scarf) covering her hair. She only spoke when she was spoken to and lived solely to look after her husband and children.

The whole family had to work the land to get food on the table. The two eldest children, Stavros and Dimitra, were big and strong, and helped Vasili carry out the hard labour of digging the soil by hand, as there was no plant and machinery back then.

"It's always us that have to do all the work," Stavros said to his sister. "That lazy Marika and Nicholas always get away with doing nothing. I hate being the eldest."

The tasks were endless and ranged from breeding livestock to harvesting crops. Kika's job was to stand on the flat roof like a scarecrow to swat the flies and keep the birds away from the *sitari* (drying wheat). Imagine a five-year-old being allowed on a flat roof nowadays!

"Father, I'm bored now," said Kika after five minutes. "Can I come down and play?"

"Yes, my precious," replied Vasili. "Go and get that lazy sister of yours to take over." As the baby of the family Kika was Vasili's favourite and nobody was allowed to upset his little princess without incurring his wrath.

Fruits, berries and seasonal vegetables had to be picked, along with olives to make oil, not only for the family consumption but for selling, to raise a few pennies.

Some crops were easy to harvest for the young siblings but it was harder to pick the *deratcha* (carobs) off the trees, as the branches were high and the *deratcha* could not be reached except with the aid of Vasili's home-made walking stick. It was a job for the two youngest sons, Loucas and Nicholas, to climb the trees and knock them off for their sisters to collect in their aprons and take back to Maria, who started the long process of making syrup and jam.

Vasili's youngest son, Nicholas, was a *zizanion* (mischievious), and he loved to wind up his younger sisters by aiming the branches so that the hard black *deratcha* would fall on their heads. He found it hysterical to hear a screech of "Ouch!" from Kika, until one day one fell on Vasili's head by mistake.

"Oops, oh shit," said Nicholas.

Vasili pulled him off the tree by his ear and spanked him as the girls looked on and chuckled. "That will teach you to try and hurt your sisters."

Nicholas was fearless and getting a spanking from his father did not stop him from misbehaving. He continued to run riot and steal eggs from the chicken coop and eat them raw until he was sick, just so that he wouldn't have to share them with his siblings.

The priority for everyone was to look after the family livelihood, which consisted of six goats, two dozen chickens, three sheep, a couple of cows and three donkeys. The donkeys were used for pulling the ploughs but also doubled up as the family's transport. One of the donkeys was Kika's pet, which she named Yarou, meaning "donkey", and she rode her with pride around the village and to the tip of Thrakontas so that she could watch the sea across the horizon. This was her favourite spot, the place where she went with her beloved Yarou to get her away from the hard labour.

"Don't worry, Yarou," Kika said, "I won't let them tire you out. We will hide here until the sun goes down." Once, she rode Yarou fifty kilometres, all the way to Apostolos Andreas Church to kiss the icon of St Andrew and pray for health and prosperity ... Vasili sent a search party to find her.

Whilst Vasili and his offspring worked on the land, Maria cooked for her growing family. She baked bread twice a week in her large, round, clay-built *fourni* (oven), baking twenty-two loaves each time because bread was the family's primary source of food. When the bread first came out of the oven, the children anxiously gathered around to eat it piping hot with dripping pre-made from pigs' fat, saved by Maria until it solidified into a thick white mass and spread like butter with a little salt and pepper. Nothing went to waste.

Meat was scarce and expensive, so it was only served once a year, usually at Easter when two whole chickens were slaughtered and barbequed on a home-made wooden spit or baked in the *fourni*. But when Kaliopi announced that she was pregnant, Vasili shouted "Slaughter the chickens and a lamb and go get my *Simbetherous* (in-laws) to celebrate this momentous occasion."

All the family mucked in to build another room for the newlyweds and the pending new baby. It is tradition in the Greek Cypriot culture for the firstborn son to be named after the groom's father and, nine months later, Vasili Junior was born, much to the seniors' delight.

Dimitra was Vasilis's oldest daughter and just turned sixteen. There was an air of excitement when Vasili came home from the *kafeneion* and said "Dimitra, get ready. A boy called Yiasoumi from Patriki is coming round with his parents and his grandparents to meet you."

"What for?" asked Dimitra.

"For *proxenia*," he said.

"But who is he? I don't even know him!"

"I don't know him either but his dad has got a *horafi* (field).

As they sat on opposite sides of the room, Dimitra and Yiasoumi watched as the priest arrived to draft a *prikosimfono*: a type of prenuptial dowry agreement which, in effect, matched the assets brought into the marriage and, was then blessed by the priest. If a girl acquired a "bad reputation" the bargaining power of a potential husband was enormously increased, allowing him the chance to make extortionate demands for property settlements. But Vasili was very proud to announce that Dimitra was a virgin, implying that he had managed to control his family well.

"Well," said Vasili to Yiasoumi's father, Kyriakos, "what are you going to give for my daughter's hand in marriage?"

"I will give my *horafi* consisting of one acre full of olive trees and a *lefkaritiko* tablecloth (made in Lefkara village) crocheted by my great-grandmother in 1879. What will you give?" asked Kyriakos.

"I will give four hand-crocheted *petsetakia* (doilies), a cow, a goat, a sheep and a bedspread woven by my dear wife, Maria."

Dimitra and Yiasoumi then watched as both their fathers stood up as soon as the document was signed, shook hands and passionately hugged and tapped each other on the back with pride, as both mothers got emotional.

"Let's drink some *zivania* to celebrate, *simpethere*," said Vasili. And, to seal the deal, Yiasoumi's grandmother was sent back to Patriki on a donkey to slaughter three chickens to feed both families, whilst Yiasoumi and Dimitra were left alone together to get to know each other, still sitting on opposite sides of the room.

"There's going to be a wedding! There's going to be a wedding. Dimitra and Yiasoumi are getting married!" yelled Nicholas riding on the back of the donkey.

As the village prepared for another wedding, Nicholas and Marika hid a bottle of Metaxa brandy in the chicken coop – just in case they got sent home early again by Maria. A merry night was had by all and, as the sun rose over Thrakontas Mountain and the cockerel crowed, the village chores began again. Baby Anastasis was soon to become the new addition to Vasili's family.

CHAPTER 2

The Dream

As the cockerel crowed "cock-a-doodle-do" throughout the years, everyone grew older. Kika was now fifteen and had developed into a beautiful, voluptuous young woman. Vasili was struggling to make ends meet, especially with the extra mouths to feed. So one Sunday afternoon, after church he rounded up the family.

"I need you boys to go and find work in the larger neighbouring villages of Patriki and Trikomo to help bring money in."

"But father, none of us are educated or qualified to do anything except for farm labouring," said Louca, Vasili's second-born son.

"You have to find anything you can, son. I'm relying on you to help your brothers find work to support this family."

School was not compulsory then, as most children were needed to help their parents on the land. In any event, very few girls attended school as it was understood that a woman's destiny was to get married and have a family at an early age before she developed sexual thoughts, and as all teachers were male most parents were unwilling to allow their daughters to stay on at school beyond eight or nine to avoid sexual corruption. The school building was a small, clay-built hut, typical of the rest of the houses in the village. There were a few wooden desks which had to be shared by three students and each child had a black slate board and a piece of white chalk to write with. There were no books to read and the part-time teacher was a parent who travelled on a donkey from Trikomo to teach. Kika and Marika, being the youngest, were occasionally sent to school if they were not needed on the land, but they were soon expelled for Kika's poor attendance and for Marika's disruptive behaviour. So, with no education behind them, the siblings were not the brightest sparks in the box, with the exception of the second son, Louca, who was adventurous and very ambitious.

At twenty-two he was very hard-working and very capable. He was brighter than the rest of his siblings and was the only one that was over five feet tall. He used to roam the surrounding villages for any scraps of work that he could find and had a huge curiosity for adventure. It was while he was on one of his rounds, in the next village of Komi Kebir, that he bumped into his friend Shailos, who was a fisherman, who told him: "I saved some money from selling fish and I have bought myself a one-way ticket on a ship sailing to England."

"What? How? Why?" asked Louca, completely taken aback.

"I heard from some sailors that the prime minister of England, Mr Winston Churchill, is inviting people from Commonwealth countries to go to England to help reconstruct London, after the war destroyed large parts of it."

Louca did not understand what that meant, exactly, but he'd always had dreams of grandeur and decided at that moment that he wanted to go with the fisherman to London. The ship was sailing in two months' time and he wanted to be on it.

He waited until that evening over dinner to announce to the family his intentions of sailing to England. The news nearly gave Maria a heart attack. So as not to distress his wife any further, Vasili forbade Louca to travel to England.

"Please father. I will send money back every month to help with the family's financial position," begged Louca.

"If you promise to stay only for a couple of years and then come back, I will give you my blessing."

"I promise father."

Once Louca had agreed, Vasili gave Louca's travel plan his

blessing – much to Maria's heartbreak. A goat and the proceeds of half the year's olive crop were used to raise the money for the ticket and, after an emotional farewell from the family and the villagers, Louca was on his way to England.

After her son had sailed, Maria was sick with worry and it was over a month before a letter was received from Louca, saying that he had arrived safely and was living in London with a cousin called Pavlos, who had travelled to London a few months earlier. The letter went on to say that Louca had a job in a restaurant as a plate washer. A one-pound note was attached to the letter with a piece of candle-wax. Everyone got excited and word soon got around the village that Vasili's son was rich, having sent a whole pound!

The letter seemed to spark off an infectious eagerness from other villagers to sail to England to seek their fortune: one of them being Vasili's fifth child, Marika. She was the second youngest child and, like her brother Nicholas, very mischievous. As a child, she had spent all her time running around the village causing havoc, trying not to do any chores. She was a pretty, fair-haired, skinny girl, who used to run very fast up the Thrakontas mountain, usually to get way from some pursuing adults after she had provoked them. The villagers nicknamed her *vourou* (runner), because she ran like a greyhound and nobody could catch her. She was very lazy and persistently made excuses to try and get the older siblings to do her chores and, when she didn't get her way, she bullied the younger children in the village to take out her frustration. She particularly picked on her cousin, Antoni, who was five years her junior.

Marika, who grew to be only four feet eleven inches, battered him for years until he towered over her and, during one of her bullying tantrums, she tried to smack Antoni, but this time he picked her up by her hair, swung her to the floor and gave her a battering she never forgot.

"That," he said, "was for all those times you beat me black and blue," and that was the last time she ever laid hands on him.

Once Marika had lost her status as a bully, she became bored with village life. She was now twenty had no friends and all attempts to marry her off were unsuccessful, as all the eligible young men in the village were scared of her.

A second letter was received from Louca. This one told the family about how excited he was that he had seen the royal wedding of Princess Elizabeth and Philipo of Greece and saw King George VI with Queen Elizabeth on the balcony. He went on to say that he was really looking forward to seeing the Olympic Games in London in the summer. That was enough to make Marika decide that she wanted to go to London.

"Please, father, I want to go to London to see the King and the Olympics," she pleaded and, after many strops and tantrums, Vasili agreed that she could go to England, but only on the condition that she took Kika with her so that she didn't travel alone.

Marika was delighted and danced with joy, but poor Kika was devastated.

"No, father, please. All my friends are here and I am very happy where I am," she cried. She thought that she was Vasili's favourite, so she was surprised that he would let her go.

Kika cried for days, hoping that her father would change his mind, but he didn't. Two goats were sold to buy the one-way tickets for the ship that was leaving Limassol docks in a few months' time.

CHAPTER 3

The Journey

It was November 1948 when seventeen-year-old Kika boarded *The Phillpo Grimani* ship with her twenty-one-year-old sister, Marika, sailing for Dover, England. Kiki was a five-feet-tall, big-busted, beautiful young woman, with a bad temper like her father, but she found herself scared and was already missing home. She was seasick and cried for most of the journey, while Marika stropped the whole way about having missed the Olympic Games. On-board ship, she had never seen so much food in her life and stuffed herself until she was sick. She particularly took a liking to an Athenian dish called *pastitio*, made with macaroni and mincemeat with a white sauce on top, which Marika called *makaronia tou fournou* (macaroni in the oven).

The ship was full of young Cypriots who had left their homeland in search of a better life. They spent their time playing backgammon and singing Greek songs, accompanied by a harmonica and violin which two young men brought with them on the ship. The journey to Dover took two weeks, setting off from Limassol, sailing through Beirut to Alexandria, Pireaus and finally to Marseilles in France. At Marseilles, the ship anchored, and the anxious Kika and Marika followed the guides onto a train to Paris, changed at Paris for Calais and boarded another boat until it finally reached England.

As the boat dropped its anchor in Dover, Louca was there waiting at the dock to greet them. There was an emotional reunion when the sisters saw their brother waving to them, as they tried to come to terms with England's exceptionally bitter winter of 1948. Louca had anticipated that his sisters would be affected by the climate change and he presented them with a thick coat and a pair of woolly gloves apiece, which he purchased from the Salvation Army.

As Kika put on her coat she said tearfully, "This is the best present that I have ever had."

Marika merely commented that she did not like the colour. "I would have preferred one like that," she said, pointing to a lady wearing a brown fur coat.

Louca gave her a dirty look and said, "I can see you haven't changed much, have you?"

The journey to London Victoria took over two hours by train. It started to get dark and for the final part of the journey Louca and his sisters took a tram to Pavlos' house, which was going to be their new home. Kika was fascinated by her surroundings and her eyes were glued to the tram window, taking it all in, but Marika fell asleep and started to snore. There was still evidence of ruins and damage from the Blitz, but the reconstruction of London was well underway. Kika saw from the window the huge structures that were to become schools, hospitals and homes, the size of which she had never seen before. They were a far cry from the small clay houses of Eptakomi.

She sniffed the air and commented that she could smell smoke.

"It is the coal from the fires that people burnt to keep warm," Louca explained. Her curiosity then turned to a yellow glow that caught her attention as the tram rattled its way over the uneven cobbled streets to Islington. "Why is London so orange?" she asked.

Louca laughed. "It is the yellow sodium street lamps that turn the sky orange but do little to light up the streets," he explained. Kika was fascinated and burst out laughing when she saw a fat woman squashed into a motorcycle sidecar, bursting out of the window.

Pavlos lived in a three-storey, rented town house on Essex Road. He lived there with his wife, Florou, and their two sons, and she was pregnant with their third child. They lived in two rooms on the third floor of the house and Louca lived in one room on the first floor, to which he had added another bed for his sisters to sleep on. Kika sat on the bed and cried. "I don't like it here. I want to go home. I miss my family and my Yarou." Louca tried to console her.

Another Cypriot man, with his pregnant wife and five children, lived on the ground floor, so living in one house there were fourteen people with two babies on the way. Each family unit cooked for themselves on their individual fireplaces, but they all socialised together every day and all chipped in to carry out the daily chores, including looking after each other's children.

As the sisters familiarised themselves with their new surroundings, Louca was promoted to waiter in the restaurant and was bringing in money to support them all. One of the waiters in the restaurant was a friend of Louca's who had a girlfriend called Anita, who worked in a clothes factory in Mornington Crescent. She happened to mention that her boss had vacancies for finishers and, as soon as Louca heard this, he took the next morning off work to take both his sisters straight to the factory to ask for work.

Having only previously worked as farmers, neither of the girls had any experience in finishing, which entailed sewing the finishing touches of a garment by hand, including things like buttons or fasteners. Manufacturing in London in the late forties was flourishing, especially the rag trade. There was an influx of demand for skilled workers and, coupled with the fact that the Jewish owner, Abraham, liked big breasted women and took a fancy to Kika, he employed both sisters on a salary of three pounds a week.

Anita took them both under her wing and, within a few days, Kika caught on like an expert finisher. She was very hardworking and this was soon noticed by Abraham, who called her into his office one Friday afternoon.

"Kika, I am so impressed with your hard work and dedication, that I am taking you off of salary and putting you on piece work to give you more incentive," he said. "Also, I am seating you nearer a heater, so you can keep warm."

Kika was delighted that she was able to earn more money but Marika, on the other hand, was a slowcoach and took longer to master the art of finishing. She preferred to cut off the excess cotton threads that were hanging off the garments, anything that was easy for the lazy Marika who had brought her lazy village ways with her from Cyprus.

In order to compensate for her snail's pace, Kika secretly kept slipping her some of her tickets to mislead Abraham into believing that Marika was quick and valuable to him, ensuring that she never got sacked along with other lazy slowcoach workers in the factory.

Kika became an expert finisher and nobody could match her on her speed and accuracy. Her impeccable work stood out among the rest and every Friday afternoon when Abraham distributed the little brown wage packet (the *fakelouin* as the sisters called it), Kika got more money than most.

Kika learned some basic English and soon mastered all the London bus routes and was always on the go. It was on one of her bus trips that she noticed an advertisement outside a factory in Goodge Street that there was a job for an experienced finisher for six pounds a week: double her existing salary. She stopped off on her way home with one of her dress samples and another Jewish owner called Jacob offered Kika the job on the spot to work evenings and weekends.

Kika was not afraid to work and held down both jobs, unlike her sister who skived so many times from Abraham's factory that he eventually fired her.

Kika got Marika a job in Jacob's factory, having lied to him about her sister being a good worker but she warned Marika "If you dare skive one single day from this job after I stuck my neck out for you, I will personally beat the shit out of you. Do you hear me?"

Marika was a lot older than her sister and very bullish by nature, but Kika was a lot bigger than her and her violent temper was enough to keep Marika in tow. Kika was strong, physically as well as mentally, and from being the baby of the family she was slowly becoming the rock.

Having two jobs meant Kika was making enough money to buy food for the household, send money to her parents and still have enough money left over to save. The new-found money from his youngest daughter inspired Vasili to want to send Nicholas to England to make something of himself and keep him out of trouble.

Nicholas was now twenty-five, five-feet-nothing, skinny and still considered himself a bit of a *munga* (dude). He was a womaniser; a *kafkajis* (troublemaker), always looking for fights and was a constant nuisance. His irresponsible childish behaviour continually landed him in trouble with the local police, and one such time culminated in him getting a one-year prison sentence for attempting to shoot a young woman called Maroullou who refused to have sex with him. Her rejection of him dented his ego and, after drinking a whole bottle of whisky and getting totally wasted, he took Vasili's hunting gun and set off to shoot her. Luckily he was intercepted by Maroullou's brother who called the police. Nicholas said to the judge, in his defence, "That floozy has slept with every man in the village, so why couldn't she sleep with me?"

After he finished his stint in prison, Vasili made an announcement to his son. "*Re Mane*! (You idiot!), I am sending you to England *perki na valeis noun* (to hopefully knock some sense into you)."

Nicholas was to set sail two months later with his brother-in-law Yiasoumi, who was struggling to make ends meet on the farm and decided to travel to England to make money to send home to his wife Dimitra and baby Anastasis, while at the same time keeping an eye on Nicholas. Vasili was heartbroken that he had to sell Kika's beloved donkey, Yarou, to be able to buy them the one-way ticket to England.

Back in London Kika had saved some money and had her heart set on buying a house of her own. She was eternally grateful and obligated to Pavlos and Florou, who was now pregnant with her fifth child, and it was time for the siblings to move out to give them more space and privacy to raise their growing family.

It just so happened that around that time Louca had started dating an Irish girl called Mona who was renting a house in Hackney. Louca stayed over at hers on a regular basis and it was while he was there one night that he happened to find out that the owner of the house was in financial difficulty and looking to sell the house. Louca persuaded him to sell the house to him for six hundred and fifty pounds but the owner only agreed to the deal on condition that he bought the house with the sitting tenant in it. Little did the owner know that the tenant was Louca's girlfriend and it turned out to be a bargain for a two-storey, three-up, three-down, terraced house with a hundred-foot garden. It was perfect for all the siblings to live in and a far cry from the cramped room which they had been sharing. Louca and Kika put their savings together and bought the house in Louca's name as it wasn't legal at the time for women to purchase property in their own names.

In October 1951 the siblings moved from Islington into Roding Road, Hackney, just in time for Nicholas and Yiasoumi's arrival on St Dimitrios day. There were eight people living in the house. The tenant occupied two rooms on the first floor with her two children, the sisters shared the front reception room on the ground floor and the boys shared the remaining vacant room upstairs.

The second reception room on the ground floor was used as the family living room, which was rarely used in the winter as it took ages to heat up. The large kitchen to the rear of the house was where all the activity took place: it served as a kitchen, where the sisters cooked for everyone, a dining room, a sitting room and, as there was no bathroom, it also doubled up as a washroom for laundry or for a quick face-and-armpit wash in the huge butler sink before leaving for work.

There was only a cold tap, so all hot water had to be boiled in a metal kettle on the fireplace. Saturday morning was laundry day and the kettle would not stop whistling all day. The washboard came out and Kika would be scrubbing the clothes, while Marika used a wooden spoon to stir them around in the boiling water. Washing machines had not yet been invented and the first launderette did not appear until 1949. There was an outside toilet in the backyard which was fine in the summer but in the winter the siblings kept a *kathiki* (a potty) under their beds so that they didn't have to go outside in the freezing cold and dark.

Most of the time everyone got on well; inevitably friction would sometimes occur between the siblings, but more regularly between Marika and the tenant. Marika was not happy about Louca having a girlfriend upstairs. She thought it was illicit and dirty, and kept calling Mona that *poutana* upstairs. Mona worked as a waitress in a Greek restaurant and knew that *poutana* meant prostitute and hated Marika with a vengeance. The feeling was entirely mutual.

Nicholas and Yiasoumi were struggling to get accustomed to the new English ways of life, and Nicolas brought some of his village ways with him. Instead of flushing toilet paper down the toilet he threw it on the floor like he did in the village.

It all kicked off one night when Louca came home after a long shift at work to find used toilet paper full of excrement all over the toilet floor. Louca was fuming as he cringingly picked up the paper off the floor and flushed it down the toilet. He was anxious to find out who the culprit was, but suspected that Nicholas and Yiasoumi would deny it if confronted. So, being the brightest of the siblings, he walked back into the house where the others were all sitting and craftily said:

"What idiot is putting the toilet paper down the pan and blocking the toilet?" Before he could finish his sentence

Nicholas proudly blurted out all smug: "It wasn't me, I throw the paper on the floor!"

"You *ampalate* (dirty layabout)," shouted Louca. "Do you think I am your shit cleaner? You're not in the village now, you donkey. Haven't you noticed that we don't have holes in the ground here? If I find any more shit on the floor I will rub your ugly face in it and flush your head down the toilet, *katalaves?* (do you understand?)"

"Yes," said Nicholas and he never threw the toilet paper on the floor again but he looked at Marika and asked, "I don't have an ugly face, do I?"

Next morning Louca took Nicholas and Yiasoumi to a restaurant in Warren Street which was managed by a friend and persuaded him to take them on as plate washers for five a week. Yiasoumi was delighted that he was finally earning money for his family and hoped that the job would keep Nicholas out of trouble.

Every Saturday night the siblings and Yiasoumi would all go together to the Hackney public baths to have a bath. They paid a shilling each and got a ticket number with a towel and a small bar of soap. They sat on a wooden bench in a crowded waiting room, shifting up one place as the numbers were called and wait for their turn to make the journey down the long steamy corridor to their cubicle.

It sounded like Niagara Falls as water gushed out from giant brass outlets until they called the attendant to turn off the water from an outside stop cock. If they wanted a hot or cold top up they had to call out their number and what they required. This bit was the highlight of Nicholas' and Marika's day. They both laughed their heads off as Nicholas called out "cold water number 3" and some unsuspecting old guy got freezing cold water gushing over him and started effing and blinding over the wall. Louca shouted at them in Greek over the wall "I'm going to batter you both when we get home," but they just couldn't stop laughing. The months rolled by and the siblings and brother-in-law Yiasoumi were settling into English life.

CHAPTER 4

The Settlement

London in the 1950s was booming but the East End had been the place worst hit by the Blitz and there were still large areas of ruins that were left derelict. Hackney was massively deprived and it was this area that gave rise to gangsters such as the Krays but the siblings created their own gang and called themselves "The Munges," which was Nicholas' idea.

Nothing fazed them, not even the "Great Smog" that blighted London for five days from 5 December 1952, caused by a combination of freezing temperatures and the mix of fog and smoke from industrial flues and domestic coal fires. Hackney was one of the worst affected areas as it had the highest density of factory smokestacks and domestic chimney pots. Low levels of visibility meant that people could not see further than a few feet in front of them, which led to road accidents and, not wanting to miss an opportunity, Nicholas pretended to walk into a lamppost so that he could make a bogus personal injury claim from Hackney Council but soon gave up when he couldn't read English to fill in the claim form and so had given himself a black eye for nothing.

Roads were brought almost to a standstill as buses had to be suspended. This was great news for Marika as it meant she could skive off work without being reprimanded, but she pushed her luck too far by skiving off for two weeks and got a written warning from Jacob.

Food rationing was still in effect and there wasn't enough meat, bacon, butter or sugar to go around.

Frozen foods were non-existent because no-one had a freezer and hardly anyone had a refrigerator. Supermarkets were yet to make an appearance and there just wasn't the variety of tinned food in the local shops. But this did not deter the sisters from cooking three square meals a day: rationing or no rationing.

Being experienced farmers they were quick to convert the hundred-foot garden into a family allotment, where they grew enough vegetables to feed an army. Kika was proud of her artichokes and *kouloumpres* (Greek radishes). Yiasoumi had constructed a chicken hut and a rabbit pen, and bred chickens and rabbits; while chicken was a luxury in most households, it was plentiful in the "*Munga*" household. On summer Sundays the barbeque would come out and one of the chickens would find itself on the skewer.

One of the neighbours poked her head over the fence when she heard a commotion in the chicken shed, only to catch Yiasoumi at that precise moment pulling the head off a chicken, which ran around the garden until it dropped. The neighbour fainted and her husband had to fetch paramedics to resuscitate her.

Winter Sundays meant that all the food went into the huge pot and was boiled but on rare occasions they would hear a horse and cart, and the cry of "cockles and mussels alive, alive oh" and as a special treat the siblings would buy a few pints of seafood and sit with a pin prizing the cockles and winkles out of their shell and eat them with a loaf of homemade bread.

Kika never missed an opportunity to take a shovel out with her, in case the horse crapped, so she could collect the manure for her allotment. She was also the first one out in the street with her shovel when she heard the milkman or the rag and bone collector call out "any old iron" not giving anyone else a chance to scoop up the *kopri*, as she called it.

Nicholas also never missed an opportunity when Kika's back was turned to dig up some of the *kopri* from Kika's allotment and sell it to neighbours for tuppence a bucketful or sixpence for a wheelbarrow-full. While he was there he would rummage through their dustbins and collect used lemonade bottles, which had a value of one penny when returned to a sweet shop and jam jars which had a return value of one farthing a jar. He was the first original Greek "Del Boy".

And so it was, that the gang were all working hard and earning money – well most of them anyway.

Kika was promoted to supervisor and Louca was promoted to chef. Marika, true to form, was eventually fired by Jacob for arguing with him about her taking a day off to watch the Queen's Coronation. He had kindly given all the staff a few hours off on the morning of the Coronation to watch the procession pass the factory but Marika decided to skive off the rest of the afternoon too. When Jacob questioned her next morning about her absence she gave it the large in front of the other workers and said, "Stick your job, *pushto evreo* (poofy Jew)" and not surprisingly he fired her on the spot and she found herself unemployed, being supported by her brothers and sister.

"That is it," said Louca "I have had enough of your irresponsible, stroppy tantrums and childish outbursts," and packed her off back to Cyprus, kicking and screaming. Unbeknown to her, he had arranged to marry her off to an unsuspecting gullible young man called Frixo who was six years her junior – they were married in Cyprus within a week.

Life in Hackney was a lot more peaceful without Marika around. Louca bought a lease to a café in Green Lanes, Haringey, right near the Haringey dog track. Everyone mucked in to clean it up and kit it out, and helped him out when they could which earned them some extra cash. The café got very busy and, just as Louca was about to employ more staff, Marika unexpectedly turned up on the doorstep with her new young husband in tow and surprised everyone. She was a changed woman, all domesticated and conscientious. Married life appeared to suit her.

Louca employed Marika and Frixo as waiter and waitress,

which surprisingly turned out to be a mutually satisfactory arrangement and Louca was very proud of his sister's metamorphosis.

Just as Marika had finally settled and was starting to pull her weight, Nicholas was abruptly fired from his job. He had threatened to kill the head chef with a meat cleaver and the five-foot-nothing Nicholas chased the six-foot-five-inch chef through the packed restaurant with the raised cleaver in his hand and, in full view of all the customers, shouted "I'm going to slice your head off, you fat Polish poof." The manager had no choice but to sack him on the spot. Louca was furious when he found out from the manager that the argument was about a French waitress fancying the chef instead of Nicholas, and Louca went for Nicholas' throat. "Who the hell do you think you are, Mussolini?" Louca shouted at the top of his voice.

"Just look at you, you are hardly God's gift to women, you little shrimp. You were lucky to get that job and now you have lost a perfectly good job for no reason. So now what you are going to do, you bloody stupid idiot?"

Yiasoumi had to hold Louca back from battering Nicholas, who made things worse for himself by saying. "I am better than Mussolini and I am better than Alexander the Great and I am going to kill that French *poutana* that's what I'm going to do, you just watch me."

Once Louca calmed down he decided that the best place for his younger brother was with him at the café where he could keep an eye on him. He gave him a job as assistant chef for ten pounds a week.

Nicholas was very proud of his new-found status and went round boasting to the customers that he owned the café, especially if the customers were pretty, English, blond girls.

With his first pay packet he bought himself a double-breasted suit and trilby hat, and walked round looking like a miniature Al Capone.

When he wasn't trying to pick up women with his corny chat-up lines, he was at the dog track flashing wads of money he had "borrowed" from the till and pretended to be a rich Greek shipping tycoon. This charade worked as it was there that he met an Italian model called Signora who was five foot ten inches, and a foot taller than him with her heels on. She towered over him but Nicholas was as proud as a peacock of his trophy model girlfriend and he soon moved her into Hackney, lying to her that he was stopping at his sister's house while his mansion in Athens was being renovated.

This new arrangement did not go down well at all with Marika, who did not want a gorgeous model living under the same roof as her husband and was now forced to live with yet "another *poutana*", as she called her. She deliberately started arguments with Signora in the hope that she would leave her brother and more importantly leave the house, but Nicholas continued to date her.

After yet another fierce argument with Marika, Signora told Nicholas out of the blue that her father had died and she had to go to Italy for the funeral. He paid for her ticket to Milan but he never heard from her again. He was heartbroken and wondered what had happened to his sweetheart but later suspected that Marika who was strutting around like a smug peacock, not being able to look Nicholas in the eye had had something to do with Signora's disappearance when he found a clump of Signora's hair in Marika's handbag.

CHAPTER 5

The Conductor

It was 1956, rationing had only recently ended and people were starting to buy things they couldn't before. Pounds, shillings and pence were still in effect and noise levels increased as more radio and television technology was introduced into homes.

There were no fast-food outlets but tea shops and fish and chip shops were popping up everywhere. This period gave rise to the first solid teenage subculture in the form of the Teddy boys with their greased-back quiff hairdos, tight drainpipes and blue-suede shoes, influenced by a new music culture called rock and roll and by the rise of a young singer called Elvis Presley.

For the siblings, home life in Hackney had become a little cramped to say the least. Yiasoumi was finally able to afford to bring over from Cyprus Dimitra and Anastasis, who was now ten years old.

They travelled over on the boat with Vasili junior who was now sixteen and three other cousins, one of which was Antoni, the poor boy that Marika used to bully in Cyprus, who was now twenty and six foot two inches. The other two cousins were Christo and his sister Katina who were both single and very attractive and, like thousands of Cypriots at that time, came to England in search of a better life. Excluding the tenant and her two children, there were now eleven people living in the house.

As cramped and chaotic as the house was, it was fun-packed with shenanigans that were going on from all the differing personalities. Louca was given an old wind-up gramophone from a customer and Vasili Junior brought some Greek records from Cyprus. They entertained themselves daily dancing away every night to the Greek folk dances of *tsiftetelia* (a type of belly dance) and *vareta* (a heavy dance).

Kika and Katina sometimes wanted to listen to Elvis on the radio and dance the Samba but the *vareta* always took priority over Elvis.

The new arrivals, Christo and Vasili Junior, were soon fixed up as dishwashers in Louca's café, and Katina and Dimitra as finishers in Jacob's factory.

Louca had to be strict with Nicholas and Christo as not only did they come on to all the women that set foot in the café, but both also had a tendency to muck about and play practical jokes on unsuspecting customers, pulling their chairs away from under their feet or unscrewing the salt pots, laughing as they watched the salt spill all over the food.

The gang took it in turns to stay home and look after little Anastasis, depending on their shifts, but sometimes they left him alone with a sandwich for his lunch and he had to fend for himself until they came home. There were no social services in those days.

Marika's feud with Mona upstairs got worse over the months, especially since the new arrivals and the gramophone had moved into the house. Mona would bang on the ceiling with her broom, come out of her room and shout out, "Will you shut up? You are waking my children!"

Kika turned the music down and said "Come on everyone quieten down a bit. Let the children sleep." But not Marika. She took offence and, not needing any excuse to spite Mona, stormed halfway up the stairs and shouted: "Shuddup, you bloody Irish *poutana*!"

Mona would inevitably then swing her door open and shout back at Marika: "Shut up, you Greek midget bitch!" And so it went on.

The Gang became notorious around the East End, and on Sundays they would all get dressed up and go out in Central London. The boys wore their best trousers and double-breasted jackets with a tie and trilby hat.

All the girls put on their best dresses, raincoats and the obligatory head scarf, which they wore folded into a triangle over their head and tied under the chin. At home or for housework they wore it turban style, tied at the forehead, usually to cover a mass of rollers underneath.

All the girls, except for Marika who said "I would not be seen dead in that head scarf, it's no good for my image" and always went out with her bright red lipstick and a hairnet to make her bouffant hairdo last a bit longer.

The Gang always hung out together as a group to limit any threat of racism or persecution, which they said they experienced regularly as foreigners. But it seemed no coincidence that, wherever there was trouble, the Gang was always there.

It was Christmas 1958 and the Gang took a trip to Oxford Street to see the Christmas illuminations and the tree in Trafalgar Square. On the way home, somewhat inebriated, they ran up the stairs to the top deck of the 22 bus, all rowdy and singing the Greek hit "*Tin Yerimin Tin Vraka*", disrupting the rest of the passengers.

They sat down near a group of drunken Teddy boys who stared at the gang. A few dirty looks went back and forth and, anticipating trouble, some passengers quickly made their way down to the lower deck to avoid being in any crossfire.

"Tickets, please," said the bus conductor and what started off as a simple misunderstanding about a shortfall of fare developed into a wrestling match between Antoni and the conductor, which lead to a fight breaking out between the Teddy boys and the rest of the gang. Punches and kicks were thrown and at one stage the conductor was pinned to the floor by Antoni and being head-butted by Marika who was sitting on top of him.

"Get off me you stupid woman or I am going to call the police," shouted the conductor.

"So you call me stupi' woman huh! I show you stupi'," and she continued to head-butt him.

A scared passenger was frantically pulling the red emergency cord and the bus ground to a halt just as Nicholas was holding a Teddy boy by the throat and was about to throw him down the stairs. The force of the emergency stop jerked everyone on the bus forward and Nicholas and the Teddy boy ended up at the bottom of the stairs in a heap.

The bus driver ran to the back of the bus to find out what was going on and, seeing the two men in a heap on the floor holding their heads and then seeing his conductor covered in blood, he reached for his walkie-talkie and requested police help.

The two gangs ran off the bus and dispersed in different directions before the police could get there.

"Count yourselves lucky I didn't knock all your blocks off, Teddys," shouted Nicholas as he ran.

The gang walked eight miles in the freezing cold to get home, laughing and reconstructing their victory over the poor defenceless conductor.

"Did you see the way I got that big Teddy man by the throat?" asked Nicholas.

"What about the way I head-butted that conductor?" said Marika.

"If it wasn't for me," said Antoni, "you would have had to pay the bus fare."

"Oh shut up all of you," said Kika "You should be ashamed of yourselves." And they all shut up.

Brawling became a fact of life for the Gang, who got themselves a reputation for defending racist attacks but which they always seemed to provoke and it was Nicholas' life ambition to come across the Kray Twins and "sort them out too."

CHAPTER 6

Mona

The daily folk dancing, the singing and laughing played a big part in the Gang's early years in England. It somehow compensated for the hard work that was endured and helped lift the mood of the Depression that was still quite raw and lingering in the background from the aftermath of World War II.

One Saturday afternoon in 1959, while Louca and Christo were working in the café, the rest of the Gang were dancing and singing to the song called "*To thiko mou paploma*". Marika had had a few too many brandies and decided to dance up and down the stairs to annoy Mona. As expected, Mona swung open her door and said to Marika "Fuck off back to where you came from you fucking bitch." Well that was it; Marika went ballistic and charged up the stairs with a frying pan.

"Come out, you *poutana*," she yelled and banged the frying pan on her door.

Fearful, Mona stayed inside the room but hurled abuse from behind the door.

"Fuck off back to your primitive village, you bloody foreigner."

More hurling abuse and banging of the pan followed until Nicholas decided to go upstairs to take over the situation. He pushed Marika out of the way and told her to go downstairs with her frying pan and leave it to him to sort her out.

"*Afisme na tin kanoniso ego pou ime anthras*" ("I am the man here, let me sort her out"), he said and tapped his chest with his fist like Tarzan. He shouted outside Mona's door.

"I give you one hour to pack your things and get out or I will come in there and throw you out myself."

"You and whose army, you fucking Greek midget?" shouted Mona from behind the door.

"Midje'? Midje'?" shouted an enraged Nicholas.

"I show you what a Greek midje' does, you *poutana*", and he attempted to kick the door down with his little legs. After six kicks the door broke off the lock and swung open. Before Nicholas could blink, Mona stormed out of the room and mercilessly cracked him over the head with a poker, just missing his crown and catching his ear and the side of his head. Blood gushed out and within seconds his whole face was covered. He lost his balance and fell down the stairs.

"O ma' God!" yelled Kika as soon as she saw the blood on her brother's face and ran up the stairs like a hurricane, quickly followed by Marika with her husband Frixo behind her. She grabbed the Irish woman by the neck and tried to strangle her. Marika punched her to the floor and the sisters beat her up in full view of her children.

Downstairs Dimitra panicked when she saw the blood still gushing out of Nicholas' head and ran out into the street shouting "Umbula', umbula'" in her limited English.

Meanwhile Marika had managed to kick Mona down the stairs and out of the front door and in a half-conscious state Mona managed to crawl to the pavement and cry for help.

"Somebody help me. Please help me."

Her children ran down the stairs crying after their mother, as everyone spilled out into the street. Upon hearing the commotion and screaming coming from inside the house, a concerned neighbour called for an ambulance and the police.

The ambulance got there within moments and put both the bleeding Nicholas, holding a bottle of whisky, and the semi-conscious Mona in the ambulance together and sped off to the sound of the deafening siren towards Hackney hospital.

As the ambulance siren faded away into the distance it was replaced with the distant sound of a police siren, which got louder and louder until it deafened the area outside the house. The police car doors opened and slammed shut, and a crowd began to gather outside the house, with anxious neighbours curiously looking to see what was going on.

The children were crying and were being comforted by neighbours.

The front door was still open and three police officers walked in to the front room, where they saw Dimitra and Katina sobbing, with Frixo trying to console them. There was a pool of blood at the foot of the stairs and blood stains all up the banisters.

Marika and Kika were in the kitchen and had just started to make *louvi with lahana* (black-eyed peas and spinach) for dinner.

The policeman asked, "Can someone please tell me what went on here?" But they were all new arrivals and couldn't speak a word of English between them.

In a panic Katina called out for Kika, who came rushing into the room brandishing the knife that she had been using to cut the *lahana*, Marika following closely behind her holding the saucepan. When Kika saw the policeman she stopped in her tracks and said: "Oh halo, Mr Polishmano," and put the knife down by her side.

"What is your name, ma'am?" he asked Kika.

"Sorry, er, no speaking the English. I'm Greek," she replied pretending not to understand.

The police officer was unable to take any coherent statement from anyone in the house, so continued his enquiries with the neighbours just as Louca and Christo turned up on foot and ran inside the house in panic as soon as they saw the police cars outside.

Dimitra was frantically trying to explain to them what had happened when she was interrupted by the policeman who came to tell them that he would be back the following day with an interpreter.

Nicholas's injuries were superficial and not as bad as first seemed. The doctor told him that he was very lucky in that had the poker hit him in the middle of his head, it would have broken his skull and in all likelihood would have been fatal.

This didn't seem to faze Nicholas at all as he said to the doctor: "I have a Greek head, very strong, like a Spartan. You know the Spartans, doctor?"

"Er, no, actually, Mr Nicholas, I don't," said the surgeon as he stitched up Nicholas' head, who didn't need any anaesthetic as he had drank the whole bottle of whiskey by then and was already anaesthetised.

Mona and her children were taken to a secret women's refuge never to be seen again, much to Marika's pleasure as she rubbed her hands together in glee.

Nicholas decided that it would be best for him to take the blame for beating up Mona as he didn't see the point of his sisters getting into trouble and they agreed to keep their mouths shut when the police came around to take statements the following morning. Nicholas admitted to beating up the tenant in self-defence, after she hit him first with the poker.

He was charged with grievous bodily harm and, after pleading guilty at the Old Bailey, he was sentenced to three months' imprisonment in Brixton prison, after the judge took into account provocation as mitigating circumstances.

During Nicholas' incarceration life changed for the Gang.

Yiasoumi and Dimitra decided that England was not a good place to bring up a family and moved back to Cyprus with little Anastasis.

Katina had *proxenia* with a young man called Soderis, who owned a restaurant in Great Yarmouth, and she moved there with her brother Christos to work in the restaurant.

Frixos realised that he was not cut out for married life with Marika. He was young and adventurous and wanted to travel the world on his motorbike without being tied down. He packed his bags and left Marika, who was nine months' pregnant. She was devastated and felt humiliated by the disgrace of being a single mum. She wept for weeks and was inconsolable at being left alone to bring up a child in foreign lands without her parents. She had a baby girl and she named her Antonia after Antoni, who proudly became her godfather and by so doing finally put to bed the distant memories of Marika bullying him as a child.

The house had too many memories for Marika so she rented a house a few doors away and Antoni moved in with her so that he could be close to his goddaughter and assist Marika with her daughter's upbringing.

Vasili Junior got a Greek girl pregnant, had a shot-gun wedding and emigrated to America, where baby Thekla was born nine months later.

By the time Nicholas was released from prison, only Kika and Louca were left in the house and, with no tenant upstairs, they each had a room to themselves.

Louca thought it was time to get Nicholas married off and preferably get him out of London to keep him out of trouble. His friend, Tommy, had a single sister called Nicolletta who lived in Birmingham and Louca arranged with Tommy to bring his sister to London to meet Nicholas the next weekend.

Nicolletta was taller than Nicholas and didn't fancy him because he was so short. But when she found out that he had just been released from prison for GBH she found this very manly and agreed to marry him. After a brief honeymoon in Trafalgar Square, the newlyweds moved in to Nicolletta's house in Birmingham, bought a restaurant which he called "Al Capone" and had a baby girl he called Maria after his mother.

With Nicholas now settled and out of the way, as head of the family Louca felt that he had one more responsibility left to carry out and that was to marry Kika off.

Kika was now twenty-five years old and was, by Cypriot standards, left on the shelf.

Louca embarked on a mission to find her a suitable husband. He took her to many *proxenia* but Louca was not impressed with the calibre of men that were offered to his sister. Eventually she was introduced to a tall, dark man with piercing green eyes, called Andreas Papadopoulos. He was quiet and handsome and Kika fancied him straight away.

He had been born in Cyprus in a village called Lefkonico and, like Kika, came to England when he was seventeen to work, ending up living in Haringey with his uncle Antrico, his wife and their daughter Rita. He was the eldest child and had left behind his parents, Yiorko and Anna and five younger siblings. His uncle found him a job as a cutter in a clothing factory but he presented himself at the *proxenia* as a tailor.

Antrico had previously taken his nephew on other *proxenia* to find him a decent wife but his uncle never seemed to like any of them, not even a gorgeous brunette with long legs, an hour-glass figure with a bouffant of jet black hair in a beehive style who looked like a brunette version of Brigitte Bardot. Andreas' eyes popped out of their sockets when he saw her but Antrico said "*den mou areskei i parpatisha teis*" ("I don't like the way that she walks,") much to Andreas' disappointment.

Kika turned up with lots of *kourapiethes* (homemade short-breads) and Andreas' uncle liked her straightaway.

"*Einai spithkiasimi toutei*" ("this one is homely") he said "she will make a good housewife and mother and I approve of this one to marry." Kika and Andreas were married in 1959 and, with everyone now firmly settled into their lives in England, Cyprus was becoming a long-distant memory.

Andreas and Kika started their new life together. Louca sold his share of the house to Kika and he moved in above the café.

Kika bought a Singer sewing machine and started to work from home as a seamstress but, as quick and as capable as she was, Andreas was the opposite. He was slow and laid back in everything that he did and was unable to hold down a job, so Kika bought another sewing machine and taught him how to sew. Together they worked side by side until the day I was born.

CHAPTER 7

Growing Up

And so here I am. My name is Annie Papadopoulos and everyone calls me Annie, with the exception of my mother who calls me Anna. I was born in the 1960s in the East End of London and my first-ever memory as a child was when I was about three. I remember waking up in the middle of the night and calling for my mum over and over again but nobody came. I was in a large, dark room and I got out of my bed and walked to the window and stared out of it intensely as I felt the tears rolling down my face.

I was petrified that my mum had left me and was never coming back. I waited for what seemed hours, staring out of the window into the dark seeing only the large, white, full moon. Finally, out of the eerie silence, I heard the front door open downstairs, with the sound of voices. As I heard the sound of my mum's voice, my heart slowly started to beat normally and I exhaled deeply with a spontaneous sigh of relief, as my tears stopped and my quivering lips turned into a smile.

I walked away from the window, got back into bed and instantly fell asleep.

My parents had left me at home alone to go and vote at a polling station.

I lived in a mid-terraced house in Hackney with my mother Kika, father Andreas, younger brother Vasili and baby sister Maria, with whom I shared a bedroom on the first floor. My brother had his own bedroom across the hall from my parents' bedroom at the front of the house.

Downstairs we had a front room which had a huge sideboard to house all of Mum's framed photos and *petsetakia* (doilies), an old wind-up gramophone with some old Greek 78 rpm records, a slide-out drinks cabinet along with our best red and gold fabric furniture, which was only used when we had visitors or on special occasions.

The rest of the time this room saw no activity, apart from me polishing it every Saturday morning and the slow movement of the snails that were crawling around in a large cardboard box full of flour which was situated in the corner of the room. I often wondered why the box of snails was there at all as it looked so out of place, until I discovered, when I got older, that the snails were kept in the box until their intestines were "cleansed" by the flour, before they were boiled in the pot and eaten. At the rear of the house we had a large room which was the hub of the house. It was our kitchen, dining room and living room, where all the daily activities took place including watching our 12-inch black-and-white TV in its huge wooden cabinet.

Hardly anyone had a bathroom in our street. We had a stone-floored yard in the garden which had an outside toilet. I was scared to go out there at night especially in the winter in the dark and freezing cold, so I had a *kathiki* (potty) under my bed and every morning my mum bellowed "Bring the *kathiki* down and empty it!"

Every Saturday night, without fail, Mum would boil our huge kettle, clear the dining table and place a large tin bath on it to bathe us. First she bathed my baby sister, then Vasili and then, in the same water, she bathed me. As I got a little older my bum got larger and only just fitted into the bath. One day I stood up and the bath got stuck to my arse, making me spill the soapy water all over the floor. I got a slap round the ear for that.

The last thing I wanted was one of my mother's friends walking in unexpectedly and seeing me washing my private parts, which often happened, and if it wasn't Mum's friends, Dad would sometimes walk in wearing his old pair of army trousers, carrying a shot gun in one hand and a string of wood pigeons in the other, rushing to get to the sink.

Luckily, by the time I neared puberty and knew what embarrassment was, my parents had a bath installed together with an invention called a twin-tub washing machine and the tin bath was no more.

With the tin bath now extinct, the room got a new secondary use as a hair salon. My mum's cousin Androulla would come and give her a home hair perm and make the whole room stink of peroxide. It was not a very pleasant experience when I was trying to eat my dinner and couldn't breathe from the choking smell.

A middle reception room contained two sewing machines and this is where both my parents worked as dressmakers.

My memories of growing up are vivid and I often wonder whether my childhood was normal. I remember playing hide-and-seek with my brother and sister in our living room, while Mum and Dad worked in the machine room. On many occasions I would find my brother sitting on a small chair in the sewing room with his hands tied behind his back and one of his legs tied to a sewing machine. His mouth would sometimes be gagged with a piece of off cut-material and I didn't quite understand why Mum had tied him up like this; I just thought that maybe Vasili had been naughty again.

The fact is that my brother was very naughty. He was a stocky kid with an exceptionally large head and a fierce temper to go with it. He did not sit still and there was not a thing in the house that he would not break and it wasn't always objects either. It was his fingers, his head, anything that got in the way of his antics. He was a danger to himself and others and he charged through the house like a raging bull, usually brandishing a stick or a hammer in his hand. He loved to break things and Mum was forced to tie him up or lock him out in the garden to distract him from smashing something in the house.

He even banged his head on the headboard in his sleep and night after night he would keep everyone awake until Mum went into his room and smacked him around the head. It worked for a few hours but the banging would soon start up again.

I would always hear Mum say that he took after Grandfather Vasili in terms of his strength and temper: "*onoma kai prama*" she used to say, meaning that he was aptly named after him.

We seemed to have hundreds of relatives and I remember our house always being full of them. The men would play cards banging their knuckles on the table on one side of the room with a cloud of smoke above them from their Rothman Royals cigarettes, and the women would be the other side of the room crocheting and chatting about the old days.

We children played outside in the street or in the garden for hours, but we were never allowed to go anywhere near the vegetable patch. "Be careful of my *kouloumbres,*" Mum would shout.

We had loads of chickens in a pen and pet rabbits in a hutch, and I loved holding and stroking them. Every now and again some rabbits went missing and Mum said that someone left the hatch open by mistake and they escaped. This used to upset me and I always blamed it on naughty Vasili.

My gang consisted of me, my brother and sister and my godbrothers who lived in the next street Theo, Jimmy and Costa who were similar ages to us. Then there was my best friend Mastra, who lived a few doors down, and at the end of the street was my cousin Antonia who lived with her mum, my Auntie Marika. Cousin Stella was the sixth child of uncle Pavlos and Auntie Florou and lived in Islington but visited every day. Finally there was my cousin Alexis who lived a few roads away with her parents, Auntie Pezouna and Uncle Rikos who was Mum's cousin once removed.

This was our Greek gang and whenever we got together, the whole neighbourhood would hear us we were so loud.

The streets were safe back then. Hardly anyone owned a car so the side streets were virtually traffic-free. This made them a good place for us to play, as a car would only interrupt our games every half hour or so – normally the milkman in his milk-float or the paraffin man.

In the summer months we played outside all day and never got bored as there was always something to do. We made our own toys using junk and vivid imaginations. The boys would play marbles or cowboys and Indians with caps that went bang: Vasili timed it to make old ladies jump with fright as they passed by.

The girls played hopscotch or French-skipped and I loved hopping around on my bright orange spacehopper until one day it burst and Vasili teased me for having a fat arse.

When all the gang were together we played hide-and-seek "It" or "Had" but if we felt mischievous we played knock-down ginger, where we knocked on neighbours' doors and ran off. The best part of the games for me was picking the teams. My cousin Antonia was the eldest so was our leader and was always in charge of picking the teams. There were many different rhymes that accompanied this elimination process. One was "Ippa dippa dation, my operation, how many people at the station?" and another was "One potato, two potato, three potato, four, five potato, six potato, seven potato, more". Whoever landed on the words "station" or "more" was out and the last one left was "It". But my favourite one of all was "Ip dip dog shit, you are not it" because it was an excuse to use a swear word and this amused me.

We were always laughing and giggling and played practical jokes on each other. Vasili and Jimmy once gave Maria a birthday present. She untied the dainty ribbon, unwrapped the paper, put her hand in the box and took out the present, which turned out to be a piece of dog shit they had freshly scooped up from the pavement. She ran crying into the house and wiped her soiled hand all over Vasili's bedcovers; Mum went mental and battered us all for that.

If we got a bang on the head or a grazed knee we held back the tears and hobbled home to get a plaster or Dettol. If we got dirty we used to spit on our hands to wipe the dirt off our faces to avoid getting a yelling-at from Mum and a wet cold flannel around the face. So this is how our Greek gang all grew up. They were happy days, until one day an Irish family of ten moved in across the street and things began to change.

No sooner had they moved in, cars got scraped, garden gnomes got vandalised and stones were thrown through windows. They terrorised our street. One morning Mum sent Maria for a loaf of bread from the corner shop and on her way back two of the Irish children stopped her in the street and forced her to hand over the change, making her cry all the way home. Mum was furious and went storming across the road to tell the parents.

The Irish mother opened the door. She was a large, tall, blonde woman towering over Mum as Mum proceeded to tell her what happened but it quickly turned into an argument where a short, loud Greek woman was arguing in a Greek accent with a huge Irish woman with a thick, broad Irish accent and no-one understood a word. Mum was shouting half in Greek and half in English and wouldn't let the Irish woman get a word in edgeways until the Irish woman shouted out "Bloody foreigner" and slammed the door in Mum's face.

Mum was spitting blood as she stomped back to our house, shouting and swearing in Greek, "*Skcato Irishtra, Shilo poutana*" ("Irish dog prostitute") and slammed the door. Dad was sitting at the sewing machine and, while Mum was foaming at the mouth with steam coming out of her ears, he said, "Hurry up I'm hungry, when is dinner going to be ready woman?"

She threw a clothes-hanger across the room at him and stormed off to the kitchen screaming at him in Greek, "*Gamo tin ratsa sou*" ("Fuck your ancestors"). How charming.

The next time my godbrothers came to visit we plotted to teach the Irish kids a lesson, "Greek style". We went outside where two of the Irish kids were propped up against our wall and one spat in Vasili's direction. Little did they know about Vasili's short fuse and bad temper. He stormed over to them like a bulldog, grabbed them both by the scruff of their necks and pushed them face down into next door's bushes. They ran home crying and within a minute the whole Irish clan came out, led by the two huge older sisters. They were built like brick walls and I shit myself when I saw them running towards me. It all happened rather quickly after that and it was like West-Side -Story-in-Hackney. The fight started when Theo grabbed them both by the hair and was swinging from their pigtails. They screamed in pain, holding their heads, and once I saw that the two hippos were being restrained by Theo, I got hold of the oldest boy, who was only half my size, dragged him across the floor and threw him in the neighbour's bushes. Vasili had two boys on the floor in a scuffle, punching them while Maria and little Costa had two little girls by their throats. I could hear the two big girls screaming "Ouch! My hair! Let me go!" and the two boys were crying on the floor with my brother on top of them screaming "Say sorry to my sister." Eventually the older girls broke free and they all ran into their house holding their heads as we cheered and laughed at them and ran victoriously back into our house.

There was a loud knock at the door. Mum got up, marched to the door, closely followed by my godfather and all of us kids behind. Dad stayed seated with his poker hand held tightly to his chest and my godmother carried on with her crocheting. Mum opened the front door and there stood the whole Irish clan.

"Do you know what your animals have done to my children?" asked the furious Irish mother. "Look!" she yelled as she showed Mum a bald patch on her daughter, a scratched face on her son and a torn jumper on her little girl. There was dead silence for a moment and then Mum became like a woman possessed with her eyeballs rolling out of their sockets. She rolled up her sleeves, stared straight into the eyes of the Irish mother who was one inch away from her face and screeched like the incredible hulk: "You go back to the other side of the street before I bend you down" and she pushed the Irish woman off the step. The woman backed off and they slowly retreated back to their house.

"*Avratinisiktimini.* (a Turkish curse) *Hade!* (come on!)", said Mum, brushing her hands together, and that was that. She walked back into the lounge, picked up her crochet from her chair, sat down and continued her crocheting.

"Come on *Koumpare* (godfather)" said Dad. "You are holding up the game."

That was the first time I noticed what a tough nut Mum was. The look that she gave the Irish woman was enough to frighten the living daylights out of her.

It wasn't long after that the Irish clan were moved away by Hackney Council and life in our street went back to normal again.

CHAPTER 8

Snowy

The late sixtes and early seventies brought in changes. People were getting used to the new decimal currency and the Hippy ideology, and fashion became part of mainstream London culture. Men were wearing flares, wide collars, kipper ties, and grew beards and their hair long. Women replaced the sixties mini-skirt with long, bright-coloured dresses with psychedelic geometric prints and high platform shoes. Our next-door neighbour, Mr Batchelor, wore high platform shoes too and Mum told us not to talk to him because "*inai pojinous*" ("he is one of them,") but I didn't know what that meant.

The film "The Godfather" was out at the cinema but I was not allowed to go and see it so I just stayed home as usual and listened to "My-Ding-a-Ling" and "Long Haired Lover from Liverpool" on the radio.

I don't remember my childhood ever being unhappy, apart from one day when I came home from school to find Mum crying. I had never seen Mum cry before and it really upset me. She told me that she had received a letter from her sister Dimitra in Cyprus to say that *Yiayia* (Grandmother) Maria had died. Mum seemed to cry for weeks.

During that summer of 1969 my family and I went to Cyprus by ship for four weeks during the school summer holidays. It was the first time that Mum and Dad had gone back to Cyprus for twenty years and Mum was sad that she was not going to see her mother.

We had never gone on holiday abroad before and the journey on the ship was so exciting. There was so much food to eat any time we liked and I stuffed my face every day. We had a little cabin with a round porthole which I loved looking out of and seeing the sea. I also loved sleeping on the top bunk of bunk beds, while Maria slept below and Vasili slept on a fold-up bed next to Mum and Dad. He kept banging his head on the wall while he was asleep and kept us awake most of the nights. At breakfast, passengers commented on the red bruises that he had on his forehead and would look over at Mum and Dad suspiciously, as if they had been physically abusing him. Mum just gave them one of her dirty looks and they soon looked away.

The journey seemed to take forever, until the ship finally dropped anchor in Limassol docks and we were finally in Cyprus. I was so excited.

We were picked up by one of Dad's brothers, Uncle Foti, in a little white car in which our suitcases didn't fit and Uncle Foti had to tie them to the roof. The rackety old car slowly made its way over dirt-track roads, backfiring regularly, passing small quaint villages and people riding donkeys.

The men all seemed to have long moustaches twisted up at the ends and wore a *vraka*, which made me laugh. The suitcases fell off the roof a few times and we had to keep stopping to put them back on.

Looking out of the car window I could see brown wasteland for miles onto the horizon and we finally arrived at my dad's village, Lefkonico, baking hot and gasping for water.

When we got out of the car it seemed that the whole village had turned out to greet us. We were surrounded by people I had never met before who were hugging and kissing us.

One woman with a hairy chin gave me a wet, soggy kiss and I had to wipe my cheek to get rid of the saliva and the itching from her brittle hairs. She crushed my bones hugging me and

Mum told me that she was my *Yiayia* Anna who I had been named after.

I smiled at her when I realised who she was and I felt a touch embarrassed about wiping my cheek.

I was introduced to my *Papou* (Grandfather) Yiorko and to all my dad's brothers and sister, cousins, aunties and uncles, and realised then that it was not the whole village that had descended upon us but merely Dad's immediate family.

My grandparents' house was a tiny, little, clay house but with a noticeably huge courtyard surrounded by small outbuildings, each used for a different purpose. One was full of huge green watermelons piled up to the ceiling. Another was full of chickens running around and another contained hutches of rabbits, two goats and a donkey.

The smallest little hut I was told was the toilet, although when I looked in it the toilet was missing and I asked *Papou* Yiorko who stole the toilet. The whole family laughed and I remember being very proud of myself that I made everyone laugh, even though I didn't understand what they were laughing at.

I later discovered that the toilet was a small hole in the ground and I had to straddle over it and aim to pee in the hole. I found this impossible and ended up with the pee running all down my leg. There was no toilet paper in sight to wipe myself with, so I picked up some loose hay that was next to the hole and I wiped my leg with it only to find out that the hay was full of shit and I had wiped it all down my leg.

"Muuuumm," I yelled and she came rushing into the hut. I unlatched the door to let her in and when she saw the mess I had made she slapped me around the head, pulled me out of the hut with my knickers still hanging around my ankles, washed me down with a hosepipe and ordered me to stand in the sun with my arms out to dry off.

I felt an idiot standing there like a scarecrow, with Vasili and Maria laughing at me, but the hot scorching sun dried me off in an instant. *Yiayia* shouted, "Leave my baby alone," and came and cuddled me. I liked my *Yiayia* Anna.

Yiayia had laid lots of tables next to each other in a long line in the backyard and I couldn't see the other end it was so long. All the family sat down and there was a suckling pig being cooked on a spit above a fire made of sticks, and Dad with three of his brothers were turning the pig round and round with a make-shift wooden handle.

It smelt delicious and, when we finally got to eat it, it tasted delicious too and was one of the best things I had ever tasted.

The conversation over dinner took hours. Everyone was talking, drink was flowing and before I knew it, it was dark.

I looked up and saw thousands of stars and I kept staring at the sky all night, as I had never seen stars before. I tried to count them but each time I tried I would get interrupted by roars of laughter at the table. It was a great start to the holiday and I sat there smiling with contentment, looking at my huge, extended family with pride.

It was time for bed and *Yiayia* Anna made up lots of camp beds in the courtyard and inside the little house there were two double beds where me, Mum, Vasili and Maria were to sleep. Dad preferred to sleep on the camp bed outside in the courtyard with *Yiayia* and *Papou*.

I couldn't sleep a wink as I was boiling hot and constantly itching. I was so frustrated and tired and kept calling Mum for water; after the third time she said: "*Hade siopa je jimithou* (shut up and go to sleep) I don't want to hear you again".

Just as I finally nodded off, I was startled by the loud noise of a cockerel screeching "cock-a-doodle-doooooo". I sat up all disorientated and for a split second didn't know where I was.

I was still very tired but I was excited about what new things the day was going to bring, so I slipped on my flip-flops and walked into the courtyard where my parents and grandparents were sitting chatting. As I appeared in front of them I saw their faces looking at me in horror.

"Holy Mary, *Panayia mou* (Holy Mary)," shouted Mum who shot up from her chair, ran towards me and grabbed me by the arms.

"*Glihora ston Yiatron*" ("Quickly to the doctor"), she said, and *Yiayia* was holding her head and crying. I heard my mum say "*Efahan din oi sknipes*" ("She has been eaten by mosquitoes"). I was covered from head to foot in red, blotchy puss spots. I looked at my blotchy hands and legs and I got scared and started to cry.

I was rushed to the village doctor by Mum and *Yiayia*, as Dad and Grandpa stayed with Vasili and Maria who did not have a single spot on them.

As they swiftly dragged me through the village on foot, I could see everyone staring at me and old ladies crossing themselves, which scared me even more as I thought I was going to die.

The doctor gave my mum some lotion and told her that I was going to be alright, making me sigh with relief. She didn't wait to get out of the surgery to smother my face and whole body with the thick white lotion, and I remember being completely embarrassed walking back through the village looking like a white clown.

It soon got around the family that I was eaten by mosquitoes and everyone kept popping in to see how I was. I loved the attention but didn't like it when Vasili and Maria were allowed to play in the sun while I had to sit in the shade covered from head to foot in a white net curtain.

My parents decided that I could not spend another night in Lefkonico in case I got mauled by the mosquitoes again, so we said our goodbyes and set off in Uncle Foti's clapped-out car to go to my mum's village, Eptakomi.

We arrived at a village at the very top of a mountain and I could see the grey-coloured rooftops of the sparsely scattered houses.

We were greeted by an old man holding a walking stick, standing outside a house with three arches. He shouted, "*Elate Irthan*" ("Come out, they are here").

Lots of people came running out of the house and I was introduced to my *Papou* Vasili for the first time.

Everyone was crying around me and it was an emotional reunion for Mum coming home and not seeing her mother, who had recently passed away. She cried uncontrollably, making me cry too. Although Mum was sad, everyone seemed very happy to see us.

We were kissed and hugged as we were introduced to the family members one by one. There was Uncle Stavro, who I was told was Mum's eldest brother, with his wife Kaliopi and their five children, all older than me. Then there was Auntie Dimitra, Mum's oldest sister, with her husband Yiasoumi and their son Anastasis, who was about twenty-five.

I had so many cousins, uncles and aunties that I lost track, but it was very exciting.

They all commented on my blotchy condition and *Papou* Vasili told Mum off for letting me get eaten by the mosquitoes and insisted that I would not sleep in Lefkonico again.

I slept like a log that night as there was a lovely cool breeze and not a mosquito in site. Within days my bites started to heal and they no longer itched.

Every day there was something exciting to do.

On our first day *Papou* Vasili put me on his donkey and rode me around the village, introducing me to his fellow villagers.

"*Einai i ankonisa mou apo tin Anglia*" ("This is my granddaughter from England"), he said proudly.

We then rode the donkey up Thrakontas mountain until we got right to the top and I could see the sea. I loved the view and it became my favourite place.

On another day he took me, Vasili and Maria with him to pick olives from the olive trees and the next day we picked carobs, knocking them off with his walking stick. My brother laughed hysterically when one fell on *Papou*'s head and *Papou* laughed and told him that he reminded him of his son Nicholas.

My cousin Anastasis drove us a couple of times to the beach at

Kyrenia and Famagusta, where the beach had white sands and the water was so crystal clear I could see my feet in it. I could walk for ages and the sea would only be to my waist. I could not digest how aqua-marine blue and clear it was. I didn't want to leave.

When we got back, Auntie Dimitra took us to a field near the house and we watched her as she milked the goats. She made me sit on a little stool under a goat and I milked it as she held its back legs. The udder was all soft and squidgy, and Vasili and Maria could not stop laughing as the milk squirted out in the metal bucket and made a noise like a fart.

The only thing I didn't enjoy doing was picking *papoutsosika* (prickly pears), as they kept prickling my fingers and they didn't taste nice either. They were all seedy and not very fleshy but my mum loved them and we picked them for her along with her other favourite fruit, *sika* (figs).

But my favourite thing of all was when Uncle Yiasoumi drove everyone to the beach on the back of his old tractor. The whole family, all the aunties, uncles, cousins, parents, everyone, all got in his trailer which he called "*Palio Karotsan*" ("old cart")and he drove us slowly to the sea. It took ages to get there and it was very bumpy but it was so much fun, with everyone squashed in the back and singing old Greek songs.

Mum was overwhelmed when we got there. She said it used to be her favourite place when she was a child and it reminded her of a little pet donkey that she once had called Yarou, and *Papou* Vasili got emotional.

We visited my Dad's village regularly but only during daylight before the mosquitoes came out. During one of our visits *Yiayia* Anna asked us if we wanted fried chicken for dinner and, as soon as we all said yes, she brought out a chicken from the pen and pulled its head off with her bare hands. We watched in horror as the headless chicken flapped around the courtyard for a few seconds until it came to a sudden halt and flopped in a heap on the floor. Me, Vasili and Maria started crying and that image remained in my head.

In an attempt to cheer us up, *Papou* Yiorko asked me to go to the rabbit hatch with him and pick a rabbit to play with. There were many rabbits there but a fluffy, pretty, little white one stood out from the rest and I picked that one to play with. He took it out of the hutch and gave it to me. She was very cute and we called her Snowy and I held her and played with her all afternoon, which helped get my mind off the headless chicken.

That evening after dinner I wanted to play with Snowy again but she wasn't there and when I asked *Papou* where she was he said that we had eaten her for dinner. I was mortified and I cried all the way back to Eptakomi. I hated *Yiayia* Anna and *Papou* Yiorko and never wanted to go back to Lefkonico again.

I felt guilty that I had chosen Snowy, thinking it was to play with but instead I chose her for execution. I couldn't live with myself and I was traumatised for days.

Apart from the headless chicken and the death of Snowy, I loved my trip to Cyprus and I didn't want to come home, but the holidays were nearly over and we had to be back for school.

Mum filled her suitcases with *halloumia*, *lounzes*, *louvi*, *sika* and a jar of *ambelopoulia* (cheese, smoked pork, black-eyed peas, figs and pickled songbirds) and checked them in at the Cyprus Airways desk. Dad carried a huge trolley as hand luggage filled with olives and Anglias Brandy and nobody said a word at customs.

We were soon back in Hackney trying to re-adapt to the climate change and the culture shock.

CHAPTER 9

The Seaside

The trip to Cyprus was the first time that I had ever travelled abroad but nothing beat our trips to the English seaside.

Most normal families went to the seaside with their buckets and spades, deckchairs and sun lotion but our seaside trips were Greek Cypriot ones and were far more interesting.

How excited we were when we woke up one beautiful Sunday morning and Mum announced that we were all going to the seaside with my godfather's family.

Mum must have been up for ages because by the time we were awake she had already packed a huge food box.

We rushed to our rooms to get our swimming costumes. Mum found our buckets and spades, and my brother was looking for his snorkel and goggles.

Mum lifted up the huge food box and carried it by herself to the car – huffing and puffing, and swearing under her breath. She gave Dad one of her filthy looks on the way back and, as he pretended to pour water into the car radiator, she muttered loudly under her breath.

"You have been pouring water into that radiator for the last hour, anything so that you don't have to carry the box into the car. You think I'm stupi'?" she said.

He ignored her as usual, which wound her up even more and put her into a rage. We would not dare say anything when she was in that sort of mood.

Once Mum had packed the car we waited for Dad to finish and we were finally on our way to the seaside in our bright red Moscovitch car. Dad was a left-wing communist supporter and was proud to show off his Russian car but I got embarrassed every time I got in it: not because it got regularly vandalised but more because it was a clapped-out old rust-bucket which rattled like a tin can and constantly backfired.

Twenty minutes into the journey Dad pulled up somewhere on the hard shoulder of a duel carriageway and waited for my godfather and his family to meet us. I saw my godfather's new burgundy Volvo estate in the distance coming up behind us flashing his headlights to let us know it was him and he pulled up behind us.

We all got out to greet each other and we children were jumping with excitement as the parents decided which route to take. They were deliberating for ages and we were getting quite impatient to leave.

"Dad, are we going yet?" Theo asked his father.

He was ignored and my parents started to walk back to their car. I was just about to open the car door and get in when Mum handed me a couple of blankets from the boot of the car.

"Take them over to that hill," she commanded.

"Why Mum?" I asked, rather perplexed.

"Just take them." She handed Maria some bottles of coke and said, "Maria, follow your sister."

I looked behind me and saw the boys walking towards me carrying boxes, followed by my godfather carrying a barbeque and my godmother carrying three huge skewers. Within moments blankets were all laid out on the grass verge ready for a picnic. There were no sandwiches in our picnic box. Mum produced huge chunks of raw chicken and lamb from the box, which she started to thread on to the skewers. So there we all were on a grass verge on the lay-by of the A12 having a barbeque, with cars rushing past us at seventy miles an hour.

While we waited for the adults to get the food ready, we

chased each other up and down the hilly verge, with cars hooting at us. I thought that the drivers were being friendly and started waving back at them: it did not occur to me that they may have been warning us of the potential danger of high-speed cars.

"*Hade!* (Come on!) Food is ready!" bellowed Mum from over the hill, at which point we all raced to the barbeque to eat. As soon as we sat down and I took a bite of my chicken leg smothered with a huge dollop of taramosalata, I heard a police siren getting louder and louder until the noise became deafening as two Panda cars and a police van pulled up next to our cars.

My godmother held her ears and muttered "*Bastardi*" as seven police officers with black armour gear and weapons got out and walked towards us. My godfather told the adults to pretend they couldn't speak any English and I had to pretend to translate.

"Do you know sir that it is illegal to stop on the hard shoulder of a duel carriageway unless it is an emergency?" said one of the officers in a very deep, loud voice.

I shook my head in fear as my godfather said, "Sorry, no speaking the English."

My godmother turned to Mum and whispered, "*Koumera, en na mas labortaroun I poushties*? ("Are they going to arrest us, the poofs?").

Mum replied, "*Theos je i psishi tous oi pesevenkies*" ("God knows. Pimps").

Another police officer started to talk to someone on his radio: "Over, over, do you copy me?" There was a hissing sound on the other end followed by a muffled voice that said, "Go ahead. We copy."

"There is no emergency; I repeat no emergency, just some foreigners having what seems to be a picnic on the hard shoulder. Do you copy? Over." He walked away to finish the conversation and I could no longer hear what he was saying.

The officer with the deep voice asked, "Where are you from?"

No one answered.

My godfather said to me in Greek: "*Pe tous imastin bo tin Kypro je en katalavoumen*" ("Tell him that we come from Cyprus and we don't understand").

I looked at the policeman gormlessly and gulped as I said. "Erm, they don't understand. They are from Cyprus."

"Is he your father?" asked the officer.

"No, he's my godfather."

"Is he the driver of one of these vehicles?"

"Yes," I answered.

"Who is the other driver?" he asked.

"He is," I said pointing at my dad.

Dad tutted and said, "*Thkiaole eprothosen mas I gaoura*" ("Damn her, she's grassed me up, the donkey") and gave me a dirty look.

"Can I have their full names please?" asked the officer.

"Andreas Papadopoulos and Christophoros Christodoullou," I replied.

"Crikey. Can you spell those please?"

As he wrote down the details in his notepad, three other policemen started walking back towards their Panda cars and drove off.

My godfather whispered to Dad, "*Pezevenkies – en na mas labortaroun alopos*" ("Pimps, I guess he is going to book us").

Indeed he did. He handed one summons to my dad and the other to my godfather, then said, "Do you realise how dangerous it is to stop on a busy dual carriageway and let your kids run around when cars are speeding at seventy miles an hour? You could get them killed. The hard shoulder is for emergencies and breakdowns only, do you understand?"

Before I could pretend to translate for them, Dad replied: "Oh yes sir," and saluted.

"Yes occiffer," added my godfather.

One saluted like an army general and the other said "occiffer" like a drunk. I wanted to burst out laughing and was trying hard to keep a straight face – I was sure that the officer felt the same.

"Get up, collect all your things and leave," he said.

"Ah OK. We finish our food first, yes?" Mum said butting in.

"No. You go now!" shouted the officer impatiently.

"Ah OK. Would you like a piece of chigin sir, is very nice?" said Mum handing the officer a chicken leg.

"No, ma'am. Now please just pack up and leave."

"*Gaourosporos*" ("Donkey sperm"), muttered my godmother under her breath, as she started collecting the cutlery.

"*Do Leshin,*" ("scum") Mum added. "He could have at least let us finish our food, *o bastartos*" and I hoped the policeman didn't hear that.

We all walked towards the cars each carrying an item of the picnic and pieces of chicken in our hands, threw everything in the boot and off we set off again – to Southend. We were whinging in the back of the car. "Why did we stop anyway, Mum? None of us were even hungry. We just want to go to the seaside."

Mum turned around, gave us one of her dirty looks and said "*Siopin prin na yiriso to sherin mou je na sas tin strapso*" ("Be quiet before I swing my hand and slap you one"), after which we were silent all the way.

We passed a sign that said Southend was fourteen miles away, so we were not that far away. A few more minutes passed when from out of the blue Mum bellowed: "*Stamata! Moloshes!*" ("Stop! Moloshes!").

Dad slammed on the brakes and steered the car to the side of the road bringing it to a sudden halt; godfather narrowly avoided hitting the back of us.

We were told by Mum to stay in the car as all the adults got out to have a discussion about something. I didn't know what was wrong. It was obviously something serious to result in an emergency stop. What were moloshes? Was Mum ill; did something happen to the car? What happened?

I could see from the rear window that the adults were returning. They opened the boots of the cars and took out some knives and what seemed to be some screwed-up carrier bags. Then Mum and my godmother put on their coats. I was puzzled and getting a little scared. Something serious must have happened. I couldn't wait to find out what was going on. My parents got back into the car.

"Mum – what's happened?" I asked.

"Nothing."

"Why did you get the knives out?"

I was completely ignored.

Mum started directing Dad as he tried to reverse the car into a field. Both cars reversed through a small, opened, iron gate, into a large field until both cars were completely surrounded by tall greenish-yellow plants.

"What is going on Mum?" But before I could even finish my sentence, Mum shot out of the car like Speedy Gonzales and started hacking at the plants with a small bread knife. Dad was holding the carrier bags open for her as she quickly filled them one by one with the plants. My godparents were doing the same a few feet away.

It suddenly dawned on me that Moloshes was a form of spinach and we were actually trespassing on somebody's land and stealing their spinach-like crops. What a great seaside trip this was turning out to be. It wasn't long before all the carrier bags were full and all their coat pockets too. No wonder they put their coats on– they needed more bag space for the crops. We seemed to be waiting in the car for ages, but I was sure that from the speed in which those bags were being filled that we could not have been there for more than ten minutes.

I had visions of the police turning up again. How could I explain this one? First we had committed a motoring offence on the highway and now we were trespassing on someone's land, stealing crops. The crop-picking was over as quickly as it started and we sped off, wheel-spinning out of the gate and back on the road.

By this time I had lost all my earlier enthusiasm, but when I saw the sea looming through the front windscreen I became excited again. We had arrived at last.

The cars pulled into the car park and we all spilled out from all directions. All us kids got together and were jumping up and down in excitement. We grabbed the buckets and spades, Vasili's goggles and snorkel and rushed towards the sea.

The adults found a nice spot just a few feet away from the water, and we quickly took off our shoes and socks, changed into our swimming costumes and ran in to the sea

"Last one in is a fatso!" shouted Theo. That was me. I was always the last one in. I was not that keen on water and was a fatso anyway. Mum kept shouting at us not to go in too deep. You couldn't miss her as she had the loudest voice on the entire beach.

The beach was full of people, all under umbrellas and windbreakers, wearing their sunhats and covered in sun cream.

The blankets were quickly spread over the sand and the barbeque was out for the second time in the day. It was no surprise that everyone was staring at us and tutting. While people were enjoying a quiet, relaxing read on their deckchairs, listening to the therapeutic sound of the waves and the seagulls, along comes this large Cypriot family yelling at the top of their voices and eating enough food to feed the entire population of the beach.

After we had eaten, Mum told us all to get our buckets and spades and that we were going for a walk along the pier. We were all up for that because there were amusement arcades at the end of the pier.

Dad was told by Mum to stay behind and keep an eye on the things, and he was more than happy to have a quiet fag and eat all the leftovers.

The rest of us all made our way towards the pier, running along the sand. When we arrived, I rushed to get on the walkway. I loved looking through the gaps in the wooden planks on the pier and hearing the noise of the sea splashing underneath. I put one foot onto the walkway and then heard my mum's voice. "Come here all of you!"

I stopped in my tracks and turned around to see where she was. She was standing underneath the pier with my godparents, with our buckets and spades. I looked closer and saw that knife again. That same knife she was holding when she hacked the crops. They were each holding one.

Oh no! Now what? I said. There were no plants around this time so what were the knives for?

We gathered around and Mum gave us each a bucket. Theo and I were given a knife too and she told us to copy her. She then rolled up her sleeves, tucked her skirt into her pop socks and proceeded to scrape a *petalina* (a limpet) from the pier bed. To my horror she prized the limpet out of its triangular shell with the knife and, as it wriggled, she put it into her mouth and crunched it.

"Yuk! That's disgusting! I feel sick," I said and put my hand over my mouth to stop me from heaving. I heard someone behind me retching and as I looked behind me, saw two little old ladies throwing up. They looked horrified and, as they walked away, I could hear one of them say, "Barbarians". She wasn't wrong.

Mum made us dislodge limpets from the pier bed and put them in the buckets all afternoon. It all started to make sense now. When did our parents ever want to walk with us on the pier to the amusement arcades? We had been tricked. They needed us to help them collect limpets.

So our day trip to the seaside had entailed committing a criminal offence on the hard shoulder of the A12, trespassing onto a field, stealing crops and finally collecting limpets from Southend pier!

Sometimes the adults would vary the entertainment. Limpets would become snails, moloshes would become spinach or asparagus and Southend would be varied to Hastings, Clacton, Brighton or Margate.

We would often get slapped around the ears if we ventured out too far and regularly got our hair or ears pulled if we answered back. Greek Cypriot mothers did not care that people were watching them as they whacked and humiliated their children in public. Where were social services in those days?

As I got a bit older I refused to go on the seaside trips and they soon fizzled out.

Getting out of seaside trips was one thing but no way could I get out of going to family weddings. Once we drove to Plymouth to the wedding of a family member I had never heard of before. It was boring as usual, sitting there eating and not knowing anybody, and Mum made me dress up in a horrible red Crimplene dress with gold trimmings which she had made especially for me and I hated it because it made me look like a fat old maid.

It was late at night by the time we were driving home in the Moskovitch and it was pouring with rain. It was raining so hard that Dad had to turn up the speed of the windscreen wipers to full.

Vasili and Maria were sleeping but I couldn't sleep due to the noise and sheer force of the rain. I was scared in case we crashed. Dad could hardly see through the windscreen irrespective of how fast the wipers were going and I could see him and Mum desperately trying to wipe the mist from inside the windscreen to help him see better, as the heater did not appear to be working.

Dad was really struggling to see and he moved his head and chair forward to get as close to the windscreen as possible. The car was swaying from side to side, crossing over the white lines between the lanes.

Dad was getting very annoyed as visibility was getting worse. He opened the window to let in some air to clear the condensation. He was muttering, "Damn it, I can't see," but he continued to drive.

"Why don't you just stop, Dad, until the rain stops?" I asked.

I was ignored as usual. Was that such an unreasonable request?

"Close that window, it's freezing," demanded Mum. That really annoyed Dad, who tutted as he closed it.

Surely our safety was more important than the temperature, I thought?

Just to get Mum back, he lit up a cigarette knowing that this would annoy her. She was allergic to cigarette smoke and he knew that she would end up asking him to open the window to get rid of the smoke, which is exactly what she did, but started by shouting at him to put the cigarette out. So not only was it wet, dark and cold, with extremely poor visibility and the car swaying from side to side, Mum and Dad were now having an argument too, which escalated into a blazing row full of insults about each other's family.

"*Gamo tin ratsa sou!*" ("Fuck your ancestors!"), Dad shouted.

"*Lampro na se kapsi*" ("May you get struck down"), she shouted back.

The car swayed even more, and Vasili and Maria woke up in a daze. Dad shook his head from side to side and tutted, as Mum continued to shout in his ear, finally gave up by throwing the cigarette out and closing the window. The insults continued back and forth and Dad started to cough and retched deeper to clear his throat as Mum continued to shout at him. He quickly turned his head to his right to spit out of the window but forgot that he had closed the window and a huge, green and white blob of phlegm ran down the inside of the glass.

I started to heave but Maria beat me to it and vomited all over my legs. Mum started to clean up my sister with a tissue and she handed one to Dad so that he could clean the window, but instead of wiping off the phlegm he spread it all over the glass.

It was a nightmare. But nightmares are for normal people. Greek Cypriot nightmares have to go that one step further.

Just as Mum was cleaning up my sister's vomit and just as Dad continued to spread the phlegm further around the glass while trying to keep his eyes on the road, and just as my sister was crying and I'm shouting at her for being sick all over me, and just as my brother is pushing her away saying "Keep her away from me, gross," the windscreen wiper on the driver's side flew off the car!

At last Dad slowed down and stopped the car on the hard shoulder. It was obviously a godsend. I believe to this day that if that wiper had not flown off we would have crashed.

But as the car came to an abrupt standstill and Dad sighed with relief, wiping his sweating brow with the same tissue that he had used to wipe the phlegm, and now had spread it all over his forehead and hair too, Mum said: "Why did you stop!!?"

"How do you expect me to drive without a wiper *Ra Beli* (you stupid woman) I can't see."

"I have a wiper on my side. You drive and I'll direct you," she said.

Would you believe it?

CHAPTER 10

School Days

1973 brought with it technical improvements to London and to our home. We got a colour television set and I was able to watch my favourite programmes, Bless this House and Fawlty Towers, in colour. "Tie a Yellow Ribbon Round the Old Oak Tree" was number one in the charts and with the changing seventies came fundamental changes to my family and my gang too.

The most significant was when Uncle Louca died suddenly of something called gangrene but I didn't know what that was and Mum was crying every day. Uncle's café was sold to a Jewish man, who sold it on to a Cypriot man, who converted it into a Greek record store called Trehantiri.

"Uncle Louca would have loved that," Mum cried.

My best friend Mastra moved to Edmonton with her family and I had to take three buses to see her; so we didn't see each other that often and I missed her dreadfully.

When we did meet it took us ages to catch up with all our gossip. She surprised me when she told me that she had met an English boy and was secretly seeing him behind her parents' back.

"Oh my God. Are you serious?" I asked. "Your dad's going to kill you if he finds out."

"I know," she said. "We are trying not to get caught."

"Wow, that's great news but be careful, won't you?"

"I will."

"How exciting though. Tell me everything. What's he like? How did you meet? I want to know everything." She updated me on her little secret every time we met.

As for my cousin Antonia, one minute she was playing with us in the street and the next she was introduced to some Greek man from Cyprus called Solomos, got married, moved to Wales with her new husband and Auntie Marika went with her.

It all happened so quickly that I don't even remember saying goodbye to them.

My godfather sold his house, bought a fish and chip shop in Chingford, and moved in above the shop. As sad as I was that they were no longer around the corner, Chingford was not that far away and I loved going to the shop every Friday to eat fish and chips – as if I wasn't fat enough as it was!

Our gang had dismantled and my family was the only Greek family left on our street.

I was eleven years old and started my new secondary school in Stamford Hill. It was an all-girls school because I was not allowed to go to one where there were boys.

Not only was Mum strict but she was also very religious. She tried to get me into a convent school near our house, so that I could be taught by nuns, but when she realised that it was a Catholic school she decided that going to that school was "against our religion" and boy was I relieved.

I came home from school one day desperate to go to the toilet. As I sat down on the seat in relief I noticed that my knickers were full of blood and I went into shock. I thought I was bleeding to death and started to cry uncontrollably.

I screamed out for Mum who rushed to the toilet to see what was wrong. I was shaking with fear so much so that I couldn't speak. As soon as Mum saw the blood she gave me the hardest slap around the face that I ever had and made me cry even more.

"Why did you hit me, Mum, what have I done?"

"Nothing, darli'," she said. "You are a woman now," and she gave me a huge hug.

I was confused. One minute she slaps me around the face and then she hugs me. What the hell was happening to me, I thought.

She asked me to wait there for a minute while she went to fetch something and came back with a huge Dr White pad and a pair of clean knickers. She shoved the pad in the knickers and asked me to wear them. It felt bulky and awkward, like I was wearing a nappy between my legs. I continued to cry and she finally consoled me by saying, "Don't worry darli', it's OK," and proceeded to explain to me that all women have periods and it is normal to bleed every month. I started to feel a bit better when she told me that my cousins Antonia and Rita bled every month too.

"So why did you slap me around the face?" I asked wiping away my tears.

"Because that's what mums do," she said all flippant.

It was years later that I discovered that it was a Greek tradition for a mother to slap her daughter around the face when she sees her first period to get her daughter out of the shock. Surely it would have been better if she had explained to me what a period was before I got one, then I wouldn't have gone into shock in the first place?

I remember that night Mum came into my room and gave me a present wrapped up in brown paper and tied with cotton.

"This is a *prezon* (present) for you for becoming a woman."

It bought a smile to my face until I opened it and saw that it was a pair of floral cotton sheets with matching pillow cases. The real purpose of coming to my room was to give me a lecture on the birds and the bees, Cypriot style. "Now that you are a woman," she said, "you must act like a nice woman. You must never talk to men in the street and when a man looks at you, you must avert your eyes away from him. Do not laugh in front of men and remember your mother's words: there are two types of men in this world, those that want a good life and those that want a good time. The men that want a good time are bad men who want to have sex with you and be very careful because sex is dirty and unbearably painful. You can haemorrhage. If you let this happen I will kill you."

When she had finished putting the fear of God into me, she snatched the present off me and said "I will save it for when you get mari'," and shoved it at the bottom of my wardrobe.

Apart from this one lecture from Mum, sex was taboo in our house, so I didn't really know what sex was until my first sex education lesson in biology when me and my new Greek friend, Soulla, seemed to be the only girls in the class who didn't know anything about the facts of life, apart from it being dirty and a painful haemorrhage.

I developed early as a teenager and by the age of eleven I was five feet two inches tall, weighed nine and a half stone, had a 36DD chest and began to feel different from my classmates. I started feeling conscious about my body when I noticed that all the other girls in the class were half my size. One lunch break, during passing conversation, I asked some of the skinny English girls what they normally tended to eat every day.

"Generally," one said, "a cereal in the morning, a sandwich for lunch and a small family meal at night."

I realised then that three boiled eggs with three pieces of toast for breakfast, a lunchbox packed with stuffed vine leaves and meatballs, half a loaf of bread with a pot of taramosalata for lunch and half a pig with potatoes and *makaronia tou fournou* for dinner was not normal. It was no wonder that I was the size of an elephant and the boys never fancied me, preferring a girl called Sharon Price instead. She was a slim, blond, sexy girl who wore black eyeliner, inch-thick mascara, ruby-red lipstick and her skirts were shorter than my belt. I thought at the time that they preferred her to me because she put herself out, what other reason could there be? It didn't occur to me until then that it was because I had hairy legs as big as tree trunks – one of which was bigger than both of her legs put together – a pot belly bigger than my Dad's, an afro hairstyle and eyebrows that met in the middle.

I attempted to go on a diet much to Mum's disapproval.

"*En na katalithies*" ("You'll waste away"), she said.

It was impossible to go on a diet when the focus of my Greek Cypriot life was food, and Mum shopped in bulk from the cash and carry and cooked huge portions.

Despite me ending up in an all-girls school, it was still much better than being at home with my arguing parents. School for me was a form of escapism, as I didn't have a life at home. My daily routine consisted of doing my homework, cooking for the family, watching television until nine o'clock and then off to bed. I was not allowed to go out and I never questioned it. I thought this was how things were meant to be in a Greek Cypriot girl's life.

I was brainwashed into believing that it was normal for girls not to go out because girls that went out were "sluts". According to my mother they were "*tou thromou*" ("ladies of the street"). I never quite knew what *tou thromou* meant at the time, so I grew up thinking that all women who walked along the streets, apart from the ones walking to school, were "sluts". It wasn't until I got a little older that I began to understand that it was all about "virginity". I had never realised how powerful this virginity thing was and how much it affected the lives of so many generations of Greek Cypriot girls. It was the second main focus of Greek Cypriot life, after food. Let me explain: traditionally, a woman's foremost duty was to safeguard herself and her family against all aspersions on her sexual modesty. In her dress, attitude and speech, her duty in the presence of men was to be virginal. A woman who conformed to this "passive" modesty was considered *timia gynaika* (an honourable woman), whereas one who didn't was considered *atime* or *adiantrope* (shameless or dishonourable). This honour and shame was not restricted to her alone but spilled over to her family and tainted her father or brothers who did not protect her honour; so families always had to be vigilant of the behaviour and reputation of their daughters.

You would think that this tradition would have become extinct once Cypriots emigrated to England but alas it was still prevalent when I was growing up in the 1970s and1980s. Cypriot girls had to maintain their chastity until their wedding day, which did not only entail an intact hymen but also implied the avoidance of sexual desire. The parents would be disgraced if their daughter was not a virgin when she got married. So important was the purity of the bride, that when cousin Rita got married her mother-in-law entered the bedroom on the morning of the wedding night to check for blood stains on the sheets to make sure that her son had married a virgin.

To avoid the humiliation of this failed hymen test, my parents spent their whole lives trying to shelter me from boys and other works of the devil such as discos, short skirts and make-up, and prepare me instead to be a domesticated housewife and mother. Why didn't they just murder me at birth?

I was not allowed to have friends unless they were Greek and preferably cousins or family friends, and even then only if they didn't wear make-up or short skirts otherwise I was not even allowed to talk to them. Even Greek girls that had older brothers were a no-go.

English girls were definitely out of the question. Having an English friend, according to my mother, meant that I would inevitably become a lady of the street.

So I only had four friends that I could mix with who fitted the "suitability" criteria: cousin Stella, cousin Alexis, my old friend Mastra and my new best friend at school, Soulla. All our parents were equally strict in that none of us were allowed out apart from going to each other's houses, where we could be chaperoned.

I would never dare mention the words "pub" or "disco" to my parents because I would run the risk of getting a smack in the mouth or getting my hair pulled out. Those places were for "men only" and of course girls *tou thromou*. I was only allowed to go to school functions as long as they were in the school with teachers present.

I will never forget my first-ever school disco. It was from 6pm until 10pm and I got all dressed up in my best red Crimplene dress, with my black leggings to hide my fat legs. I was really excited because it was a joint event with the boys school down the road but of course I didn't mention that bit to my parents. It was the highlight of my year and Soulla and I had been looking forward to it for months but at the last minute Soulla's mum did not let her go and I had to be dropped there by Dad.

I was having the time of my life as the DJ played some of my favourite tunes including Alvin Stardust's "My Coo Ca Choo". I had been watching the dance group Pan's People every week on "Top of the Pops" and had noted some of their moves so I was really going for it.

I was strutting my stuff on the dance-floor to Showaddywaddy and "Tiger Feet" when the DJ slowed the tempo down and played Marie Osmond's "Paper Roses". The dance-floor soon cleared as all the girls went and stood at the edge waiting for a loitering boy to walk by and ask them to dance.

As "Paper Roses" faded out, Charles Aznavour's "She" started to play. I knew all the lyrics and was singing to it when a cute boy walked over to me and asked me to dance. I coyly accepted.

It felt so nice having his arms around me and I put my head on his chest as we slowly stepped round and round to "She". Everything was perfect and I really liked him. He must have liked me too because he held me close and whispered in my ear that his name was Derek.

He said I was beautiful as he lifted my chin up to his and I was dying with anticipation as we were about to kiss. This was going to be my first-ever kiss and just at that romantic, intimate moment I spotted my dad from the corner of my eye standing by the doorway looking straight at me.

I abruptly shoved Derek away from me, leaving him standing on the dance-floor all bewildered trying to regain his balance from the unsuspecting push.

I ran straight out of the front door in sheer embarrassment and didn't dare look back.

As I stormed out of the door I screamed at Dad. "Why did you come here two hours early, you were supposed to pick me up at ten like all the other parents?"

"Hurry up," he said. "I'm playing poker with *Koumparo* (your godfather)."

I never went to another school disco again.

CHAPTER 11

The Prodigal Sons

I went through my early teenage years being stuck in my prison at home, learning how to cook so that I could be a perfect little housewife.

While my Greek Cypriot girl friends and I were lodged at home, being groomed to be wives, there was one rule for the girls and another for the boys. No limitations applied to sons; they were free to wander the streets and were encouraged to develop their masculinity by "sowing their oats", while, God forbid, if we were caught wearing a tampon, we would be carted off to the doctors to discuss concerns about losing our virginity.

My brother Vasili was allowed to go out whenever he wanted, even though he was younger than me. Every weekend I would watch him blow-dry his self-highlighted hair, put on his white socks, a black shiny shirt open to the waist revealing his gold medallion, tight blue jeans and a huge gold sovereign ring on his little finger, which Mum had bought him and from a distance resembled a knuckleduster. He smothered so much Old Spice aftershave over himself that he left a trail of scent wherever he went and, as he walked out of the front door, he would kiss Mum on the cheek and say goodbye. She stared at him all goggle-eyed with pride and tapped him on the back "Goodbye, *ye mou* (my son)."

These traditional double standards developed an envy inside me, as I could not understand the injustice of me being a grade-A student, a form prefect and very responsible at home, yet I was not trusted to go out anywhere, whereas my brother was a truant and could go wherever he wanted.

I once bravely asked if I could go out too and to my surprise Mum said "Yes darli'." She took off her overalls; put on her anorak grabbed her bag and said "*Hade!* Let's go to Brentford Nylons." After a brief protest she dragged me on the bus and made me pull her huge shopping trolley.

We walked into the shop and she shouted over to the shop assistant at the top of her voice: "This is shit?" and I had to quickly explain before she threw us out of the shop that what Mum meant to say was "Are these sheets?"

On the way home on the bus she shouts out "O' ma' God I forgot", and before I could ask her what she had forgotten she shot up and pulled the emergency cord causing the bus to grind to a halt.

"Thank you," she said to the conductor and got off the bus. I apologised to the conductor and chased her down the road struggling to keep up with her. She ended up in a corner shop with an Indian shop attendant. "Halo," she said to him. She opened her trolley and slapped on the counter a stack of Green Shield Stamp books. "There you go, I have thirty-three and a half books so now can I have the Kenwood food mixer please?"

She was delighted with her exchange and beamed from ear to ear when the shop attendant told her that she had provided more books than was required and gave her a set of six glasses with gold rims and a stainless steel teapot set too. She made me carry the food mixer all the way home.

That's what I got when I asked to go out, whereas Vasili used to leave home every morning but seldom made it to school. He would bunk off every day and, like his role model Del Boy from the TV sit com "Only Fools and Horses", he would roam the streets all day "finding" things from car parts, TVs, radios even wrought iron gates, anything that he could find – and he never got questioned.

It wasn't until his exam results came out with his school reports at the end of the year that my parents realised that their son was a truant, but they didn't tell him off. If that had been me I would have had my hair pulled out. He left school with no academic qualifications but he had achieved a first-class honours in life on street corners. Dad named him *Kantounometris* (street corner counter) and still he was allowed to do exactly what he wanted. How was that fair?

He could ask Mum for anything and he would get it. He told her once that he wanted to be a mechanic and needed a Ford Capri to practise on. Mum was delighted about his work initiative so she bought him the car.

His idea of "practising" on it was covering the seats with white fur seat covers, hanging two furry dice from the rear wing mirror, sticking a sun visor on the front windscreen wiper with Mungas printed on it because it was his Citizen Band handle and fitting a full body kit which touched the floor.

If that wasn't enough to make me envious, one Friday night we were in my godparents' fish and chip shop, and me and Theo, being the eldest, had to work in the back of the shop peeling the potatoes. We were playing a game which we created called "Spuds". This entailed us throwing spuds over the fence into the adjacent curry house kitchen and aiming the spud to land in the saucepan of the curry being cooked on the stove. We usually got caught and told off by the Indian chef but this time the spud landed straight in the saucepan and nobody noticed. We quickly ducked down under the fence and laughed hysterically at the fact that we had got away with it.

Just at that moment the phone rang and Dad and my godfather dashed off to Chingford Police Station leaving us to run the shop.

They were gone for ages and returned with Vasili and Jimmy; they had been arrested and cautioned for stealing an Airfix model from a local toy store. My parents only gave them a brief ticking off with no punishment and it was straight back to business as usual in the chip shop. That night I almost persuaded Mum to let me go to the cinema to watch "The Great Gatsby" but Vasili stuck his oar in and told her not to let me go. I called him a bastard and told him that one day Karma will pay him back with daughters to get back at him for being a male chauvinist pig.

This sexual discrimination and these double standards were eating away at me to the extent that I became very bitter and resentful.

I hated my parents and my brother with a vengeance and felt that they were ruining my life. I felt trapped, with nothing for me to look forward to apart from knowing that one day my parents would find me a husband of their choice and I would have to marry him. The thought of that made me feel sick especially since I had already seen the fate of my older cousins, Antonia and Rita, when as soon as they turned eighteen were taken to *Proxenia*, introduced to some strange greasy moustached guys who had just come over from Cyprus and couldn't speak a word of English, and were soon married off.

My cousin Stella told me that a friend of hers was forced to marry an old, bald guy she didn't want because her parents had already "ordered the meat". The thought of that happening to me was my worst nightmare.

I stomped around the house like a stroppy teenager, locking myself in my room pretending to revise but really I was desperately trying to think of a way to escape from Alcatraz. I had bought Elvis' "40 Greatest Hits" with my pocket-money and I kept playing "In the Ghetto" and "Don't Cry Daddy", which reflected my melancholy mood. Then something dawned on me – and Vasili was the answer. Traditionally, as part of the dowry system, parents were expected to have invested in their son's education to ensure good employment prospects in return for property or land. There was no point in educating their daughters as they were only going to get married and have children, and career women were considered to be home wreckers when their place should be in the kitchen.

I knew that my parents wanted nothing more than to educate someone in the family, but Vasili was hardly going to be my parents' educational golden boy. Recognising this as their Achilles' heel, I realised that if I fulfilled their dreams by going to university not only would I become the golden girl but, more significantly for me, I would get to finally leave home and Alcatraz.

For ages I deliberated about what to study so that my parents would be proud of me and let me go to university.

As I was stuck at home all the time all I did was watch TV and I became a film addict. I watched every American musical from "Singing in the Rain" and "West Side Story" to "South Pacific". I would fantasise that I was a Hollywood movie star like Marilyn Monroe or Elizabeth Taylor until suddenly it came to me: I wanted to be a famous actress and live in Hollywood, and that way I was sure that my parents would be so proud of me.

I was so excited about telling them the news about my chosen career that I decided to make the announcement that night while we were sitting together in the lounge watching the six o'clock news. I was just about to tell them when there was a newsflash on the TV: Cyprus had been invaded.

Dad was first to spot it on the screen and he quickly leant closer to the TV to turn the volume up. "*Apanayia mou!* (Holy Mary), what's happened?," he said. As he turned the volume up we could hear the newsreader say that Turkish troops had invaded Cyprus and a film of soldiers parachuting out of planes to the sound of machine gun fire was being shown.

I could feel the panic as Mum quickly jumped up and picked up the phone to dial someone. She started to cry in frustration as she frantically kept dialling but could not get through

"I am trying to call the village but the phone is dead!" she cried. Dad grabbed the phone off her and said he would try and call Lefkonico.

"Maybe we can get through to them," he said, but that line was dead too.

Attempt after attempt was made to call both villages but to no avail. Both my parents were frantic to find out what had happened to their relatives, and Mum was particularly anxious about *Papou* Vasili who was now in his eighties and quite frail.

It was July 1974. I was only twelve years old but I remember it being a horrible time and one that I will never forget.

There was a solemn gloom in the air for days. I heard snippets of the adult conversations and managed to decipher that Uncle Yiasoumi was missing in action and nobody seemed to know who was dead or alive.

Mum and Dad were very subdued and this melancholy seemed to go on for weeks and months. Every news channel was kept on twenty-four hours a day in the hope of hearing any snippets of further developments regarding the war.

Then we finally got word by letter that *Papou* Vasili had died and my mum's worst nightmare had come true. The letter from Auntie Demitra said that he died peacefully in his sleep but Mum was convinced that it was the shock of the war that killed him.

Auntie Marika and Uncle Nicholas came to stay with us to console Mum but I never saw her cry so much. I was very sad and prayed in my room every night that things would get better.

But there was more bad news, a few weeks later, when we got word that both sides of the family had to evacuate their villages and became refugees, living in tents in refugee camps somewhere in the south of Cyprus. In just a few short weeks forty percent of Cyprus had been occupied by Turkish troops, thousands of people were killed or injured, or lost their homes and jobs, and 200,000 people fled to the southern part of the island to become refugees, including our relatives.

Mum was frantic to find out where the families had been moved to and I saw her rummaging through our wardrobes and drawers collecting clothes, hats, socks, blankets, anything she could gather, and prepared parcels to send to our relatives in Cyprus.

Flights to Cyprus were suspended and people were stranded. Every day our house seemed to be full of visitors bringing news of fellow villagers and family friends killed or missing in action. One of Dad's cousins called Simo was stranded in London, having come over on holiday a few weeks before the invasion. He stayed with us, sharing Vasili's room until one day all of a sudden Dad kicked him out of the house and threw his belongings into the street.

I didn't know what had happened or why Dad was so angry until I eavesdropped on a conversation between Dad and his Uncle Antrico when I heard Dad say that he had found out that Simo was a *prothotis* (traitor), a member of some organisation called EOKA Beta and that he was not here on holiday at all. He had left Cyprus to go into hiding because he was wanted for shooting his brother dead in cold blood just because he supported a left-wing party. I had never seen Dad so distraught and he kept shaking his head in disbelief.

"How could someone do that to their own flesh and blood?" he wondered. "Our own stupid people have sold our beautiful island for false promises of land and money."

He shook his head and cried. "Cyprus will never be the same again." But I never understood what he meant by that.

Vasili, Maria and I were somehow shielded from most of the heartbreak of the war. We carried on with everyday life, going to school and spending time with our cousins and friends.

My dream of being an actress had taken an unexpected back seat to the Cyprus invasion. It was a sad time and nothing else seemed important any more.

CHAPTER 12

The Conference

Sometime in February 1975 I was in my geography lesson when my name was called over the tannoy by the headmistress, Mrs Edwards.

"Will Annie Papadopoulos please come to my office?" I froze and everyone in the class looked at me wondering what I had done. Usually if a girl's name was called over the tannoy, interrupting a lesson, it meant that she was in some kind of trouble.

As I made my way apprehensively through the corridors to the headmistress's office, I had a horrible feeling that maybe another relative had died in Cyprus and my heart was racing as I knocked on her door and walked in.

"Annie, it is my pleasure to tell you that you have been chosen to make the speech at the school's O-level option night. You are a confident speaker and as such you are the right girl for the job. I am sure you will be a great ambassador for the school and do me proud."

I was somewhat relieved and excited when I realised that this was my chance to show to my parents how confident I was in front of an audience and what a great actress I could be.

On the night I saw Mum, from behind the stage curtain, sitting in the middle of the third row from the front. I remember thinking that she must have got there early to get such a good seat but there was no sign of Dad. I was disappointed but not surprised as he rarely attended parents' evenings because they usually clashed with one of his poker games.

As my name was announced by a teacher, I came out from behind the curtain and walked to the front of the stage feeling very proud and confident. Everyone was looking at me.

Mum was smiling with pride and she started waving at me and then started to shout out at the top of her voice. "*Anna mou, Anna mou*". She was flapping like a mad woman as she waved frantically to attract my attention, like I didn't already know she was there. I could hardly miss her. She wore her huge black fake-fur coat which made her look like a bear.

People turned to look at her and she looked back at them beaming like a Cheshire cat as she continued to shout out, "My dota, my dota," and pointed at me.

I was so embarrassed and at that moment I decided to change my opening speech to reflect her excitable outburst.

"Thanks Mum," I said. "In case any of you are deaf and you missed that, I am that lady's daughter, not dota, and sorry but she's Greek."

Everyone laughed as Mum sat back in her chair proud as a peacock, laughing with them, pretending to understand the joke. As the laughter died down I started my speech.

My speech was going really well and I knew I had succeeded in impressing the headmistress Mrs Edwards when I saw her smiling with a smug approval after I complemented her for doing such a good job.

"It can't be easy on her especially now that we have all started our PMT," I said.

I hesitated as I waited for another laugh but that bit didn't go down too well. I could see Mum lean over to a woman next to her I presumed to ask what PMT meant. I could see shocked and blushing faces in the audience and I got a dirty look from Mrs Edwards as she shuffled uncomfortably in her chair.

"Oops, moving swiftly on," I said and proceeded to introduce the teachers and run through the formalities of the evening.

"Finally, if I can ask that you spend no more than fifteen minutes with each teacher to give everyone a chance, otherwise I'm sure Mrs Edwards will get the cane out."

I laughed but that bit didn't go down too well either, although some of the girls chuckled. I got another dirty look from Mrs Edwards and by now I couldn't wait to get off the stage.

"So without further ado ..." I introduced Mrs Edwards so she could make her speech.

The audience clapped as I turned and walked behind the curtain.

I could hear Mum shouting "Bravo. Bravo darli'. Lovely, lovely," clapping louder and faster than everyone else.

To my surprise I was congratulated by everyone who came across me, even by Mrs Edwards. I felt so proud of myself and the evening was a great success, until it was my turn to see the teachers with Mum.

My priority was to get her to go and see the drama teacher, who wanted to tell Mum that I was a born natural and had the talent to go to drama school.

I walked with Mum towards the drama room and realised that there was going to be trouble when she kept saying: "Where's the science room?"

I was trying to distract her by telling her that the science teacher was busy and we had to go to see the drama teacher first, but she wasn't having any of it.

"Thrama? Why do I want to see the thrama teacher? You are going to be a doctor." This was news to me!

"Mum, I'm not going to be a doctor. I want to do drama."

"*Stamata prin na se trihomaliso!*" ("Stop before I tear your hair out!"), she said and we proceeded to have a full-blown argument in the corridor.

"I'm not going to be a doctor."

"That's what you think," she said crossing her arms in front of her and stomping down the corridor like she was on a mission.

"I'm not!"

"You are!" And her voice kept getting louder and louder, having no regard for the other parents that were in the vicinity who could hear her. I was getting more and more embarrassed, so I gave in to her and stomped off to the science lab where my biology teacher was waiting.

She was a tiny Indian lady called Mrs Ranjita. She really liked me and so looked pleased to see me with my mum. As we sat down, I was fuming inside but I tried not to show it. Mum was great at pretending nothing had happened. No-one would have known by looking at her that we had just had a full-blown row in the corridor in front of complete strangers. Butter wouldn't melt in her mouth as she smiled all sweetly at the teacher.

"Hallo, lady," she said.

"Hello, Mrs Papadopoulos. I am Mrs Ranjita, Annie's biology teacher ..."

Mum didn't even let her finish introducing herself as she got straight to the point. "Halo Jita. Yes, my dota want to be a doctor. Er, you see, I'm from poor family and big family in Cyprus. My father and mother was farmers of chigens and *eyes* (goats), erm how you say, gots and it would be my heart to make Anna a doctor to fix the family when sick. She is very good girl so she must be doctor, OK?"

I was mortified. Did she have no shame? First she called the teacher lady then Jita and what had being poor or breeding chickens and goats got to do with anything? I was embarrassed because of her accent and I was angry that she had decided to pick my career for me.

Unfortunately, Mrs Ranjita didn't help my cause either. She went on to sing my praises. She told Mum that I was the cleverest pupil in her class, her favourite student and agreed that I should be a doctor. This was all music to Mum's ears but then she went further to inform Mum that to be a doctor I had to take chemistry, physics and biology at O level and that was all I needed! Mum now knew that I required all three sciences to be a doctor and physics clashed with drama so now what was I going to do?

We never did get to see the drama teacher.

All the way home on the bus, Mum lectured me about how proud my grandparents would be if I became a doctor. She went on and on about how she did not have the opportunity to learn because she was too poor to go to school and had therefore never learned to read or write. She omitted to mention that she had been expelled, and wasn't aware that Auntie Marika had told me that but I didn't dare mention it.

All I could think about was how I was going to break the news to her that I wanted to be an actress. I thought I would try a little diplomacy.

"Mum, did you like my speech?" I asked. "You know I am quite good at giving speeches."

"Yes, darli'. Bravo."

"Sooo, my headmistress told me that I should become a newsreader or something like that."

I figured that if I told her that I wanted to be a newsreader it would come across very intelligent and she would more likely approve. I could then go to drama school and she would not know any different. Like hell!

"Your headmistress *en belli,* (is mad)," she blurted on the bus. "Typical English woman, *stupi'*. The Indian teacher is a foreigner like us, and she has more brains and she agree with me so you will be a doctor."

She wasn't having any of it.

She barely stepped through the door when she picked up the telephone and dialled. I don't know who she was ringing but I could hear every word.

"Anna is going to be a doctor!" She was rabbiting on about how I was the cleverest girl in the whole school and how I was every teacher's favourite student.

"Mum stop lying. That's not what the biology teacher actually said", but Mum only heard what she wanted to hear.

"Shuddup! I can't hear," she complained.

I waited until she had finally finished and she had sat down. I was plucking up the courage to tell her what my real plans were and that I was not going to be a doctor. Dad was there too so it was a great opportunity. I took a deep breath and it blurted out.

"I am going to be an actress!" I stood defiant with my head held high waiting for the reaction.

"Vot Un ahtress? That's what you think. You think you are going to bring shame on this family? You think you are going to be kissing every *pezevenki* (pimp) on TV? Well, it's too late. I have told everyone you are going to become a doctor now."

Dad just said, "OK."

I was gutted at her reaction, but I knew this was the moment I had to stand up for myself. I stood away, out of Mum's reach just in case she decided to slap me: "I am not going to be a doctor. I am going to be an actress and you are not going to stop me."

I ran out of the room, slammed the door and was petrified in case Mum came after me. I had never shouted at my parents before and I felt awfuly guilty. I locked myself in my bedroom but nobody came and I eventually cried myself to sleep.

Next morning nothing was said. I could hear that they were both working at the sewing machines and it took me ages to psych myself up to walk into the room. I pushed open the door and looked at them both.

"Hello, darli'," said Mum. "Go make breakfast."

It was not unusual for Mum to act as though nothing had happened. As she carried on sewing, looking so unbothered, I had a feeling that I had not heard the last of it. She was definitely up to something, I could tell by her smug face. I wondered if she was going to grab me by the hair when I wasn't looking.

A couple of days later she announced that we were all going to visit her sister Marika in Cardiff and she said that Uncle Nick and his family were going to be there too visiting from Birmingham. I got excited because my two older cousins,

Antonia and Maria, were really fun and I loved hearing the tough-guy stories of Uncle Nick and Auntie Marika and their heyday in London's East End.

The journey in the car to Cardiff was boring as usual. Three hours with my arguing parents, annoying brother and boring tomboy sister was enough to drive anyone mad. I had nothing in common with any of them and spent the whole journey reading my *Twinkle* magazine, which normally ended up covered in my sister's sick as she never travelled well.

There was a welcoming party when we arrived, as always. The whole family was there to greet us: Uncle Nick with his wife Nicolletta, cousin Maria and her younger brother Antoni, Auntie Marika and cousin Antonia with her husband Solomos and new baby Natasha, and with the five of us, too, it was always loud and chaotic.

Solomos owned a café and the family lived in the flat above, so it was exciting for me to sit and eat in the café – especially choosing food from a menu. But it was Saturday night and the café was closed, so we all paraded upstairs and I was a little disappointed about that.

Auntie Marika had the table laid out for dinner and it was a feast as usual with her eighteen different dishes.

Mum had made and brought with her, her speciality dish called *zaladina* (pig's brawn) which looked disgusting. It was clear jelly-like brine with meat inside but when she proudly announced that the meat was a pig's head I felt sick.

We couldn't hear ourselves speak from all the loud voices shouting across the table. "Chiyess!" Mum said raising her glass and that started everybody else off.

"Cheers! Cheers!" We youngsters clashed our glasses together and said "Chiyess" mimicking their Greek accents just to take the piss out of the adults and inevitably we got a dirty look from Mum.

After dinner the adults had a nap in front of the TV.

This was a traditional family ritual and was always the same.

Mum would have her mouth wide open, her head on the back of the sofa, snoring like a pig. Auntie Marika would have her chin resting on her huge breasts, with her arms crossed in front of her resting on her big belly and hissing like a snake. Uncle Nick would be facing straight ahead like a sergeant major, with his arms hanging down on either side of the armchair, and Auntie Nicolletta would be leaning on his shoulder, quietly wheezing. Dad always got a bed.

The rest of us just watched television or talked quietly, apart from Vasili and Antoni who did not stop laughing hysterically at something or another.

An hour or so later they all woke up and the peaceful room once again become loud and chaotic. Anyone passing by outside would think that there were over fifty people inside the house.

During one unusually quiet moment Mum sat up, completely out of the blue, and looked as if she were about to make an announcement.

"Ha! Anna has decided what she wants to be when she grows up." They all sat up straight and stared at me.

"Go on, tell them," said Mum. There was a deafening silence. I had been put on the spot and was completely taken aback.

"Go on," she urged.

So after looking at everyone, I said quietly, "I want to be an actress."

There was a stunned silence for a few seconds and then a huge roar of laughter.

"Ahdress!! Ha, ha!" said Auntie Marika.

I saw Uncle Nick bend over to Auntie Nicolletta and ask "What did she say? Ahdresss? Ha, ha!!"

"She wants to humiliate the family," said Mum and continued in an over-the-top dramatic voice, "She wants to kiss all those men on TV. *Inta pou na pei o kosmos*" (What are people going to say?) I would never be able to show my face again."

She then commanded them all, one by one, to say what they thought.

"Solomos, what do you think about this *belara* (madness)?"

He looked at me and said, "That's not a good job for a Greek girl, Annie."

Auntie Marika looked at me next. "No, darli'. Is no good this thing."

"They are all on drugs," said Antonia.

" *En oulles dou thromou*" ("They are all sluts"), said Auntie Marika.

"They are dirty, darli'," said Auntie Nicolletta.

"Listen to me, darling. I am the most diplomatic person in the family. Don't listen to these women. What do they know?" said Uncle Nick "I am head of the family and you are Greek and Greek girls don't be ahdress. Greek girls are good girls and you are a very good girl and we love you, but I'm sure you don't want to give your mum a heart attack and kill her do you?"

Very diplomatic? I wondered how long before the emotional blackmail card was going to surface. I realised at that moment that Mum had briefed them all beforehand. It was all planned, that's why she suddenly wanted to go to Cardiff. The visit was a set-up to persuade me to become a doctor and not an actress.

I was in a trance and the rest was a blur as they continued to ridicule me in their own ignorant, brutal way, led of course by my own mother.

All I could think of at that moment was that most normal fourteen-year-olds would sit around a table with their parents and discuss their O-level options like civilised adults, but I had a major drama involving the whole extended family, bullying and picking on one defenceless teenager. All because I wanted to take drama instead of physics. Anyone would think that I had just announced that I was pregnant or that I was marrying a Muslim.

So like a beaten dog I conceded and had to agree there and then to take physics instead of drama and gave up my dream of becoming an actress.

I tried to hold back the tears but they uncontrollably rolled down my face as I watched them all in silence, waiting and hoping that somebody would take pity on me and stick up for me, but nobody did. I looked at Dad and I could tell by his eyes that he felt sorry for me but he wouldn't dare disagree with Mum.

I was alone, like that child at the window, and they laughed at me crying too.

"Ha ha. What a baby," laughed Vasili.

"Don't be stupi'," said Mum.

Talk about beating a man when he's down.

CHAPTER 13

Levendi

It was early July 1975 and while everyone around me was enjoying the Bay City Rollers and the rare hot weather in the school summer holidays, I was a miserable moody teenager getting bored and still coming to terms with what my family had done to me in Cardiff a few months earlier.

Mum sometimes plonked me an unexpected kiss on the cheek, which I suspected was her way of letting me know that she felt some small element of guilt for causing me such sadness, but she would never admit it and she still never let me go out.

She came to my room one morning and asked if I wanted to go shopping and said that her and Dad would treat me to something for being such a good girl at school. We started off at Barnaby's Patisserie where she bought me a huge chocolate cake and the shopping trip ended up being a stock shop at the Cash and Carry, where I ended up lugging the trolley to the car and her treat to me was a continental quilt and a colouring book as if I were five.

I spent much of that early summer with my cousin Stella at her parents' new restaurant in Bethnal Green, where they made us wash the dishes and clear tables. We were both bored out of our brains listening to our mums talk about the old days and constantly repeating that "kids nowadays are not like us anymore, they are lazy," referring to us, I'm sure.

When Mum and Auntie Florou got together they were so

loud that they could be heard the other side of the street. Stella and I started to call them 'psycho she-men' after an incident one day when a group of young boys were playing football outside the restaurant and their ball accidentally hit the window. Auntie Florou rushed outside with a carving knife, stabbed the ball three times and ripped it to shreds like a psychopath.

The only amusing thing that happened that summer was when four long-haired, scruffy looking men walked into the restaurant dressed in tight, ripped, stone-washed jeans and t-shirts. As they sat at a table I could see that Mum and Auntie Florou were not impressed.

"*Athe kilikin*" ("What a state")," Mum complained. "Their hair is longer than mine," she added.

Auntie Florou asked Mum to sit by the door and keep an eye on them. "They are tramps," she said. "They are not going to pay. They are gypsies."

Mum manoeuvred her way to the door and sat there with her arms crossed, glaring at them the whole time they were eating.

As they got close to finishing their food, Auntie Florou grabbed a frying pan and sat the other side of the door ready to pounce on them if they tried to do a runner. Just at that moment a couple walked through the door and, upon spotting the four men, went over to them and asked for their autographs.

The four long-haired gypsy tramps turned out to be the famous band called Status Quo. Well, as soon as Auntie Florou found out that there were celebrities in her restaurant she wanted pictures of them for her wall and she let them have their food complimentary, telling them repeatedly that they were "lovely boys".

So much for doing a runner and Auntie Florou did not stop going on about "Statous Quotus" the whole summer.

I still hadn't forgiven Mum for setting me up in Cardiff but I noticed that she made constant efforts to make it up to me by cooking my favourite food and making Vasili clean his own room for a change instead of me.

One morning she came into my room and told me that she had organised a weekend break to Great Yarmouth with Auntie Pezouna and cousin Alexis, along with our two younger sisters. I had vowed in the past never to go on any more seaside trips with my parents, especially after the *moloshes* and limpet trips but as Alexis was going I figured that it would be fun.

It was not until we got to Great Yarmouth that I realised I had made a big mistake.

We were not allowed to go anywhere, not to the amusement arcades, the funfair nor the beach, unless they came with us. It was a nightmare from the start.

Other children were playing in the sea and having a good time, while we had to sit there on a huge blanket on the sand with crimple hats on, our heads smothered in factor 50, and I was forced to wear my orange swimming costume with a little frilly skirt which Mum had sewn on to it supposedly so that boys could not see my private parts.

Alexis had to hold yarn for my mum while she crocheted her *petsetaki*. Auntie Pezouna was knitting a disgusting woolly jumper for Alexis, and we were getting so bored and frustrated that we decided to plot a plan to get away on our own.

The plan was that if we constantly moaned at them they would soon get fed up with us and let us go off on our own. So I started first.

"Mum, I'm bored."

"Well, eat some bread," Mum replied.

"Mum, I'm bored too," moaned Alexis and the response from Auntie Pezouna was "Shuddup."

"Mum, I'm really bored," I complained.

There was no answer because she was counting her stitches out loud in her Greek accent. "Thirdin, fordin, fifdin ..."

I winked at Alexis signalling to her to try again.

"M-u-u-m," she pleaded. "Please, I'm really bored. Can we go and play?"

"What's wrong with here? Play here," replied Auntie Pezouna.

"We don't want to play here with you. We want to play by ourselves."

Auntie Pezouna gave her a dirty look. "That's enough. Do you hear me?"

When Mum had stopped counting, I continued: "Muuuuuuum!"

"Vot?" she asked loudly, glaring at me with her beady eyes over the top of her glasses.

"We're bored. Can we go and play?"

"No" she said firmly and carried on with her crochet.

To my surprise, Alexis bravely stood and said, "Well, I'm going," at which point Auntie Pezouna grabbed her by the hair forcing Alexis to drop Mum's yarn so she could un-grip her mum's hands from her hair, and Mum started screaming at the top of her voice: "My yarn, my yarn, O ma' God, my yarn!"

Alexis broke free and ran off as fast as she could down the beach, quickly chased by Auntie Pezouna with her flip-flops and still holding her knitting needles, yelling: "Come here, I am going to kill you, *bastarda*!"

Maria starting laughing and got a slap in the mouth from Mum, which made Alexis' little sister, Pavlitsa, cry her eyes out as she screamed: "Run, Alexis run!" Mum was trying to salvage her yarn from the sand, desperately trying to unravel it and swearing under her breath "*bastarda*", as I watched Alexis running like the clappers along the seafront with Auntie Pezouna chasing her and waving her flip-flop in the air until they both disappeared out of sight.

As I stood there watching, I realised that everyone on the beach was staring at us, as Mum continued shouting like a drama queen: "*Chapin pou epatha*" (What bad luck has befallen me). O ma God, my yarn".

We spent the remainder of the weekend locked up in our bedroom, where we had a good time chatting on our own without our crazy mothers around, even though Alexis had a huge bald patch on her head from after Auntie Pezouna finally got hold of her.

By the time we got back home I was more miserable than ever and I made pretty damn sure that Mum knew it. Having learned from the master, I started to use emotional blackmail on her and made sure she never saw me with a smile on my face just to make her feel bad.

It appeared to work when one day, out of the blue, she told me that my cousin Anastasis in Cyprus wanted me to go to Cyprus to christen his baby son, Panayi, and said that she had bought me a ticket to Cyprus, leaving next week. I was given no choice in the matter and couldn't help but wonder if this was her way of making it up to me and saying sorry for hurting me.

I was excited that I was going on holiday to Cyprus but I was a bit nervous about flying on a plane on my own for the first time. My mind was soon taken off the flight when Mum took me shopping to Sali Salim warehouse in Whitechapel and bought me lots of clothes and presents for all the Cyprus cousins. I couldn't wait to see Vasili to rub it in that Mum bought me a whole new wardrobe of clothes and that I was going on holiday and he wasn't.

Only a short time had passed since the war ended in Cyprus and the aftermath was still raw. Although flights had been reinstated and it was safe to travel, both my parents' villages were now occupied by Turkish troops so I didn't know where I was going to be staying. Nicosia airport was also in the occupied territory, so my aeroplane landed in a small makeshift airport at Larnaca, in the middle of nowhere. The entire social fabric of Cyprus was destabilised. Family ties were abruptly loosened or disappeared in the chaos of the evacuation to the south, and the affects of the invasion and continuing occupation were profound.

I was picked up at the airport by my cousin Anastasis and I was happy to see him again. We drove for about forty-five minutes to a place called Kolossi on the outskirts of Limassol and we were remembering the time when his dad, Yiasoumi, put us all in the back of his tractor and drove us to the beach when we were small kids. Anastasis held back the tears as he told me that his dad was still missing and he didn't know whether he was dead or alive, and I was sad about that.

As we slowly drove through the village I saw rows of white tents where everyone had been living since the war. Washing lines were full of drying clothes and people were sleeping on camp beds under makeshift canopies made of sheets and towels.

It was hot and humid but children were running around playing and there was a strong aroma of barbeque in the air. I did not expect to see a ghetto. I had watched documentaries on TV about poverty in Angola and Ethiopia in Africa but I was not expecting it to be in Cyprus too.

The car finally came to a stop outside a small, white, single-storey, flat-roofed hut surrounded by tents and Anastasis pointed to one of the tents and said, "That is where you are going to sleep the next few weeks."

I was actually excited about this as I had never been allowed to go camping before and this seemed to be the next best thing. Despite the obvious poverty-stricken surroundings, there was a sense of peace and harmony in the air.

I was greeted by a whole new posse of family, as all my cousins had got married and had children – making our family bigger since I last saw them in 1969.

Auntie Dimitra was the first to grab and hug me. She cried uncontrollably as she tried to tell me that she sorely missed Uncle Yiasoumi. I tried to console her by squeezing her tight but couldn't stop her from crying.

Then Uncle Pavlo and his wife Auntie Kaliopi came out of the hut and hugged and kissed me for ages.

I felt so loved as all my cousins' children surrounded me. I was their Auntie Anna from England and they were so excited. I was overwhelmed and felt so important, as everyone was trying to speak to me at once, and I became even more popular when I opened one of the suitcases and gave everyone their presents.

Anastasis's wife Militsa then came out of the hut holding baby Panayi and introduced me to my godson for the first time. He was huge and gorgeous, and I couldn't wait for his christening, even though I was petrified in case I dropped him.

It soon got around the camp site that somebody from England had arrived, and small children and adults from all over kept popping in to my tent to see me. I had no privacy but it was incredible. It was as though my visit brought excitement throughout the camp and I felt like a celebrity. I got a small taste of what it was like to be famous and I loved it.

I was determined to enjoy my new-found fame during my stay and it made me want to be an actress even more.

Uncles Pavlos' daughter-in-law, Eleni, came over from her tent and told me that her cousin's eighteen-year-old daughter from England was staying with her for the holidays and couldn't speak much Greek. She asked me if I could make friends with her because she had been on camp one week and was already getting bored.

I went to her tent and introduced myself to her. Her name was Youlla and we hit it off straightaway.

"God, am I glad to hear another English voice around here. I've been struggling with my Greek," she said.

"Well, I'm glad you're here, too. I'm Annie. It's a bit surreal here, isn't it?" I said.

Every day Youlla and I would get together and cause a bit of a stir in the camp, mainly because of the way we dressed. Some campers believed that we were exposing our bodies in shorts and bikini tops and people would stare at us as if we were naked.

We would get wolf-whistled at by men, glared at by children and tutted at by old ladies, crossing themselves when we deliberately walked by their tents in our bikinis to get to the communal toilets and showers.

"*Christos je Panayia mou*" ("Holy Jesus and Mary"), we would hear them say, finding this amusing.

There were separate shower and toilet cubicles for men and women, and we had a fair walk to get to them. To wash our clothes we had to queue up outside another hut containing oversized butler sinks and endure the gaping stares of the locals, which also made us laugh as we cussed them back in English.

As primitive as it all was, Youlla and I were loving the attention we were getting from everyone, especially the guys.

When we were not walking around the camp causing tongues to wag, we would be in Youlla's tent listening to my newly acquired taste for Greek music, especially Barios, Kazantzithis and Marinella, and the rest of the time we did not stop talking and laugh hysterically – usually about the primitive surroundings we found ourselves in.

Youlla got up from her chair and put on her shoes to go outside to fetch us some water when all of a sudden she screamed the place down – scaring the life out of me. She had felt something move in her shoe and when she slung her shoe across the tent a huge black scorpion came running out. I jumped up and started screaming with her as we both sped out of the tent like Speedy Gonzales and the Roadrunner.

Youlla had had enough and she phoned her dad from the village telephone to get her a flight back to England. I was disappointed that she couldn't stay for the christening but we exchanged addresses and promised to keep in touch when we got back home.

The christening service was over and it went well and I was somewhat relieved that I didn't drop the baby.

The reception was held in the village church plaza and Auntie Dimitra asked me to sit next to her, where she introduced me to a man called Levendi. He was around his mid-thirties, quite short, with a moustache twisted at the ends and had a bald patch and a big pot belly. He smoked a cigar and the most noticeable feature about him was that he had an exceptionally long nail on his little finger.

He sat next to me and put his arm at the back of my chair, practically having his arm around me and he stank of BO. His face was about three inches away from mine and I could smell his garlic breath.

"Hallo, Anna," he said.

"How do you know my name?" I asked.

"Your Auntie Dimitra has told me all about you. I'm Levendi."

Auntie Dimitra conveniently said that she had to go somewhere and left me there on my own with him and I could see people staring in my direction.

Levendi asked me if I wanted a drink and I said no immediately, wanting to get away quickly. He was holding *paterimi* (worry beads) and was flicking them around his right hand like a munga (a dude).

He rudely called the waiter "Re" and in a bad American accent said, "scatch racks". The waiter looked at him puzzled and said, "Do you mean scotch on the rocks?"

"Yeah, scatch racks," trying to impress me. He flicked his *paterimi* around again and leant closer to me.

"I am looking for a wife and I hear that you are ripe and ready."

I looked at him in disgust and said, "Ready for what?"

"Ready to get married", he replied.

"Well, I'm not. I'm only fifteen."

"Anna, you are beautiful and I love women with *miala vizia* (big tits) as he glared at them.

"Oh my God, I can't believe what you just said to me," I shouted, but he just smiled.

He disgusted me and I kept turning my back to him so I couldn't smell him. Just then Auntie Dimitra came back and asked how we were getting on.

"We are perfect for each other," he said and I muttered, "In your dreams," but he didn't hear me. Auntie Dimitra then proceeded to tell me that Levendi's parents were good friends of the family and he owned a house which he had built himself at the end of the village, which had thirty acres of land. She then went on to say that he was a very nice and well-respected man and that he was one of the richest landowners in the village; he had more goats than the whole village put together.

It suddenly dawned on me while she was singing his praises that this was a set-up. I started to suspect that Mum had something to do with it and perhaps setting me up with Levendi the pervert was the real reason for my trip to Cyprus. I started to panic and felt myself going red with fear. "Oh God, please no," I prayed to myself. I did not want to be forced to marry Levendi whose name, incidentally, means gorgeous, but he was far from that.

I felt sick and was so overcome with emotion and anger that I started to cry. He tried to hug me to console me but he repulsed me and as I stood up to push him away I threw up all over his tight white shirt. I wasn't even sorry as I left him standing there cringing and trying to wipe my sick off his shirt with a paper napkin.

Anger set in as I tried to digest how insulted I felt. Is this what I was worth? Did I deserve to be with a fat sleaze-ball like him? This made me more determined than ever to go to university and leave home.

The christening and the holiday were over and it was time to fly back home and start my O-levels.

CHAPTER 14

The Jubilee

I was angry with Mum for forcing me to take physics and for trying to set me up with Levendi, who was never mentioned again by the way.

Every time I walked past the drama class on my way to the physics lab, my heart would sink to my stomach and I made up my mind that I was never going to become a doctor and I deliberately set out to fail physics just to spite Mum.

I began to accept that I would never go to drama school and feared that I would be stuck in the Greek Cypriot world forever.

I developed an identity crisis and started to lose interest in all my school subjects. From being a straight A-grade student, my grades started to plummet. My deep resentment spilled over into my home life as I began to answer-back to my parents and became very argumentative with them and Vasili.

I started to get very jealous of the freedom that he had and I made fun of his "Saturday Night Fever" quiff hairstyle and his John Travolta wannabe life-style but he always got the last laugh because all he had to say was, "I'm going out and you're staying home," and that was enough to bring out the green-eyed monster in me.

I went to bed at night with rage and jealousy burning inside me, hating everyone and my life.

So I plodded along like Jekyll and Hyde for the next two years and I sat my O-levels in June 1977 just in time for the

Silver Jubilee street party. This was about the only exciting thing that happened that year and Mum put a damper on that too when she sent me home to bed at eight o'clock when she saw me talking to a boy.

Throughout the summer holidays I was anxious about my results and I tried to keep myself busy to get my mind off them. I worked in my godfather's fish shop every Friday and while I was washing my hands in the sink one night I heard a newsflash on the TV. Elvis was dead. I cried for days.

The day of the results finally arrived and I passed eight O-levels with good grades but more gratifying for me was that I failed physics with an unclassified 'U' grade.

Mum was furious and I pretended to be disappointed.

"Oh, dear," I said sarcastically, "that means I can't be a doctor now. Never mind."

She gave me a dirty look like she somehow knew that I had failed on purpose and I gave her a fake forlorn look back and ignored her.

That night Alexis, Soulla and Mastra were in my bedroom celebrating our exam results and moaning as usual about our parents' strictness. I began to tell them about my plans for us all to do A-levels, go to university and escape to freedom, but I was stopped in my tracks.

Soulla announced completely out of the blue that she was getting married.

"What!" When did this happen?" I asked in shock.

Soulla explained that during the summer holidays she had *proxenia* with a guy called Christaki who seemed a nice guy, so thought it best if she married him to please her Mum and Dad.

"Wow! Do you like him?" I asked.

"Yes I do, he's quite nice," she replied.

"Well, if that's the case then I'm really happy for you" and I leant over and gave her a hug to congratulate her.

"Yes, congratulations," said Mastra and Alexis and they hugged her too.

Alexis then said "I have something to say, too. I have had enough of being a slave to my parents so I've made a pact with a Greek boy from school to get married, so that I can be allowed out and get away from my parents."

"That's ridiculous. You don't even love him," I said.

"You don't even know him, let alone love him," said Mastra. "Don't do it. There must be a better way of being allowed out than to marry a stranger!"

"Not for me," Alexis said, all despondent.

"Come to uni with me," I said.

"You've seen what my parents are like," Alexis said. "They are stricter than all of yours. They won't let me go to uni. They don't believe in women getting educated because they think it's a waste of time. No. I have made up my mind; it's for the best. He will look after me."

I felt so sorry for her. She was my favourite cousin and I could not find any words to comfort her. "Well, if you're sure that's what you want."

"Yes it is," she said and we huddled together in support. Just as I was trying to come to terms with two of my friends getting married, Mastra then came out with: "Well, I might as well tell you my news then. I was going to tell you last night over the phone but as we were meeting today I wanted to tell you out of Dad's earshot."

"Oh my God, what's happened?" I asked.

"Dad caught me and Gerry kissing at the end of my road and he went ballistic and is now insisting that Gerry marries me otherwise he will chop his legs off."

"What!"

"You have got to be kidding us!," I exclaimed.

"No, I'm not. I'm serious."

"So what are you going to do? He can't force you to get married," I said.

"No. It's going to be fine. Me and Gerry spoke about it and we want to get married anyway. I guess this has just pushed us to do it earlier, that's all," said Mastra.

"Wow. That's great," I said but for a moment I felt so alone. All my friends were getting married and moving on with their lives and, although I was very tempted to follow the same route, the thought of being with someone like Levendi the perv made me want to hang on and follow my dreams.

I had three weddings that year and I was the maid of honour at all three.

My three best friends were now married and I missed them dreadfully. I had to come to terms with the fact that I was not going to be seeing much of them anymore and the only thing that kept me going was the thought of going to university as far away from home as possible so that I could be free to live as I wanted.

I buckled down to my studies and while all my Greek friends were having sex with their husbands I was studying, producing a Chelsea FC scrapbook and stuffing vine leaves.

I continued my love for films, watched "Randal and Hopkirk" and "Starsky and Hutch" on TV and added Diana Ross, Barbra Streisand and Elton John to my music collection.

The time came when I had to choose which university I was going to attend. I tried to keep this quiet from Mum so that she wouldn't get a chance to interfere and pick one for me, but somehow she found out. I don't know how she discovered this, but I got a lecture about which university I should attend. Like she knew! Mrs Expert on education who got expelled from school!

I heard her making enquiries over the phone to my cousin Maria in Birmingham about which was the best university in London. I could feel my heart racing and broke out into a hot sweat as I eavesdropped on her conversation. Snapshots of that family conference in Cardiff where I was forced to give up on my dream career were slowly coming back to me and I had visions in my mind of another one of Mum's family conferences which would force me to go to a London university and ruin my plans to leave home.

She insisted on seeing the application form to make sure that I had listed London universities on there. She turned off her sewing machine, put on her glasses and looked carefully at the universities, one by one. I could see her little beady eyes moving lower and lower down the page. My heart was pumping and I was praying to God that she didn't make me list all London universities. She put her glasses down, gave me the form and said: "Bravo. *Theos Voithos* (May God be with you)."

I sighed with relief and I couldn't retain my excitement. I grabbed the form, dashed out of the sewing room, ran into my bedroom and shut the door. All I had to do was send the form and Bob's your uncle. My ticket to freedom!

Already I felt a heavy cloud lifting from above my head. I was almost free! All that stood in the way of my freedom were three measly A-levels.

I took English Literature, Political History and Law, and you have never seen me work so hard. I learned everything about Mussolini and Disraeli. Law was easy and interesting, and, although I found English boring, I only had to write three good essays.

I never wanted anything so badly in my whole life and as I slowly opened up the brown envelope and looked at my grades, I jumped up and down in sheer ecstasy calling out "Thank you, God!" I passed! I secured a place at university and as I got my best grade in Law, I chose to study law.

I had secured my freedom by accepting a place at the College of Law in Essex, which meant I was leaving home and at the same time I became Mum and Dad's golden girl as they were so proud that their daughter was going to "be a lawyer". Mum grabbed the phone and told everyone she knew: "My *dota* is going to be a lawyer."

Even Dad, who never said a word to anyone about anything unless it was about left-wing politics or poker, started boasting about me being a *thikihoros* (lawyer).

From being the disgraced daughter who wanted to be a

prostitute actress, I had now become the perfect daughter who was going to be a lawyer. What a result; I accidentally managed to kill two birds with one stone. Things had started to look up for me and I could finally see a bright light at the end of the dark tunnel. I was on my way.

CHAPTER 15

Mind Your Language

It was 9 September 1981. I will never forget that date because it was the day I finally escaped from Alcatraz.

I was nineteen years old and university was starting in two days' time. I packed my belongings into my little second-hand Ford Fiesta car which my parents had bought me for passing my exams and my driving test. I had loaded up all my clothes, posters, bedding and a whole ton of food.

Mum made me a huge dish of *makaronia tou fournou* which she had cut into small separate pieces and individually wrapped in tin foil ready to put into a freezer. She had also packed some koupepia (stuffed vine leaves) and meatballs for me to eat when I arrived, along with practically the whole contents of her fridge.

She gave me an icon of the Virgin Mary to hang above my bed "so that Mary can look after you" she said, and a jug of holy water "to spray in your new house to keep away the *Satana*," as she wiped away a tear from her eyes.

It took me days to convince her that she really did not have to go to the university with me as I was more than capable of unpacking everything myself.

I was counting the minutes until 2pm when I was due to set off – and finally the moment arrived. I put the last of the bags into the boot of my car and closed the door. Mum, Dad, Vasili and Maria were all standing by. I kissed and hugged them all goodbye and got in my car. As I was putting on my seatbelt, Mum started her lecture: "No mucking about," she said. "*Oi belares*, (no stupidities) just do your studies and don't listen to anyone, especially those English *poutanes*. You must eat."

I humoured her for the last time, "No, Mum, yes, Mum, no Mum." I finally started the car and off I went.

I cannot describe how ecstatic and relieved I felt as I drove away: I grinned all the way to Chelmsford.

The student house was a large Victorian semi on a main road, about half a mile's walk from the university campus. When I arrived I was greeted by a short Geordie girl called Carol, a large Chinese girl called Ling who had a strong Chinese accent, and a tall lanky African girl called Vanessa, who could not understand much English. It reminded me of a TV programme about foreign students called "Mind Your Language".

My room was on the first floor and I picked the bed nearest the wall and started unpacking. Soon my Chelsea duvet cover was on the bed and my Chelsea posters stuck to the wall with Blu-Tack. My record player and records were last to be unpacked and I instantly felt at home.

I opened up one of the foil packets and ate a *koupepi* but Carol spotted me eating the stuffed green vine leaf and said "Yuk, gross," and I was quietly offended.

It was late and I was beginning to wonder whether my roommate was going to turn up. I was excited and curious to see what she would be like, and was quite relieved that I was not sharing a room with Carol. I kept staring around my room with a big grin on my face as it started to sink in that I had finally left home. This was going to be my first night of sleeping away from home and it felt great.

The next morning, I got up early and dressed. I decided to check out the area. It was Sunday morning and everywhere was quiet. I checked everything out and found a phone box and called Mum to let her know that I had arrived safely.

"When are you coming home?" she asked.

"Mum, I've only just got here."

"So? I want you to come home every weekend so that I can feed you."

"I'm not coming home every weekend, Mum. I am eating just fine".

"So, when are you coming home then?"

"I don't know yet. Maybe in a few weeks."

"A few weeks? Oh blami'," she bellowed down the phone.

"Mum, I don't know yet. Soon. I will let you know."

"OK, see you next week then."

"I didn't say I was coming next week, I said I will let you know. I'm not promising."

"Anyway, I have to go to church now, bye," and she hang up on me before I could say anything else.

I strolled through the town and around the deserted campus feeling very happy and independent – still with the same huge grin on my face. It was the first time in my life that I felt no sense of time. I could go home any time I wanted and that felt so liberating.

My alarm woke me up at seven, I got ready and walked to campus. The university building was a huge, old-fashioned mansion house with hundreds of windows and covered in green ivy. Sunday had been very quiet but now there were hundreds of young people rushing around in all directions.

I made my way inside the building and looked for lecture theatre room one as stated in my Information Pack. I pushed open the large, carved, oak door which revealed a huge auditorium rather like a cinema complex where rows and rows of benches rose up towards the back almost reaching the ceiling. I stood for a moment just looking at my surroundings feeling completely overwhelmed. It reminded me of American movies and for a split second I thought I was in Hollywood.

There were a few students scattered around and I chose to sit half-way up the auditorium and before long every seat was taken.

I was sitting there smiling like a Cheshire cat but felt completely out of my league. I suddenly realised that the boys outnumbered the girls by about ten to one. I was checking out every guy that walked through the door and I had already spotted about twenty that I liked, one in particular.

He was rather French-looking, tall, skinny with shoulder-length straight black hair, drainpipe black jeans and big brown eyes. My heart missed a beat when I took a good look at him as he passed my row. I had never seen so many gorgeous guys in the same room before and I remember me thinking, "Boy, this is going to be fun!" My grin got even wider as the day went on.

Lecturers with robes, mortarboards and gowns appeared from a side door and stood behind a giant wooden podium at the front of the auditorium. One welcomed us all to the university while others handed out material down the rows. By the end of the induction, we all had six inches of papers to take away and read.

Ten minutes into the talk, the door opened and a girl walked in, seemingly out of breath, apologised quietly for being late and perched herself at the end of the front row. She was slim with long, frizzy light-brown hair and wore a white woollen jumper and a long, floral skirt. She looked very plain and very serious. I kept looking at her and wondering whether she was my roommate.

The induction was over and everyone began to pile out of the room. I tried to keep the girl in my sight but she soon disappeared into the crowd. I walked back to the house and, just as I was approaching the front door, there she was. She had her back to me facing the door and was about to put her key in the lock.

"Hey, I'm your room mate!" I shouted loudly.

She turned around, rather startled and looked at me in surprise.

"Oh, are you? Hi, I'm Laurie."

"I'm Annie." I rushed up to her and gave her a big hug but I must have crushed her bones because she froze on the spot and looked in pain. Either that or she was not expecting the huge over-the-top bear hug from a complete stranger.

I could see that she was slightly taken aback so I backed off to give her some space and explained that I was Greek and that's how we greet people. She laughed as we went upstairs to our room.

We sat down on our beds and she began to tell me that she lived on a farm in the Norfolk countryside, with her parents and sister and all her animals. She grew her own crops, loved organic food and her passions were classical music, ballet and opera.

The more she was telling me, the more I was cringing and thought that this person couldn't be more different from me. How were we going to get along? I knew nothing about all the things she had mentioned. I hated opera and I was more into Lionel Ritchie, Voskopoulos and Barios.

She went on to tell me that she had travelled extensively throughout England and Europe, she was very good at geography and history, and had a particular interest in world politics and environmental initiatives. She even made her own clothes and knitted her own jumpers.

My eyebrows were rising higher and higher.

In her spare time she read novels but what really made me cringe was when she told me that she liked to go to bed early and get up to see the sunrise. "Great," I said but what I was really thinking was this is going to be a nightmare especially since I went to bed late and got up at lunchtime.

"Oh, Laurie, from what you've told me, I don't think we could be any more different. I come from the East End of London and I've never travelled anywhere apart from Cyprus where my parents came from and I've never even been to the countryside. I love football and pop music and I'm a TV addict."

"I don't have a TV but I like listening to the radio," replied Laurie.

"You don't have a TV?" I asked incredulously.

"No, I prefer to read."

This was the first time I realised how uncultured I was and had nothing else to say. I was too embarrassed to tell her that the only things I read were *The Sun*, *Twinkle* and football magazines. I knew nothing about art, geography, history and definitely not world politics, apart from the history of Cyprus and I thought I'd keep quiet about Dad being a smoking, left-wing, poker-playing communist.

I felt ignorant and I could see from her face that she was not impressed.

"Oh, I see," she said.

I felt inadequate and I was overcome with anger and bitterness towards my parents for keeping me locked away for so long. They had stunted my artistic growth. I was a pleb, common as muck, and completely ignorant about life and the world around me.

Laurie and I came from two different worlds, which was apparent from our belongings. On my side of the room there was the conspicuous blue Chelsea duvet cover, with posters of the Chelsea football team above my bed. My bookcase held my record collection, my small furry dog football mascot, my icon of the Virgin Mary and a small, cheap bottle of Lancôme perfume. My Chelsea scarf was sprawled across the top shelf with not a book in sight.

On Laurie's side there was a feminine pink and white floral duvet cover with matching pillowcase which she said was from Laura Ashley. I pretended that I knew who Laura Ashley was but I had never heard of her or knew that it was a shop.

Her duvet, she said, was made of soft goose feathers as she "couldn't bare synthetics" and on her wall were framed prints of "The Sunflowers" by her "favourite" artist Van Gogh and her David Shepherd elephant print which she said was signed by the great man himself.

Her bookcase was filled with poetry books and volumes by Shakespeare, Charles Dickens and Jane Austen – exactly as a bookcase should be apart from the top left-hand corner where she had a picture of Jesus and a photo of her two dogs and her horse.

Her side of the window-sill was full of vases of beautiful flowers and pots with plants, from ferns to cacti, and my side was where I kept my Afro comb.

Her wardrobe was full of homemade Aran jumpers, as she called them, and a green Barbour jacket; while mine was packed with cheap clothes bought from Walthamstow Market crammed together into disorganised chaos – from Lycra tops, leggings and fake Pringle jumpers to a black fake-leather bomber jacket covered in zips that kept getting stuck.

Her underwear drawer housed her frilly knickers and delicate thongs; while mine housed my huge Bridget Jones knickers to cover my huge Greek Cypriot arse, and my 36EE bras which took up a whole drawer by themselves.

Whoever would have thought that a fat Greek girl with an Afro hairstyle, Lycra leggings with legwarmers and matching wrist bands would be such an aphrodisiac?

There were so many gorgeous boys around who completely outnumbered the girls, it was very easy to pick up guys. Boys were attracted to us like flies, constantly being approached by them like dogs on heat. I could have any guy I wanted, it was that easy, and I didn't have to look like Sharon Price from my old school either.

To my surprise the gorgeous French-looking guy made a beeline for me. His name was Alan but he was hardly French. He was from Leeds and had a squeaky high-pitched voice that really put me off him. To make it worse he was a wet, sloppy kisser and I hated that, so I ended up avoiding him until he got the message that I really didn't want him hanging around me anymore, cramping my style.

It was one continuous party, night after night, especially during Freshers' week. I went from jelly and ice-cream parties to pancake tossing in togas, doctors and nurses in fancy dress, kissing booths and strip poker nights. Thanks to my Dad, I was an expert poker player and a great bluffer, so my clothes always remained intact.

It was the first time that I had seen a willy in the flesh and I was so not expecting it to be so small, floppy and wrinkly. I guess that was the real reason why I dumped poor Alan.

I must have gone to every fancy dress party that there was and I dressed up as anything, from Charlie Chaplin to a Moulin Rouge dancer. It was easy to find me. I was either in the Rose & Crown pub, Dukes Disco or the student union bar dancing to Dexys Midnight Runners' "Come on Eileen".

I visited home once a month just to keep Mum off my case and to stop her making her sarcastic comments like "I forgot what you look like" and "you think that you are too good for your family now?" I stopped going as regularly when everytime I turned up, there would be a strange man sitting in the lounge whom mum had invited as a potential husband for me. On one occasion it was a bald, middle-aged man and I ended up throwing my drink over him and walking out in protest.

As it turned out, Laurie and I got on like a house on fire. She got up at the crack of dawn and slowly crept out without making a sound and I, in turn, tiptoed in during the early hours of the morning so as not to wake her.

We had a secret pact that if one of us was going to bring a boy back, we would leave the other's pyjamas and toothbrush outside the door, so that the other would know to go and sleep on the couch in the lounge.

Everyone else in the house got on well too – except for Carol. We all took turns to cook a variety of Chinese, African, Greek and English meals, apart from Carol who walked into the kitchen holding her nose and wanted to cook her own frozen ready-made shepherd's pie, pizzas and Fray Bentos steak and kidney pie in a tin.

Laurie and I became close to two girls in our class called Jo and Sarah, and between the four of us we were the most desired girls on campus and boy, did we revel in it.

By this time I was seeing the captain of the rugby team, Richard. He was really strong and immensely popular, but was paralytic most of the time and was constantly throwing up everywhere. So I ended up avoiding him too.

Despite the attention and the opportunities I had with the most gorgeous guys on campus, I realised by the end of the first term that the virginity culture that had been rammed down my throat from an early age had actually worked on me. I found myself living in fear of losing my virginity in case no Greek man would marry me later.

I was twenty years old and still a virgin!

I kissed and flirted with guys, got them all hot and bothered and then when things hotted up I made them stop, leaving them in limbo.

Word soon got around campus that I did not "put out" and I became the college prick teaser. How's that for a claim to fame?

Before I knew it the first year of university was over and I was dreading going back to my parents for a long four-month summer holiday.

CHAPTER 16

Welcome to Fawlty Towers

There were some significant changes at home since I had been away.

My parents had sold our family home in Hackney and moved to Enfield in North London to be closer to relatives and friends.

We were now living in a three-bedroomed, mid-terrace house in a nice tree-lined avenue near Mum's beloved St Demetrios Church and she was in her element.

Vasili had turned eighteen, and he and Dad were both unemployed and getting shouted at by Mum. "Stop lazing about the house smoking like chimneys and go out and find work."

Auntie Katina had remained in regular telephone contact with Mum since she left London for Great Yarmouth many years ago and it was during one of their conversations that she persuaded Mum to invest in a small hotel in Yarmouth with the remainder of the sale proceeds of the house in Hackney. Thinking that it would create employment for the lazy men in her life, Mum bought it.

What did my parents know about running a business – a hotel at that? They were in the rag trade for God's sake and could barely speak the language so, not surprisingly, I had reservations.

The small boutique hotel was called The Towers Hotel and it was only open for business in the summer months. When I saw it for the first time I was pleasantly surprised. It was a very quaint two-storey traditional detached building with fourteen bedrooms and a fantastic bar, with a 24-hour licence, built to look like a ship's cabin until Mum decided to hang some worry beads and Greek religious icons under each of the nautical paintings.

My concerns were soon realised when I was lumbered with the running of it in the busy summer months.

It was during this time that I noticed how much my sister Maria had grown up. I had only ever seen her as my annoying, tomboy, baby sister who was always throwing up. But now she was seventeen and had grown up suddenly. She was a little taller than me and wore her brown, straight hair short and neat behind the ears. She dressed older than her age – very sensibly and mature – and was quietly spoken. I was very proud of her and felt that finally there was someone in my family who was on my wavelength. Together we ran the hotel; from manning the reception, waitressing, chamber maiding, to guest entertainers.

Vasili's one and only job was to be the barman and he stayed up through the night and slept during the day. Most of the time he was giving it large to the guests, acting the big *fouartas* (Mr generous) pretending to be the owner of the hotel and giving out free drinks. Other times he drank the profits until, in a drunken stupor, he went to bed legless and left the bar unmanned for all to help themselves.

Mum was the cleaner and cook, while Dad was so slow and hopeless at everything that his sole responsibility became frying the eggs for breakfast. The rest of the time he would walk around wearing a shirt that didn't quite cover his stomach with a cigarette hanging from his mouth, dropping ash all over Mum's freshly vacuumed carpets, which would set her off in a rage. Slowly, over the summer months I witnessed my parent's relationship breaking down before my eyes.

They constantly argued, usually because Mum couldn't bear to watch him fry the eggs as slowly as a tortoise with one hand, while holding a cigarette in the other, and splashing most of the oil over the cooker which she later had to clean.

If that didn't drive her insane, he would disappear into the toilet just when it was time to fry the eggs, which would not only delay the breakfasts going out to the guests but the rest of it would get cold too.

This infuriated Mum and if she decided to step in and fry the eggs herself to save time, Dad would freak out when he came back and find her at "his" cooker doing "his" job.

"I knew you were going to do that," he would yell. "I tested you to see if you would go behind my back and cook them. You think that you can cook them better than me, huh?"

Mum was not one of those women who could keep quiet and not answer for the sake of keeping the peace, and within earshot of fifty guests in the dining room next door, they would have a full-blown slanging match in Greek.

"*Lampro nase kapsi!*" ("May you get struck down!") "May you burn in hell!"

"*Yamo din ratsa sou!*" ("Screw your ancestors!")

I laughed at the start as I just couldn't understand how these words could be so offensive and cause such rage, but as utensils started to fly through the air, and huge carving knives were raised and aimed at each other's throats, I didn't find it funny anymore.

It was just as well that the guests didn't understand Greek. As the rows raged in the kitchen, Maria and I had to show our faces in the dining room and serve the guests like nothing was happening.

I cracked jokes to make light of the situation in the hope that it disguised the noise, "Welcome to hell's kitchen," I said, long before Gordon Ramsey came on the scene, or "That's what will happen to the next person who doesn't eat their breakfast."

I found that this made the guests laugh and left them wondering whether we were putting on some kind of a show for their entertainment. This gave me an idea to produce a type of "Fawlty Towers" show based on the TV programme to cover up what was really going on behind the scenes.

In addition to the rows things were always going wrong in the hotel: wardrobes falling on people's heads, showers leaking into the bedrooms below, blocked toilets and jammed locks. I started to rename the hotel "Fawlty Towers" and as people first arrived on a Saturday morning I greeted them by saying: "Welcome to the Tower Hotel, otherwise known as Fawlty Towers." They would usually laugh and then I would be rude to them just like Basil Fawlty.

"What's so funny, you think I'm joking. Wipe that grin off your face or I will wipe it for you. In fact get out of my hotel. Go on?"

To my surprise it worked and pre-empted the cock-ups and raging rows that would inevitably soon follow.

As guests queued to complain I dismissed them with the banter.

"The wardrobe fell on my head!" said one guest.

"Well I hope you didn't make a dent in my wardrobe. Now go away. Shoo."

"The upstairs shower has leaked into my bedroom," another said.

"Get out of my sight before I charge you extra for an en-suite room."

Once I accidentally spilled soup over a guest and I made it look as if I had done it on purpose and continued it as a theme, picking a different victim each night as the guests laughed in anticipation, wondering who the next victim was going to be.

Our grand finale was a game of Mr and Mrs on the guests' last night but with a twist. The twist was that we paired the couples up ourselves. We put the grandfather from one family with the grandmother from another, or the son from one family with the daughter of another. Sometimes we even put two men or two women together just to make everyone laugh and that in itself caused hysterics.

It was genius. I had created the first themed Fawlty Towers hotel. The guests loved it and I found that spilling soup, being rude to the guests, having Mum and Dad screaming at each other in the kitchen, and the shower leaks provided them with endless entertainment, and they recommended our hotel to their friends. People came to stay just so that they could be insulted but in reality the hotel was a complete and utter shit hole.

My parents' rows got unbearable and I couldn't wait for the season to be over so that I could get back to law school.

The first summer season at The Towers was finally over and I drove back to Chelmsford at top speed, completely exhausted.

CHAPTER 17

The Beach

It took a while before I switched off from my summer holiday with my parents and got back into university life.

The partying started all over again and my prick-tease reputation went before me. Guys soon started to lose interest in me, especially once the new first-year Fresher girls came on the scene.

I, in turn, soon lost interest in the constant partying. The heavy drinking every night, people being sick from the yard-of-ale races, and the whole rugby and drinking culture and smoking pot was really not my scene. I realised that I was a little prudish and I was OK with that.

I went through the whole three years of university with my virginity intact. This was unheard of in the uni world but I was proud of myself.

I did sometimes wonder why I hadn't used the opportunity to experiment with sex and drugs but I left university with no regrets.

I gained other experiences, better ones in my opinion. Going to uni and meeting Laurie had been the best experience of my life and she helped me to grow as a person.

I learned to appreciate other people's cultures, religions and beliefs. Laurie was Catholic, Ling was Buddhist and Vanessa was Muslim, and we all lived happily together under one roof. I stood up to Carol against her class snobbism and cultural racism.

I particularly learned that Greek Orthodox was not the king of all religions as I was brought up to believe, and the Acropolis was not the highest and most sacred temple of all. The world had moved on from the Acropolis and so had I. I had become cultured.

Laurie taught me how to make jam, how to make my own clothes and even how to knit jumpers and look after house plants. By the time we left law school, I had learned to appreciate Shakespeare and Charles Dickens, and I loved Jane Austen.

I acquired a love for antiques, something which in the past I would have referred to as second-hand rubbish or junk, as I thought that MFI and Brentford Nylons were the "in" places for furnishings.

I learned to appreciate classical music and I began to frequent traditional country pubs instead of the cattle market bars and chavvy Dukes Disco.

Thanks to my roommate, I was no longer the ignorant, common, narrow-minded, blinkered Greek girl that had walked into that auditorium three years earlier, not knowing anything about Shakespeare, Van Gogh or Tchaikovsky. Not only did I now know who they were, but I had read their books, seen their paintings and listened to their masterpieces.

I had been to the ballet and the opera, and had no interest in clubbing at A'mbres and Anabelles, like my friends back home. I visited art galleries and museums and enjoyed architecture. By the end of my three years at university I had metamorphosed from a stupid, blinkered Greek girl into a cultured, rounded woman.

I would like to think that I taught Laurie a thing or two as well. I taught her to cook Greek food for one. She loved *makaronia tou fournou* and *koupepia* and even learned how to pronounce them in Greek. I taught her a bit of Greek and she was able to string some sentences together in a fantastic Greek accent, which made me laugh. Although I never managed to convince her to like pop music, apart from my new idol,

George Michael, or to wear Lycra, she did learn the off-side rule and by the end of our time at university she had become a Chelsea supporter. Ironically she went on to date a Greek boy called Costa.

I got a better education in life from Laurie than I ever did from my law degree.

I went on to pass my exams and I was now one of the first Greek girls of my generation to achieve a law degree.

Law school finished with a bang in May 1986 with a huge farewell party.

I had a place confirmed at Guildford College of Law in October to do my Law Society finals to qualify as a solicitor if I wanted it. I didn't want to be a solicitor but there was no way that I was ready to go back to live with Mum and Dad, so I accepted the place without any hesitation. Laurie and Sarah were going to Guildford too and I was going with them. But before I could do that I had three months' summer break to endure at Fawlty Towers again.

Nothing had changed. Mum and Dad were still at each other's throats and the hotel was falling to bits around us as I tried to disguise it as a theme.

I soon got back into the routine and had a lot of hours to kill during the day. On sunny days I went to the beach and sunbathed and on rainy days I went to the amusement arcades or film matinées on the pier.

One sunny day, I was sunbathing on the beach when one of our hotel guests came up to me.

"Hello, Annie," he said.

I looked up at him. He was a young man, quite good-looking and he was holidaying with his parents and two sisters.

"Oh, hi," I said. "You're Kevin, aren't you?"

"Yes."

"Where is your family?"

"They went for a walk along the pier."

"Oh, OK. And what are you up to?" I asked.

"I came to sunbathe a bit."

"Oh, great. You can join me if you like," I said.

"Can I?" he asked.

"Of course. Put your towel here." I made some room for him next to me, where he put down his towel and we started to chat.

He told me that he lived in Leeds and he was a student and that next year he was going to university in Sheffield to study engineering. He was lovely, very polite and boyishly cute. I could tell that he had a bit of a crush on me as he was quite nervous but he still managed to throw a couple of sexual innuendos my way.

Just as we were talking I heard a woman's voice shouting behind me.

"*Thkaole mavre, thkaole mavre*" ("To hell with you, to hell with you").

It was Mum's voice and as I turned round to see what she was shouting about, she grabbed me by the hair and dragged me to my feet.

"What the hell are you doing, Mum?" I shouted as she tugged my hair.

I tried to release her grip by unclasping her fingers one by one until she finally let go. I stood there in shock with my mouth open, just staring at her. My eyes were streaming partly from the pain of my hair being pulled and partly from the humiliation.

She shrieked at the top of her voice, making everyone on the beach within a half mile radius turn to look at us.

"Why you with this boy?" "*Esso glihora, ximarismeni!*" ("Dirty cow. Get home now!"). I could not believe what she had just done.

She was angry because she had seen me talking with a boy. I was twenty-two years old for fuck's sake. She didn't even stop to see that the boy was one of our guests and charged in like a bull in a china shop.

I stood there for ages frozen to the spot, unable to say a word. Nothing would come out of my mouth, and it brought back memories of Auntie Pezouna doing the same to Alexis all those years earlier.

All I wanted at that moment was the sand to open up and swallow me but as it wasn't going to I just ran back to the hotel not saying goodbye to Kevin and certainly not looking back.

I could feel everyone's eyes on me as I ran and I could not get away fast enough.

I was livid with her. She had humiliated me in front of a hotel guest and everyone on the beach. How could I ever face that boy again? What must he have thought? I wanted to kill her.

I got to the hotel and stood in the kitchen, out of breath and seething. Within a few minutes I heard the front door slam and Mum appeared. As soon as she stepped one foot through the kitchen door, I shouted: "What's the matter with you stupid woman? Are you mad?"

She started shouting back at me. "Am I mad? You is mad. How could you embarrass me in front of those peoples? What if family walk by and seen you with that boy? What they think, huh?"

I couldn't believe that she thought I had embarrassed her like she was the victim.

"How did I embarrass you? You're the one that pulled my hair in front of all those people on the beach."

"*Kala na sou kamo. Kala na patheis. Pioios itan jinos o pesevenkis?*" ("Serves you right. Who was that pimp?")

"He is a guest at your hotel," I yelled," that's who he was! How can I ever face him again? I hate you!"

I stormed out of the door, slammed it and ran to my room. I heard her shout behind me.

"Eh, how was I to know? You should have told me," she said – like she gave me a fucking chance. I was fuming.

The summer season was coming to an end and I could not wait to leave the godforsaken place and go to Guildford.

I managed to avoid Kevin for the last two days before he went back to Leeds with his family.

My parents were hardly speaking to each other and Mum was not talking to me either because since the hair pulling episode I deliberately walked past every restaurant that belonged to a relative with a different male guest in tow to give them the impression that I was a slapper just to spite her.

CHAPTER 18

The Finals

At last it was September 1985 and it couldn't have come soon enough. I swiftly packed my things into my car and drove at high speed to Guildford.

Our new student lodging was a three-bedroomed traditional town house situated in the old picturesque village of Godalming, and we all had a room each, apart from Sarah who shared with her boyfriend, Peter. My housemates were already there when I arrived and was I pleased to see Laurie and Sarah again. After we had all unpacked, we sat down in our enormous low-beamed lounge and caught up on all our news over the summer. They had all been on lovely beach holidays and were all wonderfully tanned, while I had to tell them about my adventures in Great Yarmouth and they all laughed at me.

Godalming had many old pubs and crooked houses, and was like going back in time. It was calming and peaceful, a far cry from Great Yarmouth with my crazy family.

The Guildford Law School building was an impressive, huge, old mansion covered in honeysuckle in places. I stood in the grounds for ages admiring it before I went to my first lecture. The classroom was small with only eight rows of benches and I chose to sit in the middle of the fourth row. I looked around and checked out the talent as the room was filling up. I spotted three guys that looked cute but they all went and sat behind me. We were told by the lecturer that we had to keep the same seats for the rest of the year and I wished, then, that I had sat at the back.

I noticed a guy sitting in the front row who kept looking behind him as if he was looking for someone. Every time someone walked into the room, he would turn and look behind him, towards me and smile. I wasn't sure at first whether he was smiling at me so I looked behind me to see who he was smiling at but there was nobody acknowledging him. I realised then that he was smiling at me, so I gave him a half-grin back.

He had his back to me most of the time so I couldn't really see him properly but at the end of the lecture the front row had to leave first so I got a better look at him and he was handsome. He had shoulder-length dark, straight hair, was about five-feet-eleven-inches tall, and I particularly liked it when he smiled at me. As he walked out, he turned and smiled at me once more. This time I smiled back and coyly looked down. I half expected him to be waiting for me outside but he had gone – much to my disappointment.

The next morning the same thing happened, a few smiles back and forth but nothing was said. At the start of each lecture a register went round for all attendees to sign. It started from the front and worked its way along the rows towards the back. When it got to me I counted the seats and the names down, and saw that his name was Jack Ross. At the end of the class he asked the lecturer a question about the topic and I noticed that he had quite a posh voice which I found quite a turn-on. On the third day, as the register got to me, I saw that a little smiley face had been drawn next to my name. It made me smile and I looked up to find him looking straight at me and realised that it was him who drew the face. The following day he drew a little heart next to my name and the next day a kiss. It made me smile and it became our little ritual as I started to put little kisses against his name too.

A week went by and we were smiling and writing little notes to each other but we still hadn't spoken. He always left the lecture room first but he never waited for me. I always wondered why but I was excited at the mysteriousness of it. I met Laurie outside her lecture room and, as we walked through the car park to the car, we spoke about our respective lessons and I was telling her about Jack and the message he had left me in the register that day.

"Ah," she said, "that's really sweet."

" I know," I replied, "it's so nice."

"Do you like him?"

"Yes, I do actually. He's not usually my type but there's something about him that is really nice."

We got to the car and there was a red rose poking out from under my windscreen wiper and I smiled smugly. I knew it had to be him and I looked around to see if he was hiding somewhere – watching me – but he wasn't.

"Oh my golly gosh," shouted Laurie. "That is so sweet. It's him, isn't it?"

"Yes, I think it is." I was not able to wipe the smugness from my face.

"Oh, Annie. He must really like you."

"I know. Isn't it romantic? Nobody has ever done anything like that for me before." I had such a nice warm feeling inside and I could not stop smiling. I took the rose from the windscreen and we drove home.

That first week at Guildford was Fresher's week and there were lots of parties and social events. My housemates and I went to as many as we could, sometimes to more than one a night. We were meeting lots of new people and it was fun, but I was disappointed that I never saw Jack at any of them. I only ever saw him during lectures where we continued our daily ritual of sending messages to each other in the register and I looked forward to seeing him. It became the highlight of my day but he still hadn't asked me out and I was a little disappointed about that.

Two weeks into the term my housemates and I went to a pub in the village of Sheer. They were all planning to go home for the weekend and we were having a quick drink until the Friday evening traffic died down before they set off. As we walked into the pub, I was stunned to see Jack sitting there with two other guys. Laurie also spotted him and elbowed me in the ribs to attract my attention, but I had already spotted him. Peter bought some drinks at the bar and when he got his change he went over and sat with them. He seemed to know one of Jack's friends so we followed him and sat down. Laurie asked me out loud to move nearer to Jack to make some room for her. I felt so embarrassed at her obvious manoeuvre, but suddenly there we both were sitting next to each other at last.

He looked at me and said: "Hi, Annie."

"Hi, Jack. It's nice to finally meet you."

"Yes, indeed."

We both smiled and sipped our drinks.

"So, where are you from?" he asked me.

"London. What about you?"

"Birmingham."

"Oh, I have family in Birmingham."

"Oh, really. Where?"

"Moseley."

"I'm from the other side of the spaghetti junction, in Little Aston."

We talked about our lectures and then I commented on the fact that I had noticed that he asked a lot of questions in class. He laughed.

"Well, I've noticed that you have a lovely smile." he said.

I felt myself turning bright red and then he apologised for embarrassing me. I felt so good being with him. I didn't want the evening to end. I happened to drop a hint that my three housemates were all going home for the weekend and that I was going to be home alone. He told me that his two housemates were also going away for the weekend so he was going to be home alone too. We both grinned at the same time and simultaneously took another sip of our drinks. I just knew what was coming next.

"Well, then," he said, "it will be a wasted weekend if we stayed at home all alone, so I'll pick you up and we can go and explore some of the villages around here. What do you think?"

"Yes, that's a good idea," I said all smug.

"Good, I'll pick you up at eight then."

"Great," I said loving his assertiveness. Laurie had been eavesdropping on our conversation and she discreetly winked at me.

Jack picked me up at eight in a silver MGB. He opened the passenger door for me as I sat down in the seat and fastened my seatbelt. He drove me around the surrounding villages for about half an hour and it was beautiful. There was not much conversation just some huge smiles on both our faces; as he reached over and held my hand my heart missed a beat. He then stopped the car in a small country lane and put on his main beam lights revealing a really great view of the next village in the distance. It was peaceful and romantic.

"Sorry," he said. "I just had to stop the car because I have been dying to do this all evening."

He leaned over and kissed me, slowly and sensual at first, and then harder and more passionate. My heart stopped and I could hardly breathe with excitement. From that moment on, we were inseparable. We spent the whole weekend together, touring around Surrey discovering crooked houses and two-hundred-year-old inns. I loved every minute of our weekend together and I didn't want it to end, but our roommates were due back and our weekend was coming to an end. I couldn't bear the thought of being without him and it was music to my ears when he said the same thing to me first. I had never felt like that about anyone before. He did not stop holding me the whole time we were together. I was in his arms every moment and it felt so good. We got back to my house and my housemates were due back any moment.

"I have to go," he said as he was holding me in his arms.

"I don't want you to go," I said, squeezing him tight.

"I don't want to go either but your housemates will be back soon, baby." I loved the way he called me baby.

"I don't care. I want you to stay with me."

"I really want to but, believe me, if I stay I will never leave."

"That's OK with me," I said half joking but really wishing it to be true.

He looked at me and smiled. "OK then. You speak to your housemates and I'll go and pack my things."

"Are you serious?"

"I am if you are."

"Yes. Definitely."

"OK," he replied. "Call me later and if it is OK and I will come back."

"Oh my God, I can't believe this," I said.

"Neither can I but it feels right."

"I know I feel the same."

We kissed and kissed until we finally stopped to catch our breath and then he left. My heart was racing. Butterflies were fluttering in my stomach and I felt sick at the thought of him not being with me. I wondered if this was love. That was the moment when I understood what people meant when they said that you will know when the right person comes along.

My housemates were delighted with the idea of Jack moving in and Pete said "it would be great having another guy around the house".

The following day Jack was due to move in but I was getting second thoughts. I had never slept with anyone before and I didn't know what to do. My sexual knowledge was obtained mainly from Mum and the immediate family, whose misconstrued ideas were inevitable from such sources. I was scared in case I was dreadful but I was more frightened about losing my virginity and if my parents found out they would kill me. I so badly wanted to sleep with Jack but the risk was high. If he didn't end up marrying me then no Greek man would want me as I would be soiled goods.

I was in turmoil. One minute I wanted to tell Jack I had changed my mind and the next minute I didn't want to lose him. My heart was battling with my brain. Should I end it now before it starts or take a gamble and go with my heart that he was the one? As soon as I saw Jack walk through the door with his suitcase and his smile, there was no contest. I lost my virginity that night and I cried.

"Why are you crying darling?" he asked but I didn't know.

I felt a sort of relief that it was over with and there was no going back. Quite frankly, I couldn't see what all the fuss was about. I expected either some kind of ecstasy and fireworks or some excruciating pain, what with being brought up to believe that my virginity was so sacred, but it was an anti-climax really and I shrugged it off thinking, "oh well, it's done now".

Jack and I had a whirlwind romance and we were so much in love. We couldn't be apart, not even for a moment. I lived and breathed him and he felt the same. We were joined at the hip so much so that our friends ridiculed us all the time.

"Oh dear, here come the lovebirds."

"Yuk, how sickly. Go get a room!"

We laughed and told them that they were jealous and to really rub it in we would snog in front of them until we had something thrown at us, usually one of Sarah's fluffy slippers. The weeks and months went by and I loved him more each day that passed and he reciprocated his affection. There was no doubt to anyone or to ourselves that we were besotted with each other and it was not just a fling. We spent our days in lectures and then we would come home and spend it with our housemates.

He taught me how to play bridge and he was great at it. Trivial Pursuit was another one of our pastimes and Jack was brilliant at that too and to my surprise all those hours of watching films and musicals when I was not allowed out had finally paid off, as I answered all the film questions and discovered that my knowledge of football was unmatched too.

My boyfriend was so intelligent and that really turned me on. I learned something new about him every day and he never ceased to amaze me. He was an A-grade student, having got eight O-levels all at grade A. He was a great speaker and very confident, verging on cockiness, but he was such a humble, laid-back, easygoing guy. Everybody loved him and wanted to be his friend but all he wanted was to be with me. I felt so privileged and completely fulfilled.

Before I knew it the second term was over and we each went back home for the Easter holidays.

CHAPTER 19

Happy Easter

I drove to Enfield and was missing Jack before I even got there. I opened the front door with my key to an earful of shouting and screaming from Mum.

"*Fihe po thame je afisme isihin*" ("Get lost from here and leave me alone").

"Hello," I shouted and got an abrupt "halo" back from a stressed Mum.

I saw her sitting by the kitchen table in her hair rollers, covered in flour with two large plastic bowls, packets of self-raising flour and holding a rolling pin.

"What's up with you, Mum?"

"I am trying to make *flaounes* (a savory easter cake) "*je exitheosen me* (and he's infuriating me)," she said giving Dad a piercing dirty look.

"What's he done?"

"He's smoking that stupi' cigarette of his and filled the whole house with his dirty smoke."

Dad was standing in the lounge in a pair of tatty old pyjamas sucking vigorously at the last stub of cigarette before he put it out in the ashtray, while cussing her under his breath.

"What a great welcome home this is" I said.

"Take your coat off and come here," Mum said. "Help me wrap the *flaounes* so I can finish quicker."

"Mum, I have just walked through the door and I'm hungry.

Is there anything to eat?"

"Yes. There is *louvin* with *lahana* (boiled black-eyed peas with spinach)."

"Oh my god, you know I hate that. Isn't there anything else?"

"No. It's Easter and you should be fasting because tomorrow morning you are going to church *na medalaveis* (to take the Holy Communion)," she said.

"No, I'm not. I hate queuing up and drinking from the same spoon as old people."

"Shuddup. Don't be blasphemous. You are going."

I shut my mouth as I could see she was worked up and didn't want to get her off on one of her outbursts. I made some bread and butter. When I finished eating I sat with her to help her make the *flaounes* and it didn't take her long to start lecturing me.

"I will roll the pastry and you put the chiz in the pastry, not too much chiz and cover it with the pastry but not too covered and then press the ends together with a fork but not too hard, like this." She showed me what to do – as if I didn't already know. I had been making *flaounes* with her every Easter since I was ten years old and I was an expert. She then went on to explain to me the quantities of all the ingredients, including the amount of seasoning that was used. I was so bored and wanted to slash my wrists as she listed all the ingredients one by one and made a point of telling me that I have to mix cheddar with *halloumi* otherwise the *flaounes* are too salty. It took three hours to finish them and I was exhausted as well as having brain damage. I sat down to relax and watch TV and she shouted out "*Hade!* Get ready to take me to church, it's the *Epitaphion* tonight."

The *Epitaphion* is a religious Greek ceremony that takes place on Good Friday and which depicts the story of the crucifixion of Christ. The ceremony entails carrying Christ's tomb, made of flowers, on a procession, through the streets around the church grounds, with the congregation following behind and concludes by them walking underneath the epitaph, through the church door and back into the church. For the religious followers this event is one of the most religious days in the Greek Orthodox calendar. For the non-religious it is an opportunity to meet up with old friends for a chat or for single guys to pick up girls and for married men to take a glimpse at their mistresses.

Dad was an atheist so he wasn't going to go because he believed that all priests were fascists or gay, who *kleftoun ton kosmo* (con people).

"Mum, I'm not going."

"Yes, you are. You have to."

"Why do I have to?"

"Because its *amartia* (a sin) if you don't."

"Of course it's not *a sin*."

"Shaddup and get ready. *Hade*."

I had this sudden urge to keep her sweet and thought that if I took her to church and stood there next to her she would feel very proud of me and I would be in her good books just in case I had to tell her about Jack one day. So I reluctantly got ready and took my mother to the local St Demetrious Church in Edmonton. She stood very proud in her best clothes and her black fake-fur jacket linking arms with me as she walked down the aisle to the front of the church, introducing me to her friends on the way.

"*I gori mou* (my daughter) Anna, the one who is studying to be a lawyer," she boasted loudly making sure everybody heard, while I cringed.

She took her place in the front pew and beamed from cheek to cheek. What I hadn't realised was that she had tricked me into getting to church early so that she could get a good seat at the front and we had to wait an hour before the service started, forcing me to cuss her inside a place of worship. After she placed her cardigan on her seat to reserve it she pulled me up and dragged me with her all around the church and made me kiss all the icons one by one as she narrated.

"This is Ayios Demetrios and this is Apostolos Andreas. *Thoxaso to onoma tou.* (I bless his name.) And this is Ayia Anna who you are named after so do your cross and kiss her," and so she went on until she announced as we approached Ayios Yiorgios that she had a plaque with her name on it because she donated some money for its purchase and proudly showed it to me as she wiped the silver plaque with her sleeve.

We made our way back to our seats as the service finally commenced in front of a packed congregation. It soon came to the moment when the *Epitaphion* was to be carried around the streets and Mum shot up, pushed her way in a hurry to stand next to the priest, pulling me with her so that she could be right in front of the procession as if she were a part of the church establishment. If anyone tried to muscle their way in front of her she elbowed them out of the way and gave them a dagger look which put the fear of God in them.

The procession was over and members of the congregation made their way back inside the church for the service to recommence. There was chanting, praying and a lot of "*kirie eleison*" ("may God have mercy on me") while the priest chanted out his sermon. There was an overpowering aroma of incense flowing through the room which was distributed at regular intervals by the priest hurling a brass chalice on a chain up and down in each direction of the room chanting in "the name of the father and son and holy spirit".

The chains of the chalice could be heard right at the back of the room but not half as loud as the people at the back laughing and chatting to each other like they were in a cattle market. The priest halted his chanting, tapped his microphone to a deafening sound of feedback, looked to the back like a prowling eagle and shouted across the room on his microphone. "*Sas parakalo, stamate na milate then ine karnavali etho,*" ("Please stop talking, it is not a carnival here"). He told them off like children in a playground and there was dead silence for a few minutes but the chatting soon started again. And so this was how the biggest religious day in the Greek Orthodox calendar was celebrated in St Demetrious Church.

The following night was the Cypriot midnight mass called the *Kalo loho.* This is the night that the resurrection is celebrated and I took Mum again. The service sounded the same as the night before with lots of chanting, "*kirie eleison*" and the noise of the chains hurling the brass chalice in the air filling the room with the aroma of incense once again. At the stroke of midnight the lights all went out leaving the whole congregation in complete darkness for a short moment. To the sound of slow-ringing church bells, the priest lit up his candle called the *Ayios Fos* (the holy light).

No sooner it was lit, there was a mass surge forward of bodies pushing and shoving to get their candle lit from this one solitary *Ayios Fos.* Like a stampede of animals, they elbowed, pushed and stamped each other out of the way to get to the light first. The priest again had to halt the service to sharply announce, "*Sas parakalo siha siha.*" ("Please slow down.") "There is no need to push. You will all get the light in time." One poor old woman's hair caught alight in the surge and, while some members of the congregation were frantically trying to put out the flames on her, some man stole her handbag and disappeared into the crowd. The poor woman was distraught when nobody gave chase to the thief then another old lady asked her to shush and keep the noise down.

Mum of course was the first to get her candle lit. She stood there looking smug while trying to transfer it to her state-of-the-art glass-covered lantern which she had brought especially for the occasion to ensure that she took the *Ayios Fos* safely home with her.

The church slowly started to light up, as candlelight passed from one candle to another from the front of the church to the back. I watched people as they desperately tried to shield their light from the slightest breath, movement or jerk that could blow out their *Ayios Fos* and superstitiously doom them to a year of bad luck.

Mum's covered lantern ensured that she got her *Ayios Fos* home still lit – much to her relief. She went from room to room blessing the house and then she blessed me, wishing out loud that God send me a good Greek man to marry.

The next few days I spent eating like a pig. For all Greek Cypriots, Easter Sunday was the end of a forty-day fast, and people could finally eat meat (and they certainly made up for it). Feasts fit for a king are eaten in every Greek household on that day and for weeks later red-painted hard-boiled eggs and *flaounes* are consumed until they are sick to death of them. I put on half-a-stone in weight during that time and all I could think about was Jack, impatiently counting the last few days remaining before I would be with him again.

CHAPTER 20

The Rolls Royce

Easter was over and I was back in Guildford in Jack's arms. We both breathed a huge and prolonged sigh of relief as we hugged each other intensely. I soon got back into our life and my Easter break was quickly forgotten.

Exams were fast approaching and I was beginning to dread the day when our exams were over. Jack and I hadn't discussed anything about the future and I didn't want to mention anything as we had enough pressure dealing with the exams. The thought of going back to London without Jack made me feel sick, but I tried to make the most of every moment that we were together.

The last weekend in May, Jack asked me if I would like to go back to Birmingham with him to meet his family and friends. I was so chuffed that he had asked me but I was really nervous. I didn't want to spend a weekend without him, so I agreed to go there with him. We set off early in the morning to avoid the traffic and two-and-a-half hours later we were driving up a long drive in front of a huge house. He looked at me, smiled and said: "This is where I live."

"You're kidding me, right?" I gasped.

"Nope," he replied, smirking.

My mouth dropped open as I smiled at him. "You kept this quiet. Why didn't you tell me your parents were well off?"

"I didn't see the point," he grinned, knowing that I would be impressed with his surprise.

I was even more nervous now. I had not been aware that Jack came from a well-to-do family. He had mentioned that his grandfather was a doctor and his dad was a lawyer, but to me that just explained why Jack was so clever. It never dawned on me that he was rich too, as he was so laid back and modest. We were sitting in the car on the drive and my pulse was racing. My heart was beating so fast that it felt like it was coming out of my ribcage.

"Jack, I can't do this," I said. "I really can't."

"Don't be silly, darling. It's going to be fine, you'll see. Now come on, give me your hand."

I got out of the car holding a huge bunch of flowers that I had brought for his mum and we walked towards the front door holding hands. I couldn't stop looking at the Jaguar, the Mercedes and the Range Rover parked on the drive; all I could picture in my mind was Dad's clapped-out Moskovitch. He opened the front door with a key and we walked into a long hallway to be greeted by his parents and two giant Dalmations. His mum was a slim, pretty lady with blonde hair pulled back into a ponytail. She wore a blue flowery dress which flared below the knee – and she looked really young. His dad was dark-haired, slightly grey and looked a lot like Jack.

"Oh, don't mind them," his mum said struggling to pull the dogs into a room by their leads. She finally managed to get them in and closed the door.

"Hello, sorry about that," she said reaching out to shake my hand. "Are these for me?"

I gave her the flowers. "Yes, hello. Nice to meet you."

"Hello, darling," she said to Jack kissing and hugging him.

His dad then reached over and shook my hand. "Hello, my dear. Welcome."

"Thank you, sir."

"Oh, please, don't call me sir. Basil will do, my dear."

"Maybe even Sir Basil," said Jack. We all laughed.

"And I'm Sheila and the two naughty ones are Ruby and Titch," said his mum referring to the dogs.

The ice had been broken with the Sir Basil joke, so I was able to breathe a bit easier. My nerves had been slightly settled.

I followed Jack into a room to the left of the hall. It was a huge lounge at least four times bigger than my parents' lounge, with lots of traditional sofas and armchairs.

I was in awe of the house as I had never been inside one this big before. Even my wealthiest relatives lived in semi-detached houses in Southgate. I felt very inadequate and unworthy, especially when I saw some official photos on the wall and Jack explained that his grandfather had been the Mayor of Aldridge a few years earlier. I was having an out-of-body experience. What the hell was I doing with these people? The only claim to fame for my family was that my mum was senior finisher in Jacob's factory in Goodge Street. What could I possibly say to these people? I could hardly tell them that my Uncle Nick was part of the Greek mafia in the East End in the fifties and was jailed twice. There was nothing I could think of saying that would impress them, so I stayed quiet and smiled a lot at whatever they said or showed me. All I could say was: "Oh, that's nice" or "Really!" or "Oh, how lovely!"

I was completely out of my depth and scared of saying anything in case they thought I was a complete pleb. They made me feel very welcome throughout the day and conversation flowed comfortably during dinner. Sheila had cooked a roast chicken dinner with Paxo stuffing and little sausages wrapped with bacon. I'd seen them on television but had never eaten them before. Basil thinly carved the chicken breast and put three thin slices on my plate.

"Is that enough, my dear?" he asked.

"Oh yes, thank you. That's plenty," I politely answered but really I would have normally eaten the whole breast myself.

It was quite tasty actually, but I was still hungry when we finished. Luckily Sheila brought out some cake and custard for dessert, which I had plenty of room for but politely pretended to be quite full. After dinner we "retired" to the lounge to watch the news and then Sheila showed me the guest bedroom where I was to sleep. I never had a boyfriend before let alone slept in a boy's parents' house, so felt very awkward.

Next morning after breakfast we said our goodbyes and thank yous and Jack then took me to his grandfather's house, which was a few miles away. He lived in a place called Four Oaks Park, which meant nothing to me until we drove down his road and I realised that he lived in an exclusive private road like Beverly Hills in Hollywood. There were road humps and most of the houses were hidden behind electric gates or high hedges. On his drive was an Aston Martin, a Rolls Royce and a Mercedes sports car. I felt scared before, but this time I was petrified. We were greeted by a gentleman who was immaculately dressed in a pin-striped suit, a red bow tie and a red rose in his lapel. He reached out his hand to shake mine.

"Oh, hello beautiful," he said. "I'm Dr Haris Ross."

A lady had appeared behind him who was also immaculately dressed in a peach-coloured suit, lace blouse and a triple row of pearls around her neck. Her hair was blond and put up as a magnificent bouffant on top of her head, revealing matching pearl earrings.

"Hello my love," she said. "I'm Angel. Welcome. Let me take your jacket."

There I was, standing in a magnificent hallway full of antique furniture and a ticking grandfather clock, wearing a pair of black leggings, a baggy sweat top with an afro hairstyle which resembled a bird's nest – having forgotten to bring my gel. I looked like a thorn among two rose bushes and that's how I felt too. I stood out like a sore thumb, under-dressed and scruffy, and wished that the floor would open up and swallow me. Nevertheless I was greeted and treated like a princess.

Both the grandparents were adorable and I felt a warmth from both of them that made me feel at home. I hit it off with

Angel straight away. She wanted to show me around the house as the men caught up on each other's news. The garden was huge and magnificent with brightly coloured flowers all pruned and trimmed perfectly and the grass immaculately cut. Roses and carnations of all colours were in abundance and there was an outdoor swimming pool near the back of the garden with lots of seating areas surrounding it. I had never seen anything so beautiful in real life.

The rest of the house was equally magnificent too and after the tour we ended up in a lounge, as big as my mum's entire house, filled with antique furniture, ornaments, rugs, chandeliers and paintings. Angel told me that she was a jeweller and owned an antique jewellery shop. I was completely overwhelmed. I had only seen such splendour in Hollywood movies and I never dreamt that I would ever be in a house like it.

I sat for hours in the magnificent lounge with Angel while she told me her life story and I instantly developed a bond with her and did not want to leave her presence.

I hardly saw Jack or his grandfather at all that day, as they were in another room, I guess catching up on Jack's progress at Guildford.

We drove back to Guildford and I was still digesting my visit to Jack's family. I was so in awe of it all and in a sad sort of way I felt quite lost inside. I kept thinking that I would never be suitable for such a family and for a moment I had a horrible thought imagining my parents and Jack's parents together in a room. I mean what would they talk about: Moloshes? Snails? Poker? Just the thought of it made my stomach churn. From that day on, I had begun to accept in my head that in a few weeks' time, when Guildford was over, Jack would most likely go his way and I would go mine.

CHAPTER 21

The Shortbreads

Before I knew it, the exams were finally over and our tenancy was soon to be over too. It was the end of our education and there would be no more studies after this. We were all about to part and go our separate ways, back to our respective families, full of hopes and dreams for our futures, excited about the prospect of becoming lawyers.

The last few days at Guildford were like our first few days: full of parties and drinking – like it was Freshers' week all over again. We were in our local pub when Sarah commented on how the year had gone by so quickly and we all reminisced about the time we had all met.

Sarah and Peter were still loved up, Laurie was there with her Greek boyfriend Costas and other student friends were also there. The boys were playing pool and darts and I was sitting with the girls in a corner chatting as usual, discussing plans for the summer. I cringed at the thought of having to work in Fawlty Towers again. There was no planned summer holiday in Spain or America for me. The boys finished their games and came to join us. The conversation continued about the summer holidays and Peter said he was going to Majorca and Laurie was going to tour around France with her sister. Jack said he had no plans for holidays as he had other very exciting plans. We all looked at him, waiting to hear about these plans – me in particular.

"How come I don't know about these plans?" I asked, rather put out.

I saw Peter smiling and Sarah nudging him. From out of nowhere Jack then produced a little box, opened it up, revealing a huge solitaire diamond ring, got on one knee, looked at me, smiled and said, "Annie, would you do me the greatest honour of becoming my wife?"

I sat there looking like a gasping goldfish with no sound coming out. I was shell-shocked. Everyone was looking at me and smiling, waiting for an answer, but I was frozen to the spot, staring at Jack.

"Go on Annie, say something. You're killing us," said Sarah.

All I could think about was how much I loved him, how much I wanted him, how it felt so right being with him and how I couldn't bear to be apart from him. I adored him. He was the love of my life. Although it seemed that my answer was taking forever, I had no hesitation in exclaiming: "Oh my God! Yes!!"

There was an almighty sound of screaming and tears were rolling uncontrollably down my cheeks. Sarah was crying, Laura was crying, even the barmaid was crying, and, for me everything seemed to be happening in slow motion. The boys were all shaking Jack's hand one at a time, as he wiped his brow and said: "Phew! Thank God for that!"

I heard a champagne cork popping somewhere behind me and there was more cheering and clapping from other people around the bar. I was in a complete daze. It took quite a few moments for me to snap out of it and come back to reality. The girls were all grabbing me and hugging me. I could hear: "Oh, my God! We are so happy for you, Annie."

"You make such a great couple," gushed Sarah.

"You're so meant to be together. He adores you. You're so lucky," said Laurie. "He's such a lovely guy," she added, but I was still in a daze.

"He's been so nervous all day about doing this," said Sarah.

It was only then that it dawned on me that they may all have been in on the secret.

"Did you all know about this?" I asked.

Laurie and Sarah looked at each other and smiled.

"I nearly slipped up earlier," confessed Laurie. "We were finding it really hard not to say anything. He told us all yesterday what he was planning. All we had to do was make sure that you came to the pub with us – which wasn't hard." They all laughed.

"Oh my God! You bastards! I never had a clue. You had me hook, line and sinker."

Then Jack leant over to me and whispered in my ear, "I love you baby. I love you so much."

"I love you the same," I whispered back. We kissed and everybody cheered.

As the night went on, more things began to unravel. Little did I know that, over the past few months, behind my back Jack had been to Birmingham to order a ring from Angel; she was a jeweller after all. On the day he took me to Birmingham to visit his family he had actually gone with his grandfather to pick up the ring from Angel's shop, while I was chatting with Angel, thinking they were catching up in the next room. That weekend, his family had known that they were meeting Jack's potential new wife for the first time and I didn't have a clue. But what stunned me the most was when Jack smugly told me that he had driven all the way to Great Yarmouth the week before, introduced himself to Mum and Dad and asked them for my hand in marriage. I was mortified.

"What? When the hell did this happen?" I screeched.

"Last week, darling, when I told you I was going up to Birmingham for the day."

"Oh my God! What did they say?"

"They gave me their blessing."

"What? Are you sure?"

"Of course, I'm sure."

"Are you telling me that my parents have known for a week

that you were going to propose and they never said a word to me?"

"Yep," he said again smugly.

"That's impossible. I can't believe it. Did you pretend you were Greek, or something?"

He laughed. "No darling. They know I am English and they gave me their blessing, honest. Your Mum said, you were an old maid and it was about time somebody asked you to marry them?"

"Oh charming. I still don't believe you. You must have misunderstood. I'm going to ring Mum."

"Go on then. There's a phone box in the foyer."

I rushed out to the phone, put my 50p in and dialled the number at the hotel. Mum answered it.

"Hello, Mum. It's me."

"Hello, darli'. Huh, now you remember to call me."

"Er, Mum. Is there something that you know?"

"Wo' you min'?"

"Did my friend Jack come to see you in Yarmouth?"

"Yes."

"And what did he say?"

"I dunno."

"Mum, he's asked me to marry him." I moved the receiver a few inches away from my ear waiting for a loud reaction.

"Ah, OK. Good."

"OK, good? Is that it? What do you think about it?"

"I dunno. Is good. Huh?"

I was puzzled at her lack of emotion.

"What does Dad think?"

"*Xero yo* (How do I know) Is good. Anyway, I have to go to your Aunt Katina now to make *kourapiethes* OK? See you, darli'."

"Mum wait ..." but she had already hung up before I could say anything else. I hated it when she did that. I was sure that there was no way that I was going to get away with marrying a non-Greek that easily. I suspected that she was going to wait and shout at me face to face; that was more her style. But then I suddenly had this horrible thought about something which she had just said on the phone. "*Kourapiethes*" was a type of shortbread that was usually made as offerings to guests at weddings and I had a terrible feeling that maybe she was making them for my wedding. Why else would she be making *kourapiethes* ? I had an awful vision of Mum already organising my wedding, having had a week's head start and, with that horrible thought, I put the receiver down and walked back into the pub, where the celebrations continued, with my brow sweating.

The last day in Guildford had arrived and our cars were all packed to the hilt. It was the end of an era for us and there was a sadness in the air. Student days were over as of now and we were on our way to start our careers. We all hugged and kissed each other separately, and finally all got into a big group rugby scrum, wishing each other good luck.

"Keep in touch."

"Call us."

"Have a great summer."

"Let us know your news."

"Please come and visit."

"Let us know about your wedding plans! I hope you are going to invite us!"

"Of course we are silly," I responded.

Finally and reluctantly, we broke free from the group hug, got into our respective cars and drove away, waving with tearful smiles.

CHAPTER 22

Never the Twain Shall Meet

I was parked at the back of the Towers Hotel feeling nervous. This was the first time I was going to see my parents since Jack had proposed and was very apprehensive and a little embarrassed. My mum's calm reaction on the phone had been totally out of character, so I suspected that she was saving her real thoughts to tell me in person. As I walked into the kitchen, I saw Mum sitting on a chair with Auntie Katina. They both got up on their feet when they saw me and rushed over to me.

"O, hello darli'," said Mum and she grabbed and hugged me long and hard practically breaking my ribs. Auntie Katina did the same.

"Congradulaishon, darli!" They were genuinely pleased and Mum's face was beaming with pride.

Dad then came through the door and his face also lit up when he saw me. He was holding what looked like a needle or a pin.

"O, hello, *gori mou* (my daughter)," he said. He then opened the fridge took out a bowl of snails, sat down and proceeded to surgically prise one of the snails out of its shell with the pin with great precision and loudly slurp it into his mouth. I looked at him in disgust as he discarded the empty shell back in the bowl and picked up another one. I could see that Auntie Katina wanted to laugh at the loud slurping but Mum's face was like thunder and she quickly started a conversation to stop herself from thumping him over the head.

"Where is Jacki?" Mum asked.

"He's gone to Birmingham but he will be coming down in two weeks time to see me."

"Ah, good. Tell him to bring his Mum and Dad, and I will arrange for the priest to be here to bless the rings."

"No Mum. We don't want the rings blessed; we can do that at the wedding. I don't want any fuss."

"No! Don't be silly. *Prepei* (You must)."

"I mean it, Mum, I said no."

Auntie Katrina backed me up by saying to Mum. "The youngsters these days don't bless rings. They do it all at the wedding."

"Thanks *Theia* (Aunty)," I said in gratitude.

Mum tutted and mumbled under her breath. "OK, OK. Just get him to bring his parents. I want to meet my *sympetherous* (in-laws)".

"OK, I will," I said as Dad let out another almighty slurp as he tried to suck out another snail from its shell. He was oblivious to everything.

The next two weeks dragged by and I was missing Jack terribly. Although we had been speaking on the phone every day, I was longing to be with him. We had been discussing our future over the phone, especially about the property boom and the house prices being sky high in London. We decided that, when the holiday season was over, I would move to Birmingham with him and he had picked out a little house near his parents. It made sense to move near to him, especially as he had a training contract already lined up with a Birmingham City practice and actually I was quite relieved because I just couldn't imagine us living in London near my parents.

The night before Jack and his parents were due to come to

Great Yarmouth for the weekend, Mum scrubbed the floors and polished the cutlery. She disappeared for a couple of hours and returned with a huge crochet tablecloth, which she said she had borrowed from Auntie Katina, and started to lay the dining table. I must admit that it all looked lovely and she had made a huge effort to make sure the napkins all faced the right way and that the place mats were all straight. I started to help her so that she could finish quicker.

"Anyway, when are you getting marri'?" Mum asked.

"I don't know, Mum. We haven't talked about it yet. First we both need to get a job and a place to live, and I'd better tell you now that we have decided to live in Birmingham because houses are cheaper there and Jack already has a job lined up." I cringed as I waited for her to start shouting, but she didn't.

"OK. But I want you to get marri' quickly. Is no good like this."

"Like what?"

"Er, you and Jacki living together and not be marri'. You get marri' first and then buy house. "This is the right way."

"No way, Mum. I am going to live with him and that's the way it is. We've been living together for a year anyway, so what difference does it make?"

"*Christos je panayia mou*!" ("Jesus and Mary!") she yelled and crossed herself. She rushed into the kitchen and I thought she had gone to collect more plates or something. Instead, she came back holding a small plastic jar. She unscrewed the lid and, to my horror, she chucked the whole contents of the jar over me. Water was dripping from my hair onto my clothes and I was drenched.

"What the hell was that?" I screamed.

"It's holy water," she said.

"What did you do that for?" I yelled as water dripped down my face.

"I'm cleaning your soul so God can forgive you," she said.

"What planet are you from?" I yelled.

She had thrown holy water over me so that God would forgive me for sleeping with Jack out of wedlock and I was livid.

"You are stark raving mad, you stupid woman. This is 1986 in England, not 1896 in Cyprus! Look what you've done to my clothes. I'm soaked!"

"Huh, now you call your mother stupi'," she shouted out as I ran to my room to dry off and change my clothes. I was fuming and wanted nothing more than to leave this godforsaken place and move to Birmingham with Jack.

The next day Jack was due to arrive with his parents at around 2pm. I was very nervous during the hours leading up to their arrival because I was terrified that Mum and Dad would humiliate me with their ways. At first I kept surprisingly calm, until I suddenly noticed that the place settings for dinner had increased from eight to eighteen. I reminded Mum that there were only three on Jack's side and five of us and I queried the increased plate settings.

"Well, what about your cousin Anastasis and his wife Militsa from Cyprus who are coming to stay with us?" she said not looking at me in the eyes.

"OK, fair enough," I said, "but that only makes ten. Where did you get eighteen from?"

"Well," she said sheepishly, "I had to invite my brother Nicholas and his wife Nicoletta, and my sister Marika, and I can't invite her without Antonia and Solomos because they have to drive her."

"What? But they live in Cardiff and Birmingham. Don't tell me you made them come all the way here just to meet Jack and his parents?"

"E, was wrong with tha'? They are my family!"

"It's a first meeting Mum, not a flipping party. I don't believe this." I was holding my head with worry and then she added, "Well you are getting engaged. How can they not be here?"

"I am already engaged. I have accepted Jack's ring. You are just meeting his parents, that's all," I yelled.

"E, same thing," she said shrugging her shoulders, as she then flippantly added, "... and how could I not invite your Auntie Katina when I borrowed her tablecloth ... and she wanted to bring her son too, so I could hardly say no, could I? Anyway, one more person is not going to make any difference, is it?"

"It's not one more person, is it?" I shouted, "it's eight more people!" It's not fair on Jack's Mum and Dad. There are only three of them."

"Oh, shuddup! We are Greek, now I need to go check the ovens." And she calmly walked out of the dining room and ignored me. She was just great at changing the subject and walking away.

All I could think was: "This is going to be a nightmare."

By lunchtime the whole extended family had descended upon us and the dining room resembled Piccadilly Circus. I was dreading Jack's arrival.

Jack and his family arrived a little late and everyone waited in the dining room while I went with Mum to greet them at the car. Uncle Nick gave Dad a shove in the back to make him come with us, but he said he needed to go to the toilet first.

Jack got out of the car first. "Hello all." He then leaned over and kissed me on the cheek. I had warned him the night before not to snog me in front of my parents, so he secretly squeezed my bum instead, making me jump as I affectionately glared at him. His Mum and Dad got out of the car and I went to greet them. I kissed Sheila on the cheek.

"Hello Sheila. I hope you had a good trip," I said.

"Oh yes. It was lovely."

I then went over and kissed Basil on the cheek. "Welcome to Great Yarmouth."

"Thank you, my dear. This is super."

"Everyone, this is my mum, Kika," I said as I introduced her.

"Oh hello, Kika. I'm Sheila. Very nice to meet you," and she handed Mum a bunch of flowers.

"Thank you Shilla," said Mum and then she curtsied. I

cringed with embarrassment at the curtsey but luckily Sheila broke the ice.

"Oh, Kika, you don't have to curtsey for me. I'm not the Queen, you know." We all laughed.

Mum then shook Basil's hand. "Hello Kika. I'm Basil."

"Ah, Basil," she said beaming. "Basil is Greek and means Vasili, my son is Vasili and my father was Vasili too."

"Well, Basil is English too," said Basil.

"Yes but *Ahios Vasilios* is a Greek saint ..." Oh God, I thought, she's about to break into her religious mode.

"Oh is he?" said Basil. "Did you hear that, wife?" he asked Sheila." I'm a Greek saint," and they both laughed.

Mum then added "Oh yes and *Ayios Vasilios* is Father Christmas."

"Anyway, Mum," I interrupted. "Shall we go in?" I shoved her towards the door, as Basil whispered to Jack, "Do we have a Saint Basil?"

"We do now," responded Jack and they both laughed.

I was dreading taking them to the dining room with all those people waiting, so I sent Mum ahead and kept the others back to pre-warn them that there were going to be a few extra people for dinner.

"Oh, that's OK," said Sheila, "the more the merrier."

"Is that OK, Basil?" I asked. "I hope you don't mind but Mum invited the whole village to show off her future son-in-law."

"Don't worry, my dear," he replied. "Jack warned us that you had a big family."

As I led them into the dining room, I noticed that Dad had already started eating the taramosalata and had spilt some over his shirt. I tried to catch his eye to give him a dirty look to make him stop eating but he just carried on regardless. And Mum butted in saying, "Is OK, it is Greek caviar."

"Hello, everyone," I said. "This is Jack, and these are his parents, Basil and Sheila."

Uncle Nick looked over at his wife and asked "*Iben Shilla? En Shilla*?" ("Did I hear right. Did she just say bitch?") and he laughed out loud as Auntie nudged him in the ribs to be quiet.

I pretended not to hear what he had just said as I was not about to translate to my future in-laws that "*Shilla*" in Greek meant bitch but I did manage to give my uncle a dirty look as he caught my eye.

Everybody said hello and stood up to shake hands, apart from Dad who carried on eating and now had taramosalata all over his mouth too.

"If I do the introductions," I said smiling, and under my breath I whispered: "*Sikou pano!* (stand up!)"

"This is Uncle Nick and Auntie Nicoletta from Birmingham."

"Oh, really," said Sheila. "Whereabouts?"

"Mozli'," said Uncle Nick.

"He means Moseley," I translated.

"Yes, I have a restaurant, Al Capony."

"Oh, that's nice" said Sheila.

"Do you know it?" asked Uncle Nick with excitement.

"No, actually I don't," said Sheila.

Uncle Nicola then proceeded to tell her that "you go through the spaghetti jungshon, take the exit to Brod Stri' and Harbo'..."

I interrupted him. "He means Broad Street and Harborne. But *Theie,* (Uncle) you can tell them about that later. Now this is my cousin Anastasis and his wife Militsa, who have come over from Cyprus on holiday, my mum's sister Auntie Marika and her daughter Antonia with her husband Solomo, and my auntie Katina with her son John."

"How do you do," said Sheila and Basil together.

"And finally this is my brother Vasili, sister Maria and my dad, Andreas."

"Hello Andreas. I'm Sheila and this is my husband Basil."

Dad wiped his mouth on his sleeve.

"Oh, hello." He shook their hands. "Come on, sit down and eat food. My wife makes much food to eat. You like chiggin?"

And to my horror he then said "Do you want some cock?" I nearly died on the spot and had to quickly butt in and say, "He means coke."

"Please take a seat here while I help Mum bring the food in," I said and couldn't wait to get out of the door, but Auntie Marika jumped in suddenly and said "No Anna, you sit with Jack, and me and my Antonia will go and help," she said nudging Antonia in the ribs. All the women got up and went to the kitchen, leaving me and Sheila alone with all the men.

Basil turned to look at Sheila. "That's what you should be doing, woman. Looking after your man."

"I'll look after you alright," she replied. "Just you wait till I get you home."

We all laughed just as the platters of food starting arriving. I watched as the roast chicken with roast potatoes came in on Mum's silver platters, followed by the *macaronia tou fournou*, *koupepia*, *pizeli yiahni* (pea casserole)and beef *stifado*, then another huge platter of lamb *kleftiko*, pork *afelia* and finally finished off with Mum carrying her glass crystal bowl filled with *kolokassi* (taro).

"Oh my God," said Basil. "Have you forgotten anything?" he joked. The whole table was covered in food and everybody got stuck in.

"You really shouldn't have gone to all this trouble, Kika," said Sheila.

"This is perfectly normal for a Greek Sunday lunch," I told her.

Everything was all going quite well until Mum suddenly shot up and made everybody jump by squealing: "Oh ma' God! *din zaladinan mou!* (My pig's brawn!)". She ran to the kitchen and came back with a clear Pyrex dish of *zaladina.* I cringed.

"What is it?" asked Basil.

"You really don't want to know," I said, but Mum was very keen to tell him as she was serving it up that it was a pig's head in lemon brine. She didn't know what brine was in English so she described it as the "fat juice of pig's jelly". I cringed again and had to hide my face as I watched Dad pull out a pigs' hair from his mouth.

I just wanted to die when Basil looked into the Pyrex dish and tried to focus as he said: "What's that round little black bit?" It was partly protruding through the brine. Mum prodded the brine with her fingers and said "Let me see, ah, it's OK, it's the pig's eye." She picked it out with her fingers and showed it to Basil nicely poised in her hand.

"Would you like it?" she asked.

"Er, no, thank you. I'm fine with what I have." I could see he was trying not to laugh and Sheila was about to heave.

"What about you, *Shilla*? Would you like it?" asked Mum moving it over towards her.

Sheila was struggling to speak.

"No, Mum, it's OK. I don't think Sheila wants it," I said.

"OK," said Mum and she put it in her mouth and crunched it.

Everyone around the table winced except for Dad and Uncle Nick, who both asked Mum if they could have the other eye.

I wanted the floor to open up and swallow me. I knew this was going to happen. I had feared that my family were going to humiliate me but this was worse than I had anticipated. My uncle had topped-up Sheila and Basil's glasses with ouzo for the fifth time and as the alcohol flowed my family were getting drunker and louder by the minute.

I kept shaking my head in disbelief, knowing for sure that Jack was never going to marry me in a million years after this. My family were villagers, actually worse than villagers, they were Neanderthals and there was not a damn thing I could do about it. I sat back in my chair deflated.

Just when I thought things could not get any worse, the doorbell rang and I watched in horror as a priest walked in fully gowned with a beard down to the ground. I nearly fainted. Mum shot up all excited, went over to the priest and kissed his hand as she bowed to him, quickly followed by Auntie Katina and Auntie Marika. My heart missed beats as it pumped through my ribcage. As Jack looked on in horror, his parents just laughed and Basil shouted out, "Oh look! It's Father Christmas." Everyone burst out laughing apart from Mum, who came up to me, yanked my engagement ring off my finger and produced from her apron pocket a huge gold sovereign knuckleduster ring and gave them both to the priest who said a quick prayer, blessed the rings by crossing them with a huge gold crucifix on a string around his neck, chanted some words in Greek and ended with "*Sto onma tou Patros kai tou Ahiou kai tou Ahiou Pnevmatos, amin*" ("In the name of the father, the son, and the holy spirit, Amen"). Everyone said Amen in unison.

Mum forced the huge sovereign on Jack's finger as he looked at it and said in jest, "Mmm very nice."

"Cheers! Here's to the wedding," said Uncle Nick.

"Here, here I drink to that," said Basil toasting his empty glass, "and here's to Greek food too," he said.

"And ouzo," added Sheila downing the drink and toasting her empty glass too.

I looked at Jack, he looked at me, winked and mimed: "I love you." I smiled back at him and mimed "Ditto".

To my surprise, the evening turned out to be a success. Basil and Sheila got drunk and became as loud as Mum after their eighth glass of ouzo. Uncle Nick was telling Basil the story about his restaurant in "Mozli" and how all the local constabulary used to go in after hours and drink, and boasted that he used to spike their drinks so that they would let him stay open for longer after hours. He was slurring his words by this point, but Basil seemed to be fascinated. Sheila was admiring the tablecloth and Auntie Katina was telling her how she had crocheted it with her own hands. Auntie Marika and Auntie Nicoletta were asleep in the lounge and everyone else was in the kitchen washing up. Dad had gone off to have a cigarette two hours earlier and hadn't come back. I guessed that he was either in bed or had gone to the casino.

So, despite being in the same room as my rowdy, overpowering Greek family, crunching on pigs' eyes and pulling out pigs' hairs from their mouths, everyone enjoyed themselves and, more importantly, Jack still loved me.

CHAPTER 23

The Lemon Scented Geranium

It was 5 May 1987 and it was my wedding day.

The build-up to the wedding went surprisingly smoothly. I was able to pick my own dress, venue, flowers, limos and the band with little interference from Mum and this was primarily because she was severely distracted when Vasili had recently announced that he had an English girlfriend and all hell had broken loose. Mum was distraught and demanded one of her family conferences, where she got down on her knees and begged him to dump the English girl and marry a "nice Greek girl".

"Pliz', darli'. I will kill myself if you marri' her. There is no point in me living," she pleaded, faking a cry and pulling her hair with both hands.

"Mum," I said, What's your problem? I am marrying an Englshman."

"You, shuddup. That's different. I don't want my son eating sauasage rolls and those vol-au-vent things."

Thus I was able to make my own wedding plans, while Mum concentrated on plotting to split her precious son up from his English *poutana* girlfriend.

To keep Mum out of mischief and to cheer her up somewhat, I delegated to her the job of sorting out the church as I knew little about the Greek ceremony and Mum was an expert in all things religious: she proudly booked her favourite Ayios Demetrious church.

Traditionally the bride's parents were responsible for the cost of the entire wedding, which in the past entailed hiring a room in a town hall for the wedding reception, primarily because it was cheap but more significantly because they were the only venues large enough to hold a thousand guests, which was normal for a Greek Cypriot wedding.

The food was prepared and cooked at home by the female members of the bride's family the day before the wedding and it would be taken to the hall in the morning of the wedding by the men, ready to be served to the guests on paper plates and disposable cutlery. There was no bar at Greek weddings, so instead bottles of whisky, brandy, wine, beer and soft drinks would be taken to the hall in box loads and plonked on each table for the guests to help themselves.

This is what Greek weddings were like in London in the sixties and seventies, and I still remember cousin Antonia's wedding fourteen years earlier. Mum took me and Maria to our Auntie Marika's house a few doors away to help with the food preparations. The house was full of women and I recall it being chaos! Women were in the kitchen rolling up *kyioftethes* (meatballs), while others were by the cooker frying them in huge catering size saucepans. Auntie Marika was getting stressed about wrapping up *koupepia*, while some woman was cutting up pre-cooked chickens into pieces and placing them into large cardboard boxes. They were all busy working in a tiny kitchen with a strong potent smell of *sikoti* (liver) cooking on the stove.

Mum rolled up her sleeves and got stuck into making *thahtila* (finger shaped pastries covered in syrup). I was given the job by Mum to stand at the butler's sink outside in the backyard with a hosepipe and wash sticks of celery piece by piece. Four hours and fifty boxes later, I was still washing celery, cursing my mother and wishing I were dead.

These old Greek wedding traditions had moved on and weddings had become a bit more civilised by the eighties. The "Big Bang" of 1986 made London one of the world's major financial capitals and from this new-found wealth developed a weird form of pretentious snobbishness and the Greek Cypriots became the epitome of it.

With their brick-size mobile phones and leather-covered filofaxes, some started to consider themselves as a kind of elite society, quickly forgetting their roots. They developed overwhelming shows of jealousy and arrogance, with a sudden mad rush to keep up with the Joneses or, in their case, the Georgious. If one bought a Mercedes then the other had to buy the top of-the-range one. If one built a porch outside the front of their semi in Palmer's Green, then the second had to build an even bigger porch with huge pillars. Then the third would have to buy a detached house in Southgate and ultimately a huge house in Hadley Wood hidden behind electronic gates, which they mortgaged to the hilt and couldn't really afford. Power dressing became the fashion, as clothes once bought in Stavros' factory in Fonthill Road were ditched for designer labels.

Middle-aged men started revealing their hairy gorilla-like chests through their silk shirts, unbuttoned to the waist to show off their *24*-carat gold medallions resting on their big pot bellies, after they flashed their thick *24*-carat gold identity bracelets, with their names boldly engraved, and their oversized Rolex watches and gold Sovereign knuckleduster rings. At *bouzoukia* (Greek clubs) they started to openly parade their young, blonde mistresses with their large shoulder pads, fur coats and diamond earrings, which they had purchased for them while their wives were at home cooking, cleaning and taking care of the children. As long as they were left with the credit card and lavished with Gucci handbags and Jimmy Choo shoes, the wives were happy to stay home and obey.

There was no greater arena than a Greek wedding to show off this newly found wealth, and the huge chaotic town hall venues were replaced with expensive hotels and lavish banqueting suites with caterers and the eighties introduced another extreme form of Greek wedding.

As each wedding came and went, it had to be surpassed by the next one. Banqueting suites were sought in central London and I lost count of the number of weddings I had been to at the Café Royal, the Bloomsbury Hotel and the Grosvenor Hotel.

Every wedding was the same except for being more flamboyant than the last. Wedding cakes which started off with one tier developed into two, four and even six tiers and, as the pretentiousness grew, the pillars grew and in between each one were introduced elaborate swans with gold-plated trimmings. Little cute bridesmaids were joined by an entourage of grown-up bridesmaids. The wedding dress still had to be white, God forbid, not off-white or cream to avoid whispering around the hall that the bride was "soiled goods". So prevalent was the virginity thing still, that non-virgins visited a gynaecologist to ask for hymenorrhaphy, a hymen repair operation to fool the potential husband and avoid being belittled or disgraced by the "expert" spouse who thought he could differentiate between a virgin and a non-virgin by the penetration of his penis.

The basque bodice of the wedding dress would be very tight around the waist like a girdle to hide the Cypriot bulges and the skirt would be a humungous flared ball the width of a tent, followed by a train as long as a bus and finished off with a huge bouffant hair affair with the obligatory diamond-encrusted tiara on top.

The bride's parents would make sure that the whole world knew that their daughter's wedding cost more than their neighbour's daughter's wedding a year before and so it went on.

The highlight of every Greek Cypriot wedding is the traditional money-pinning dance, where the wedding guests pin money on to the couple's attire as they dance to the song "*Psintri Vasilija mou* ('My beautiful Basil Plant')". This tradition was invented in good faith by the villagers in Cyprus decades earlier and was intended to help newlyweds get off to a good financial start, as guests gave small financial contributions as wedding gifts.

However, this money-pinning tradition called *the bloomisi* had somehow been hijacked over the years and made into an opportunity for pretentious parents to get their wads of fifty-pound notes, pre-pinned together in a chain, and unreeling it for everyone to see them wrap it around the bride and groom like tinsel on a Christmas tree.

Sadly, the flamboyant wedding exhibitions became all about money instead of love and at my cousin Paraskevou's wedding, her newly betrothed husband went AWOL with the money and at a friend's wedding her father-in-law stole the money and ran off to Vegas with his Russian mistress, never to be seen again. Far from *the bloomisi* being a "good financial start", spoiled newlyweds did not need the money to help set up their first home, as their parents would have already bought them a house as a wedding present, so would use the *bloomisi* to lavish on themselves cars, diamonds, holidays and plastic surgery instead.

So now it was my turn to get married and over my dead body was I going to get married in the Bloomsbury with a thousand guests I didn't even know.

I had already decided a few years earlier that if I ever got married it would be in a beautiful little old moat house called Churchill Hall in a remote village in Essex, which I accidentally come across while driving to Chelmsford one day. I discreetly booked it and paid the deposit before Mum got a whiff of the fact that it only seated two-hundred people at the most. When I finally told her about the venue and that it only seated two-hundred guests she automatically assumed that I meant two-hundred guests each.

"No, Mum," I said. "A total of two-hundred people, and even that is too big."

"Vot! O blami'! That's not enough for all my friends and family."

"Oh yes, it will be. You do a list and I will decide who is and who is not invited to my wedding," I said.

She was not happy until I told her that Jack was only inviting thirty people.

"That's only three tables, Mum, so I'm sure we can manage to cut yours down to a hundred and seventy people."

"OK, OK," she said very put out and I could see from her thoughtful expression that her mind was racing ahead. To my surprise she managed to restrain herself on the numbers but at the last minute, after the table plan had been handed to the catering manager, she insisted on adding five strange people to the guest list and wouldn't tell me who they were. She said that they were a secret and threatened not to turn up to the wedding if they weren't allowed to attend. I gave in to her to keep the peace and remained curious as to who these "secret" wedding guests were.

My wedding dress was simple but elegant, with a tight bodice, narrow skirt and a short train. It had tiny little pearls sewn all over the dress which were not supposed to be there but the dressmaker sewed them on my dress by mistake, instead of on a sample dress that was due for a wedding exhibition. How lucky was that?

Everything was going like clockwork. Jack's grandfather lent us his Rolls Royce and chauffeur for the day, and I negotiated with the venue manager to allow us to bring our own drinks and not pay corkage. My parents had taken a day trip to Calais with my godparents a week before and stocked up with cheap wine, beer and spirits.

Everything was in place and I was extremely relieved that I had managed to organise most of my wedding without too much interference from Mum, as I had kept her busy making the three bridesmaids' dresses and three-hundred *kourapiethes.*

The wedding day arrived and Mum's house was packed with people that she had invited to watch the "changing of the bride", which is another Cypriot wedding tradition. There was no room to swing a cat, and people were falling over themselves in the tiny lounge. The photographer was clicking away, tripping over the video man's leads, while the violinist was blurting out some traditional Greek Cypriot wedding tunes and bursting people's eardrums.

Dad looked very proud in his new blue suit that he had bought in secret and had hidden away in his wardrobe. He looked very dapper and a far cry from his usual dirty beige, stained trousers and torn, worn shirts with missing buttons and was scrounging cigarettes from the wedding guests.

Mum had taken out her best silver trays and candelabra which she had boxed away for decades waiting for this moment to display. She was ferreting around all morning with her apron on, dusting and polishing everywhere but conspicuously she was nowhere to be found when the photographer called her for the family photos. She was busy concentrating on starching Vasili's shirt collar because she wanted him to look his best for a Greek girl that she had lined up for him at the wedding reception. I had earlier found out from one of her friends, who had let it slip, that this was the "secret" family that Mum had insisted on keeping anonymous and I had a bad feeling about it.

Mum kept everybody waiting as I watched her rush out into the garden, pick two huge leaves from her *thkuli* (lemon scented Geranium plant) and proudly stick one in Vasili 's buttonhole and one in Dad's.

"What the hell is that?" I said when I saw the huge leaves sticking out of their lapels to just below their chins. "Take them out," I yelled.

"No, leave them," she said. "They smell nice."

"Mum, the buttonholes are supposed to be for carnations, not *thkuli.*"

"I don' care," she said loudly, crossing her arms in front of her chest, about to go into one of her tantrums.

I didn't see Dad or Vasili objecting so, in imminent fear of incurring one of Mum's outbursts, I just shut up while digesting the fact that *thkuli* was going to be the theme of my buttonholes.

Mum took off her apron and we all posed in the lounge for the family wedding photos: me in the middle with Mum and Dad either side of me, and Vasili and Maria at either end. The photographer clicked away and took a moment to change his film. During the brief interlude Dad attempted to put out the ash from his cigarette, which had grown longer and longer during the photos, but before he could get to an ashtray the ash fell on the carpet. Well, that was it! All hell broke loose as Mum went into one of her fits, with absolutely no regard to the fact that the room was full of guests. She started bellowing at the top of her voice: "*Apanayia mou, thkyaole mavre ekrousen to peftjin mou*!" ("Holy Mary, damn him, he has burnt my carpet!") and gave Dad a vicious look as she ran into the kitchen and came back with a huge, yellow sponge dripping with water. She shoved guests out of her way, got on her hands and knees in her wedding outfit and vigorously started to scrub the floor, squirting water over anyone that was near her.

"Mum. That's enough," I said. "It's only a bit of ash and it's gone now so stop exaggerating." But she wasn't having any of it. She stood up slowly and, pretending to be all wobbly at the knees, she put the back of her hand on her forehead and said: "*Enimboro, en na firto.*" ("I can't, I'm going to faint").

It was obvious to me that this was all an act which had nothing to do with the ash on her carpet. She used the opportunity to milk the sympathy vote for Vasili's attention, which was meant to make him feel sorry for her and give up his English girlfriend.

She was helped up onto the couch by two of her friends who held her up by each arm whilst a third soaked her face with the same dirty, wet sponge she used to wipe the ash off the carpet with. A fourth friend was fanning her with the Cypriot newspaper, Parikiaki. Dad sneaked out to have a fag and Vasili secretly went out to phone his girlfriend away from Mum's earshot to arrange a time to pick her up to take her to the reception.

Mum miraculously recovered when it was time to do the religious part of the ceremony called the *kapnisman*. This is another tradition where parents bless the bride by burning some *elian* (olive leaves) in a terracotta pot and moving it around in a circular motion above the bride's head and crossing themselves. This is supposed to keep away bad spirits and the evil eye off the bride.

Mum shot up from the couch to be "the one" to light the *elian*. She bought the terracotta pot back from the kitchen fully smoking and circled it above my head. She was shorter than me and struggled to reach over my head and was so heavy handed that some of the burning olive leaves fell out of the pot, brushed my veil and fell on her carpet.

Everyone in the room gasped loudly, anticipating another outburst from Mum about her carpet, but she just bent over picked the hot leaves up off the floor with her asbestos fingers and put them back in the pot without a single word. No shouting, no drama, no tantrum no nothing. She just carried on as if she hadn't done anything. If Dad had done it, it would have been a different story and nobody bothered to tell me that I had a burn mark at the back of my veil, either.

Finally the traditional formalities were over and I couldn't wait to get out of there. I gathered up my dress and veil and turned towards the door ready to go to the Rolls to take me to the church to marry Jack.

I heard a screeching sound which appeared to be coming from Auntie Pezouna. She started singing *tsiatista* at the top of her voice and made everybody jump out of their skin. *Tsiatista* is a loud Cypriot rap where words are made up on the spot about the bride and groom. I wouldn't have minded but her voice sounded like a horrendous foghorn, which deafened everyone.

I had to stand there for five minutes and listen to the agonising wailing of all eight verses, none of which rhymed. While everyone was biting their lips trying not to burst out laughing, I wanted to slash my wrists. As soon as the last verse and screeching were over, I made a beeline for the Rolls and told the driver to put his foot down, only to realise that I had to wait for Dad who had just gone to the toilet.

I was completely deflated and sat at the back of the Rolls wondering if I was ever going to get married.

As I walked down the aisle with Dad I noticed that his fly was open and everyone was looking at that and the burn mark on my veil instead of looking at me but when I saw Jack at the end of the aisle, staring at me with such adoration, I felt the luckiest girl in the world.

I was now Mrs Ross. The church bells rang and the confetti was thrown. There were lots of happy faces and Mum was crying tears of joy as she wiped them away with a blue J-cloth. Auntie Marika grabbed it from her and gave her a white silk handkerchief.

The reception looked beautiful as my husband and I entered the room to clapping, cheers and a standing ovation. Within minutes the band was playing, the food had reached the desert course and the drink was flowing. It wasn't until Jack got up to say his speech that I realised just how much the drink had been flowing.

He was swaying from side to side and slurring his words. He had been drinking triples for Dutch courage and was absolutely legless. The English tables were all laughing and clapping as they were equally inebriated, while the Greek tables did not appear to be at all amused.

All that was going through my mind at that moment was remembering Mum's words a year or so earlier, when she was trying to justify to her friends why I was not marrying a Greek man.

"Our *Engleso*," she said, "is different from other *Englesous* because our one comes from a very good family of lawyers and doctors and doesn't drink and become like a donkey."

I caught a glimpse of Mum across the other end of the head table and she was crossing herself. To my relief the band stepped in and started playing music, ending the incoherent speech prematurely and preventing Jack from further humiliating himself.

As the guests danced the night away, I began to feel a little more relaxed and started to enjoy myself. The time had come for me and Jack to dance the traditional money-pinning dance. Some of the English guests looked on with great interest, capturing the moment on their cameras where they pinned a five pound note on my dress, while others conveniently disappeared into the toilets to prevent pinning any money on us at all.

Auntie Marika was given the task by Mum to sit on the head table and guard the money with her life, and she sat there all night clutching the black bag with both hands like an armed guard giving dirty looks to anyone that came within three feet of her especially if they were English.

The dancing continued and everyone seemed to be having a great time until I saw Mum suddenly shoot up from her chair, charge through the dance floor like a rhino and, to my horror, grabbed some blond girl by the hair and wrestled her to the floor. As the girl struggled to release her long hair from her grip, a guest tried to pull Mum off, exposing her long johns in the process. I was mortified when I heard someone shout out that the girl was Vasili's girlfriend, Tracey.

Mum was screaming. "What you doing here, *shillo poutana,* (prostitute bitch) leave my son alone!" as Vasili just stood there crying. Jack's Uncle Frank stepped in to try and yank Mum off Tracey to appease the situation but Uncle Nick, who was by now also paralytic, thought that Frank was going for his sister, so jumped on top of the unsuspecting Frank and started to beat him over the head.

All hell broke loose and within moments a huge fight broke out. Punches were thrown, hair was being pulled, chairs went flying across the room and crockery was smashed until the band ceased playing the music and the management stopped the wedding.

Auntie Marika missed it all as she had nodded off, still firmly clutching the money bag.

And so this was how my wedding ended. Well, not quite! As the guests bid us farewell and wished us good luck, me, Jack and the black bag made our way outside towards the complimentary honeymoon chalet. Ten feet away from the front door Jack slipped and fell headfirst onto the concrete floor.

As blood gushed from his forehead we were rushed to hospital in an ambulance and our wedding night was spent in casualty and, as it was a head injury, Jack had to be kept in for forty-eight hours for observation – so we missed our honeymoon in the Bahamas too.

CHAPTER 24

Happy Birthday

I watched the bright lights of Birmingham in the distance as we drove towards them with Jack's head still heavily bandaged. I was excited about my new life as Mrs Ross.

I loved cooking for my husband and cleaning our little one-bedroom house. I remembered Laurie's recipe for coffee and walnut cake and started baking cakes for Jack and his family. I regularly invited Jack's friends around with their wives for dinner and we developed a nice circle of friends.

Once I had settled into my wife routine I managed to obtain a training contract to do my "Articles" with an old established general practice in Tamworth, and on 5 January 1989 I qualified as a solicitor.

Look at the Cypriot girl now! My family was so proud of me being the first woman in the history of my family to become a lawyer.

Mum couldn't wait to tell everyone in the neighbourhood and Dad couldn't wait to tell everyone down at the café and the betting office. Dad went around the Cypriot community boasting that his daughter was a solicitor and gave everyone my mobile number, and suddenly I was on twenty-four hour call. It wasn't long before I was getting calls from Greek strangers asking for advice on anything from income support, neighbour's disputes and tree damage, to squatter's rights.

I tried to help the callers as much as I could at first, but after a while it began to annoy me. Not only was I getting calls at ungodly hours but Cypriots did not seem understand that I was not a specialist in everything and some got aggressive if they did not get the answer that they wanted.

One night I was having an argument with a bolshie Greek man who was insisting on coercing his elderly mother into making a will in his favour, and when I refused to do it he told me to "fuck off". I phoned Dad and told him to stop giving my number out to strangers. He said that he thought he was doing me a favour by sending me clients until I told him that they wanted everything done for free and he said: "*Na pasein na kopsoun ton lemon tous*" ("They can go and cut their throat"), and I had no more calls after that.

I specialised in property law and because I had trained in a general practice instead of a departmentalised firm where trainees only spent six months in each department, I learned my trade better than most. It was not long before I was headhunted by one of the largest commercial practices in Birmingham.

I could not resist. As much as I loved the country practice and the people there, I was offered triple my salary and I took the job without any hesitation.

The transformation from a village practice to a large city firm was incomparable in terms of its pace and quality of commercial work. I found myself working with the city's top commercial practitioners – and they were ruthless!

I loved watching them in action, with their power dressing and articulate vocabulary. They oozed confidence and arrogance, and were formidable opponents. Their reputations had laid the path for me and I was proud to give my business card to anyone I came across in the business. Anyone who took the card and saw the firm's name automatically assumed that I was ruthless because of the precedent that colleagues had set among the City's legal circles.

In time, I proved that I was exceptional at property law and soon leapfrogged over a few conveyancing colleagues, progressing quickly up the hierarchy of the firm. I was getting pay rise after pay rise and promotion after promotion.

Jack and I bought a large detached house in Lichfield and I was on the verge of the biggest promotion of my career, Associate Partner, when something unexpected happened.

"How can I be pregnant?" I said to the doctor. "I'm on the pill."

"Well," said the doctor. "The pill is only 99% effective so you must be one of the 1%."

"Oh, great." It would have to be me.

When I broke the news to Jack, he was shocked too.

"I thought you were on the pill?"

"I am."

"Oh, well. It looks like we are going to have a baby, then."

"Yes, it looks like we are."

You can imagine the hysteria when I broke the news to Mum over the phone.

"Oh, lovely. About time you made me a *Yiayia*." Calls were flooding in within minutes from aunties, uncles, cousins, even Mum's neighbours and friends, congratulating me.

Mum had obviously gone through her whole address book and called everyone to tell them the news. I even got a call from my cousin in America – anyone would think I was going to give birth to Jesus of Nazareth.

Everyone was delighted to hear the news, especially Jack's grandfather, who beamed with pride. Everyone apart from my boss, that is. Telling a senior partner in a big city law practice that you are pregnant is like telling him you have leprosy.

From the moment that I told him, I was no longer the golden girl but the firm's letdown. He was convinced that I had fallen pregnant on purpose just to get maternity leave and it didn't help that I had just qualified for maternity benefit by a whisker.

I made a point of telling him that I was on the pill when I fell pregnant but it did not seem to make any difference because as far as my boss was concerned, I had stitched up the firm and that was that.

I was very uncomfortable towards the end of the pregnancy and was tired and stressed as I worked to the last day before going into labour.

I had gone into hospital on Monday morning with contractions and was still dilating by Wednesday. I had been in labour for three days, gone through two bottles of gas and air, pethidine and six top-ups of epidural before my son came out weighing 7lb 2oz.

I was the woman who had been giving it large and boasting during her pregnancy that I didn't need an epidural and was going to have a natural birth. Like hell! By the end of the first day I was screaming like a lunatic.

"Get me that fucking epidural, you fucking idiots! Now!" I yelled at the poor nurses.

By the time the poor baby was born he was drugged to the hilt and I was exhausted. All I wanted to do was sleep but how could I when I was put into a room with an insomniac mother and her screaming baby. I was slowly metamorphosing into a killer grizzly bear who wanted to claw them both to death, limb by limb.

It was as though the midwives were getting me back for my appalling language and behaviour during the labour. I had gone through three shifts of midwives and sworn at all of them until the epidural had finally set in by Tuesday night. If I hadn't been so cocky about having a natural birth in the first place, I would have had an epidural booked beforehand and everything would have been fine, but oh no, the "hard" East End Greek Cypriot girl thought that she was above all the drugs and that she was going to shed like a pea.

Cousin Antonia had shed like a pea twice and she only weighed six stone so I was sure I could tolerate a little pain for a few hours.

Suffice to say, I didn't know where to put my face when the midwives came back on their shifts one by one looking at me as if I were Satan, especially the one that I had called "a fat bitch whore". I was so ashamed of myself and knew that saying sorry was not going to be anywhere near good enough to make up for my despicable behaviour.

I just wanted to get out of the hospital as quickly as possible but as luck would have it I caught an infection and had to stay in for an extra week.

I had my twenty-seventh birthday in the hospital – which everyone seemed to have forgotten. Cards were arriving for the baby but not a single one for me. I had become insignificant, a nobody, as the baby took pride of place like a king. When I finally got over my lack of sleep and the midwives were talking to me again, only then did I notice my little bundle of joy properly.

He was so adorable with his full head of spiky, black hair. I wanted to call him Andreas after my dad but Jack said he didn't like the name and wanted to call him Piers. "Piers," I said not being able to hide my disapproval. Over my dead body was I going to call my baby Piers so George Haris Ross was named.

Jack's grandfather beamed from ear to ear, gloating that the middle name was named after him, and he kept visiting us every day in hospital, sometimes twice a day. My father-in-law Basil made a joke that his father had seen this baby more times in one week than he had seen his own grandchildren in their whole lifetimes.

I took my son home, desperate for some peace and quiet so that I could sleep, only to find when I got there my whole extended family had descended upon us as a surprise.

Huge boxes of nappies and baby wipes from the cash-and-carry, a highchair, dozens of baby-grows two sizes too big, a swing and a see-saw "not suitable for under 5" were blocking up the hallway. Mum grabbed George and took things over. "You wrap him like this, you hold him like this, and you feed him like this. Ahh, he looks just like me," she said.

"He looks absolutely nothing like you. He doesn't even look like me. He looks like Jack," I said.

"What does your mother know, she's stupi'?" she said to the baby and kissed him on the forehead before whisking him away to the kitchen.

Mum had cooked loads of *makaronia tou fournou* because it was Jack's favourite and Sheila then walked in with a Beatrix Potter baby cup and saucer for the baby, much to Mum's amusement.

"Is that all she brought for the baby?" she whispered giggling.

"Stop it, Mum," I whispered back and gave her a frowning look.

George was adorable and thankfully he was not a cry-baby. He ate and slept most of the time and when he was awake he would just gurgle and kick his little, podgy legs. He was so good that no-one even knew that he was in the house half the time.

Maternity pay was low and things were hard with only one salary coming in, and my career was left in limbo. After an agonising deliberation, I decided to get a nanny and go back to work, much to Mum's disapproval.

"You are going to let an English stranger look after my grandchild and feed him fish and chips?" she belted down the phone.

"I feel bad enough as it is without your stupid comments, Mum."

"So I'm stupi' now. I'm your mother and I know what I'm talking about. What do your generation know about bringing up children? You bring him to me and I will raise him like I raised you." She was getting on my nerves.

"Mum. I have to go. Speak to you soon," and I hung up on her just like she always did to me.

My decision to go back to work was made a lot easier knowing that George was very happy with his nanny. She was great with George and he bonded with her straightaway.

She looked after him until he was nine months old, when he walked, and that's when I thought it was a good idea to take him to a nursery where there were lots of children to play with.

I took him for a one-day trial to a local nursery near our house to see how he would get on. He was used to being at home all the time so I didn't quite know how he would take to it.

As I walked into the nursery holding him in my arms, he started to flap his arms and kick his little legs, wanting to get down.

I put him on the floor and he made a beeline for a sit-in car that was on the grass in the back garden. He climbed right in and started pedalling it, bumping into everything that got in his way, including other children.

He was hilarious to watch, especially when he started making car noises and blowing bubbles, spitting all over his little Thomas the Tank engine t-shirt. I had no hesitation in leaving him there and my decision was further ratified when I went back to pick him up after work and he didn't want to leave.

He was still clutching onto the car and the nursery teacher told me that he had been sitting in that car all day and wouldn't let anyone else have it. She said that they had tried to prise him out to have lunch with the rest of the children but he had screamed the place down and they had to feed him his lunch in the car.

This fascination with cars developed into an obsession and by the time he was one, he was able to recognise the make of a car just by its badge on the wheels.

George had heard me once refer to a friend's clapped-out Volvo as a banger and since then he identified bangers with Volvos.

During a family wedding the bridal car was a brand spanking new gold Volvo and as soon as George spotted it he ran towards it as fast as his legs could carry him and shouted: "Banger, banger!" We all laughed hysterically – all except the owner of the Volvo.

George was growing up by the day and every morning he would wake up with a huge smile on his face, put his shoes on, usually the wrong way around, and run to the front door, waiting excitedly until his dad took him to the nursery.

There was a property boom in the Midlands in 1989 and I was headhunted again, this time by Tarmac plc, which was one of the biggest construction company in the country in the eighties.

They offered to triple my salary, give me a company car and eight weeks' holiday a year. I knew that having a baby had severely reduced my chances of being made partner at my current firm. So I accepted the job without an interview and became Legal Manager of one of Tarmac's subsidiary companies a few miles from home and didn't have to commute through the dreaded spaghetti junction again.

The work was interesting and it broadened my horizons. I attended and sometimes conducted the board meetings and conferences and gained invaluable business and organisational skills, but most of all I loved the attention working in a company where the staff were predominantly male, especially when I paraded around the construction site with a hard hat and Wellington boots, inspecting sites and doing spot checks.

I loved the power and money too. I was the main breadwinner as Jack was doing legal aid criminal work and his salary was low, but he was a great advocate and had great future prospects.

As for my social life, I had Angel who I regarded as a grandmother. Angel always made me feel so welcome and treated me like her own daughter. She gave me an overwhelming sense of belonging and was always there to ground me if I started getting thoughts above my station.

She was a classy lady and I aspired to be kind, wise and humble like her.

We tried to visit my parents in London at least once a month, although Mum would ring most days to speak with George.

She had an annoying habit of phoning and waking everyone up every Sunday morning at nine, the only day I could get a lie-in. I dropped a few hints about her waking us up and to phone a bit later, so she started ringing at ten past nine. When I told her it was still too early, she said she had to call then because she had to be in church by ten. I told her off one morning for waking us up again and suggested that it would be better if she called after church but got she the hump and didn't ring for a couple of weeks.

At least it gave us a couple of Sundays to lie in!

When we did travel down to London to visit, a fuss was understandably made of the baby and Mum always cooked the food that Jack liked, never what I liked.

"What about me?" I asked. "I like *stifatho.*"

"Er, Jaki no like *stifatho* so I make *macaronia tou fournou* that he like. You like Jaki?"

"Yes, Mum. I love it. Thank you."

"You see. Jaki like my cooking. Why you no cook *macaronia tou fournou* for Jaki?"

"When do I get time to do that? I work all day."

"Huh? You are a solicitor and you think you are too good to cook now? Sunday. I wake you up early on Sunday and you make him *macaronia tou fournou.*"

"No, Mum," Jack said. "It's OK, really."

She tutted as she looked at me with one of her disapproving looks, and yanked the baby from his high-chair.

"I'm taking him to church to *metalavi* (take Holy Communion)," she said. "He has to *metalavi* otherwise he will be Muslim."

"And what's wrong with being a Muslim anyway? At least they don't go to the Mosque and get told off for chatting and selling cakes outside the building."

"Shaddup and go and wash your mouth out, *E bellanes* (You have gone mad)," Mum bellowed and crossed herself.

"And how do you think are you going to take him to church. You don't drive?"

"You are going to take us so that you can make a confession for God to forgive you for your blasphemy."

It is another Cypriot tradition that if a woman is on her period, she is not allowed to go to church and take Holy Communion. I learned to manipulate this tradition over the years to avoid sitting in church with Mum for hours and luckily she never kept a diary of my period dates.

"Well I can't go to church because I'm on my period," I said lying through my teeth. She gave me a dirty look and said," Well you can drop us off and wait at the back then."

It was her way of making me light a candle and "*proskinisi*" (kiss) the icons for good luck.

CHAPTER 25

D-Day

I was twenty-nine years old and Jack and I had been happily married for two years. We were "Yuppies" in the Thatcher years and had surpassed all expectations, living in a newly built four-bedroom detached house in a desirable village near Lichfield. One evening, I had just put George to bed and gone down to the lounge as Jack was watching a film on the television.

I caught a glimpse of him wiping away a tear and immediately teased him.

"That will teach you to laugh at me when I cry at weepies," I joked.

"It's not the film," he replied.

"What is it then?" I asked with a smile on my face trying not to embarrass him.

"Annie, since I fell and hit my head on our wedding day I haven't felt the same about my life. It made me realise that life is too short and you should live it as you want to."

"That was ages ago and what's wrong with your life? You have everything. We have a lovely home, great careers, a beautiful baby boy and great friends and family around us."

"I don't know, I just feel trapped. I feel like a butterfly in your hands. I feel as if you have closed your hand around me and broken my wings."

"Oh my God, darling. This doesn't sound right to me. I've actually noticed that you haven't been your bubbly self recently but I didn't realise that you have been feeling this way since you hit your head. What if we go to see a specialist? They might be able to X-ray you to see if there is a problem".

He held his head and sobbed, "Yes, that could be it. I should see someone. You make the arrangements and I'll see a specialist as soon as possible."

"OK darling, don't worry. I'm sure that they will get to the bottom of it," I said and kissed him on the forehead as he continued to sob.

I got up and slowly walked out of the lounge into the kitchen to hide my tears. I had to be strong for him but I felt very sorry for him and was concerned about his state of health. I didn't want him to see me worrying.

His memory had not been the same since he hit his head at our wedding. Prior to that day he had been very sharp with an excellent memory, but since the fall his spark had gone – the sharpness and spontaneity that had attracted me to him were no longer present. I still loved him, though, and wanted to help him. Just at that moment the phone rang.

"Hello darli'. How are you?"

"Oh Mum, hi, erm can I call you back later? I'm doing something right now."

"What's the matter?"

"Nothing, Mum, honestly it's fine."

"I am your mother. I can tell from your voice that there is something wrong."

"Mum, honestly, it's nothing. Jack is just going through a bad time at the moment. He is going to the doctor to get a brain scan. We think it is something to do with when he fell at our wedding and hit his head."

"Oh dear. Make him some *avholemoni* (egg and lemon soup). That will make him feel better."

"What's that going to do Mum?"

"Trust me. It will warm his belly. That's what he needs."

"OK Mum. Whatever. I will call you soon. Bye."

I composed myself and walked back into the lounge. "How are you feeling babe?"

"I feel worse when I am here and I have all these memories. I need to spend some time alone so that I can clear my head. As long as I am under this roof my feelings are never going to change. I don't want to be this person that I have become. I want to be the person you first met and the husband you married. I think it will be best for both of us that I move out for a few days."

I felt a lump in my throat.

"But why? Where will you go?" I asked.

"I thought I would move in with my parents. I'm sure if we explained the situation to them they would be happy to help. What do you think?"

I was choking. "I don't want you to leave but if you think it will help, then let's do it."

"It will. Thanks for being so understanding babe. I think it's probably a good idea to put the house on the market too."

"What? Why? That's a bit extreme isn't it?"

"Our mortgage is too high and we should get something smaller. Then we would have more money to spend on ourselves and each other," he said," it would relieve some of the financial pressure."

"OK, that might be a good idea. I will phone the estate agent tomorrow."

"Good. I feel a lot better now," he said smiling.

Somehow, I didn't feel at all better. I pretended to be fine and helped him pack a few things in an overnight bag. I was confident that things would be all right if he had some space.

The next day Jack phoned to see how I was.

"I'm coping. How are you? I said.

"I'm miserable, I didn't know it was going to be like this. How do you fancy meeting up at the Crown tomorrow?"

"Yes, that would be nice. I'll get a baby sitter," I said smiling, "it's like we are dating again, how funny."

"OK, see you tomorrow at eight."

"OK. Bye."

Jack was sitting at a small table with a pint in his hand, which was half empty, and a diet coke for me.

"Thank you sweety ," I said as I sat down.

"That's OK. How are you?" he asked?

"Fine," I said. "I can't eat, can't sleep and missing you like crazy but apart from that, I'm fine," I said and chuckled.

"Yes, I know," he said "but I still can't help the way I feel. I've realised now that I am always going to feel the same way. But Annie, I want you to find happiness with someone else. I really do."

He squeezed my hand and he sobbed, "I really wish you the best."

"Don't be stupid," I said. "I don't want anyone else. I'm not stupid you know, I know what you are doing," I grinned.

"What?" he said looking rather surprised as he stared straight into my eyes.

"You are saying all this to make me to finish with you. I'm not going to leave you just because you're not well. In sickness and in health remember? I'm going to help you to get through this. I know you are only trying to protect me and I love you for it but get it into you're thick head that I'm not going anywhere."

He said nothing.

"Look darling," I continued, "I've had time to think about us over the last two days and you are right, we need more time for ourselves. In two years, darling, we have gone from being carefree, dossy students to being married, getting jobs, a mortgage and a baby all at once. That's enough to make any sane person stress out. I'm tired too. I get up early every day to get the baby ready, rush to a full-time job, cook, clean and look after you and our son. I just don't have time to look after myself anymore and I've let myself go. I look like a hag."

"Don't be so hard on yourself," he said.

"Anyway, I've thought of some ways to make things better

for the both of us. We'll sell the house for something smaller to release the capital and spend it on ourselves. We could have a proper honeymoon. We can take George to my mum's on some weekends so we can spend some time on our own and do more things together, and I promise you I will lose some weight. What do you think?"

"I don't know. I guess there is no harm in trying," he said rather subdued. "Let me think about it."

I sipped my coke, gave him a few moments, leaned over to him and with a huge smile said, "So, now that you have thought about it, sexy pants, when are you coming home?"

"You don't get it, do you?" he said.

"Get what?"

"I'm not coming home Annie. I want a divorce."

"I'm sorry, Jack, but have I missed something here? You never said anything before about a divorce. You said you needed some space and a few days to clear your head."

"Well, I've had time to think about it and I am never going to change the way I feel. I don't love you anymore. I'm sorry."

"Sorry for what, exactly? You haven't even had the scan yet."

"I don't need a scan. I'm fine."

My heart was beating so fast I couldn't breathe and through the panic and anxiety could feel my blood boiling inside.

"Oh, so now you are fine. Two days ago you told me you felt so bad that you needed a brain scan and now, miraculously, you feel fine."

He remained silent, gazing at the table.

"OK," I said, "What the hell is going on here?"

"What do you mean?"

"I mean I have proposed all these things to make our lives better and you are not having any of it! You haven't even tried to compromise. Nothing. So there must be something else, something you haven't told me yet. What is it?"

He looked at me with his woeful, melancholy eyes.

"I just want you to know that this is not about you, it's

about me. I want you to know that since we split up, I've met someone else. But I promise you, she had nothing to do with us splitting up."

It was only at this moment did the penny finally drop.

"Oh my God!" I said as the truth finally dawned on me that he was having an affair. I shook my head in disbelief. "Oh my God!"

"What a fucking idiot," I said out loud referring to myself. "It all makes sense now. I have blamed myself for putting on weight, and being too ambitious when all along you're sleeping with someone else. No wonder you wanted to get out of the house you bastard. How long has it been going on?"

"I only started seeing her last week."

"Bollocks. That's bullshit, you're a fucking liar. What do you take me for?"

My voice got louder and he looked around him at the people watching us.

"I swear to you it's the truth. I met her last week but only because she needed my help. Her husband beats her up."

"Ahh, poor thing. Does she have brain damage too?"

"Stop it, Annie. That's not nice."

"Oh, I'm sorry but you fucking someone else isn't nice either, is it?" I said as the tears streamed uncontrollably down my face.

He took my hands in his, wiped my tears and said: "Annie, I will never let anyone hurt you."

"Oh, so, you want the copyright as well, do you? Fuck you," I yelled, pulling my hand away.

I stood up, looking at him with piercing eyes.

Then I picked up his pint of beer and poured it all over his head. Slamming the glass down on the table, and watched the liquid drip down his head onto his face. I turned my back, walked out of the pub, got into my car and drove off without looking back.

That drive back home was a nightmare. All I remembered was turning into the drive, parking the car and bawling my eyes out for ages.

Not knowing what had come over me, I marched around the house on automatic pilot, filling up black bin liners of everything that Jack owned and drove them to his house.

I noticed that he was sitting in his car so parked behind him. I started taking out the bin liners, one by one, throwing them onto the front lawn but when I reached the last three sacks my rage got the better of me and I emptied the whole of their contents onto the lawn. Clothes were flying all over the place and Jack jumped out of the car, desperately trying to gather up all his belongings.

"Why should I let you have my fucking bin liners?" I shouted out as the last of his belongings were flung onto the floor. I got great satisfaction from watching his sorry, lying arse bending over to pick everything up.

Suddenly I noticed some movement from the corner of my eye and realised that there was a woman sitting in his car. "Oh my God it's her!" I shouted out and made a beeline for her charging across the lawn like a mad woman.

Jack saw me heading straight for her, dropped everything and started to run towards his car. He got there a split second before me and spread his arms across the passenger door.

"Keep her out of this, Annie. It's nothing to do with her."

"Nothing to fucking do with her? You're a married man and I'm your wife so how could it have nothing to do with her? It has everything to do with her. Get out of my way before I knock your block off. Let me see what you have left me for. Come on, get out here you chicken shit slag."

"Don't call her that," he said.

"Oh, diddums," I mimicked his pathetic tone. "Please don't call my slag girlfriend a slag. All right, then. Come out you fucking bitch whore. Is that better for you darling? And when did you grow balls to stick up for anyone? Are you pretending to be macho in front of your bird? You are pathetic! If only she knew what a lying coward you really are. Have you actually told her that you have a wife and a one-year-old child? Huh?"

"Yes, she knows."

"Oh, so she does, does she? So that must make her either a desperate cow or a fucking bitch. Which is it?"

The passenger door opened and she stepped out of the car. She was short with straight dark hair cut short like a boy, plain, with no make-up. She wore tight white jeans exposing chunky legs and not what I was expecting at all. I was somehow quite relieved.

"Is this what you have left me for?" I said to Jack. "Are you blind as well as stupid? What the hell is the matter with you?"

"Annie," she said "I must emphasise that I had nothing to do with your break-up. Jack was there for me when I was having problems and things just happened. I assure you we never meant to hurt you."

"We? We, never meant to hurt you? So, all of a sudden it's we, is it? You and him are a 'we' now, are you? I looked at Jack and said, "Considering that you only 'got with her'," as I made inverted commas with my fingers, "a week ago, you are already 'we', you fucking liar?"

Suddenly, he turned away and ran into the house and even she looked surprised.

"Ha, ha, you fucking wimp!" I shouted and laughed out loudly. I turned to the woman, "You see what a coward he is? He's left you out here with a mad woman. He must really like you. What a fucking loser. Do you really want to be with a lying, cheating wimp like that? If he's cheated on me he will do the same to you."

"Trust me," she said in a posh voice "He won't do the same to me. I am a matrimonial barrister and I know how to deal with these kind of emotions."

For a moment everything about her was funny and I started laughing hysterically "Oh my God – you arrogant, stuck-up, stupid cow. If there was a female Mr Magoo you would be it. Do you know what? Mr and Mrs Magoo, you deserve each other."

I continued to laugh hysterically as I drove home, maybe it was nerves but whatever it was I couldn't stop. What did I ever see in that pathetic lying coward?

CHAPTER 26

Hell Hath No Fury …

The next morning, the adrenaline rush wore off and reality set in.

I had been taken for a ride, a complete sucker. I analysed everything over and over in my head and the more I analysed the more I realised that maybe I had not been happy in my marriage after all.

Maybe I had just been in love with the notion of being married. I loved the idea of being somebody's wife, having a nice home and children. That a woman's place was in the kitchen was embedded in me since childhood and I had actually believed that.

Did Cypriot parents inject their female offspring with a drug called "Wifee" which stunted their intelligence gene?

The one thing I did know was that over my dead body, was I going to let him get away with what he'd done, especially since he had not mentioned his son even once in any of this. My mother-in-law was supportive in the days that followed. I told Sheila my innermost feelings about Jack and she made the mistake of telling me the "bitch's" name: Madison James. That was all I needed to know; the rest was easy. I looked up all the chambers and found her boss.

"How could you allow a marriage wrecker and an adulterer to represent your chambers in matrimonial matters? It is a disgrace and a scandal," I said to him.

She was fired that night.

I told Sheila what I had done and we both laughed as we waited for Jack's reaction.

I had been trying to get some kind of reaction from him about seeing George but he ignored my calls and the letters from my solicitor. "I will explain everything to him when he is fifteen" was all Jack had to say about the subject of his own son. Most couples who divorced, usually, ended up in court fighting tooth and nail for custody of their children, but not my husband. Yet as soon as his poor little girlfriend was reported to her bosses and gets fired, I get a reaction: "You, nasty, vindictive, spiteful cow. Now I am sure that I have done the right thing in leaving you," he said.

I laughed as I said: "Any excuse to pass your blame onto me. You are a pathetic, low-life loser who has chosen his dick over his own child. You are the amoeba of all scum. You are not a rat as that would be insulting to rodents and a flea on a rat's arse should be given more respect than you. Call yourself a father? Go fuck yourself!"

Was I bitter? You bet I was! "Hell hath no fury like a woman scorned" was definitely true of me then. I don't know how other women would have dealt with that situation, but I'm Greek, and my way was to became a woman possessed with revenge. I wanted to go to his football club and put posters up saying: "Beware! Lock up your wives because Jack Ross is a lying cheat!", then turn up at court where he was appearing and cause a scene by shouting out "cheating liar" and "child neglecter".

I wanted to slash his car tyres and punch them both in the face, but Angel kept me sane and discouraged me from looking like a lunatic. "Annie, stop being Greek and act like a lady," she said. I tried to remember her words but at times just couldn't help myself.

The only request Jack ever made was to obtain possession of his record player, with never any mention of George. This made my blood boil and I took a pair of pliers and pulled the volume buttons off his record player before he collected it. These little things made me feel better, albeit for a short time. My friends were getting sick of the sound of me going on and on about the next daily instalment, as I became a neurotic fool.

I tried to shield George from my heartache but sensed that maybe he knew something was going on when he saw me crying and came over to hug me. It broke my heart to pieces and that was the moment that I knew that I had to pull myself together and regain control of my emotions and my life. I had kept George with me in that environment in the hope that his father would see him but I could see now that it was not going to happen.

I couldn't face having to break the news of my break-up to my parents so I phoned Maria to ask her to tell them, and she agreed to take George to London for a few days until I sorted myself out.

"He needs some fun, Maria, not his miserable, neurotic mother," I cried "It won't be for long I promise. I will come and get him in a few days."

But a few days turned into a few weeks and I was missing him dreadfully.

I don't actually recall the moment when I started to calm down and stop my irrational behaviour but I came home from work one day to find a note had been put through my door: "Hi, you don't know me. My name is Justin and I'm Madison's husband. I would like to talk to you so please call me."

I was surprised when I first clapped eyes on him. He was tall, slim and really good looking. In fact, I fancied him as he was much better looking than Jack.

"When I first met Madison," he said, "she weighed eighteen stone and was very insecure. I paid for her to go through university and put her through law school."

I started to laugh hysterically; especially when Justin then went on to say that she was a shopaholic and that she had left him with debts of £30,000 on his credit cards.

"What are you laughing at?" he asked?

"I'm sorry Justin but Jack is really tight with money and hates fat women, and I just had a vision of an eighteen-stone woman using up all his credit cards to their limits. His worst two nightmares could come true and he so deserves it," and we both laughed.

Justin rang me every day for the latest updates on the "happy couple" as we called them and, despite hurting inside, we found comfort in each other's pain.

As it happens, Justin was a considerably better kisser than Jack! It's funny how things turn out, huh?

We kept in touch for a while, until he accepted a job abroad and I never heard from him again. But that's when my anger stopped, along with the lunatic thoughts of revenge. I realised that if I just bided my time and left it to karma, Jack would get everything he deserved.

Then, one more thing happened which turned out to be my biggest lesson in life, and it was all thanks to Angel.

I opened my post and there was a letter from Sheila. It said, that I was a nasty person for not returning Jack's calls and putting obstacles his way of seeing his son.

I could not understand why she wrote such a thing when I had been confiding in her and knew the truth. I could feel myself seething inside.

I scribbled a reply back telling her exactly what I thought of her and her precious lying, loser son.

I was about to post the letter when my phone rang and it was Angel. I burst out crying trying to tell her what had happened.

"Stay put, do not do anything, go put the kettle on, my dear, and we will be right there," she said.

When Angel finished reading my reply to Sheila's letter she slowly lifted up her glasses from the edge of her nose, placed them on the table and tore my reply into pieces as I looked on in surprise.

"Now, Annie," she said, "that woman tried to trick you. She

knows that you are emotionally vulnerable right now and act like a bull in a china shop. She was hoping that her letter would provoke you into writing a nasty letter back, rather like the one you did, so that she could show to all her friends what a horrible girl you are to make her son appear justified in leaving you. Luckily I was here otherwise you would have sent that letter and fallen right into her trap. So you will be all sweetness and light, write her a nice letter back and that will put a stop to that."

"How could people be like that?" I cried, with tears rolling down my face. "I watched "Dallas" and "Dynasty" when I was younger and thought that deceitful people like Alexis Colby and JR Ewing only existed in films."

"No, Annie. I am afraid that there are people like that everywhere around us and it's always the ones you least expect. Jealousy and deceit could be hidden behind people who pretend to be your closest friends. Please remember that and always be wary."

"I can't thank you enough, Angel. You are my guardian angel. I have decided that I'm going back to London to my family. There is nothing left here for me.

Angel started to cry and made me cry too. "There is a God above," said Angel, "and he works in mysterious ways, you mark my words Annie, Jack will get what he deserves one day, I promise you."

CHAPTER 27

The Return

It was June 1991. I was driving back to London with what was left over from my marriage in boxes and black bin liners.

As I looked in the rear view mirror and saw the Birmingham skyline disappearing into the distance, it reminded me of the day I moved to Birmingham with my new husband, full of hope and excitement about our new life together.

My eyes filled with tears and I cried uncontrollably from the minute I saw the view to the moment I arrived in London.

I parked the car a mile away from my parents' house and just sat there for ages, wondering how it had come to this. Here I was, back at my parents' house which I had left twelve years earlier. Secretly I hoped that Jack would miss me and George, and come to get us in an emotional reunion. I smiled at the thought, wiped my eyes and drove the last mile to my parents.

As I was parking the car, the front door opened and there was Mum standing there with George in her arms. He was flapping his little arms in excitement and was reaching out towards me. I rushed to him, grabbed him and held him in my arms. He put his head on my chest, held me tight and would not let go.

I sat down with him in the lounge feeling his breath panting on me. His little heart was racing and he never loosened his grip until he fell asleep in my arms. I was riddled with guilt and as I took George upstairs to bed, I whispered to him, "It's just you and me now, baby. Don't worry, I will look after you. Mummy is here now."

I opened the bedroom door and saw his little bed with his Thomas the Tank Engine duvet cover, next to a double bed, which was to be my bed for the near future. We had moved from a four-bedroomed luxury house where George had a whole house to play in, into one room. My heart sank as I put him down and lay next to him.

I wanted to cry but did not want to cry in front of my baby ever again. From the moment I felt my little boy's heart racing, I promised myself that my son was to witness only joy from that day on.

The first few weeks back with my parents were excruciating. Mum wore black and cried everyday like she was mourning.

"What are the neighbours going to think? *Ekamesmas rezilin.*"("You have made us a laughing stock.") I had to put up with Mum's constant digs and comments, "You should never have married that stupi' *Engleso* drunk. Levendi was not a drunk, but oh no, *proxenia* wasn't good enough for the solicitor. You wanted to find him yourself, and look where it got you."

One day I just lost it, "Oh why don't you just shut up and leave me alone. It's your fault that I fell for him. If you had allowed me to go out when I was younger and got some experience of men I might not have fallen for Jack's shit."

"Oh, it's my fault now that you married a foreigner?"

"I give up. Me and George are going out." I slammed the door.

On the inside I felt constantly sick, lonely and lost. No words could describe the anguish I was feeling. On the outside, however, I had built up a defensive wall for the benefit of George and my parents. I wanted to hide away from everyone but I soon had to face the world when my sister got married and I had to put on a brave face.

People saw me looking strong and smiling as I pretended that I didn't have a care in the world. "Jack was never any good for me anyway," I would say, "I'm happy and much better off without him," but I could never look anyone in the eyes or be in a room long enough with anyone in case they saw me break-down. I had always wanted to be an actress and now, here I was, an Oscar winner.

I woke up every morning with the realisation that I was alone and within seconds the butterflies in my stomach would travel up to my throat and choke me.

I wanted to sleep for months and wake up six months later pain-free. But it didn't happen.

Mum would come into my room or call me to come and eat and I would force myself to eat a morsel so that she wouldn't worry. I lost a lot of weight, so something good came out of it at least.

George settled happily into a new nursery school across the road from my parents' house. He would get up at the crack of dawn, put his shoes on, usually the wrong way around, and couldn't wait to go to school. He always came home covered in mud with his shirt hanging out, his trousers green with grass stains, and paint all over his face and hands. He made me smile every time I saw him like that and this made me feel good inside, knowing that he was happy. Mum would tell him off for getting dirty but I soon put a stop to that.

"How can you tell off a two-year-old for having fun?" I snapped at her.

"Eh, he has to learn to be clean."

"He's two for God's sake Mum, leave him alone."

I felt guilty that he did not have his father around and overcompensated by taking him everywhere with me. Alexis and Mastra had children the same age, so we spent most of the time together taking them to parties, Clown Town, bowling and face painting. George used to get so excited and run around, all hyper. He was the first one up the slide, the ladder and the climbing frame, and he was fearless. If he fell off he never cried, he just got straight back up and carried on as if nothing had happened. I used to watch him for hours as his little face got so excited. The dirtier he got the more I knew he was enjoying himself.

He never complained that he was bored as he always entertained himself with his Power Rangers or his smack down wrestlers. He was an angel and the only thing that kept me going. His cheeky smile and little hugs eased my pain. He was my little hero and he didn't know it.

Alexis and I had lost touch after she got married and I went away to university, but since my return to London we got together practically every day. She had recently divorced and become a single mum, so we both knew what the other was going through.

We reminisced about our hair-pulling days and we laughed, which provided a temporary escape from the pain that we were both going through.

Slowly I began to notice that my heart was mending, second by second, millimetre by millimetre, until one morning in August 2002 I woke up and there was no pain. There was no lump in my throat, no butterflies in my stomach, no feelings, no nothing. The pain had gone just like that over night, without cause or explanation.

Maybe this was the day God decided to release me from my pain or maybe my heart just could not take any more and detached itself from any feelings. Time is a great healer and no truer words are spoken.

With the pain gone I slowly began to see things a lot more clearly. The pain had taken with it the clouds that had been blinding my judgement and draining my energy. I bought some new clothes for my smaller figure and gelled my hair.

I sat down and wrote a list of all the things I needed to do, things that I could not previously face. With George happy and settled, my next priority was to find a job.

My CV was impressive. I had a law degree, great training, excellent work experience in a top city law firm and a multinational company, and I received endless job offers. I decided to accept a job doing criminal law, after watching *LA Law* on the TV – quite fancying the idea of dressing up in smart suits and speaking in a court room. It was a bit like being an actress on stage and I thought that this could be my chance to be famous, albeit as a lawyer. The thrill and the glamour appealed to me, so I accepted a job as criminal clerk in a small criminal practice.

My job primarily entailed taking statements from clients whom the firm represented. I would attend police stations, prison cells and ID parades to take statements and ensure that my clients were treated fairly.

I became familiar with most of the police stations and Crown Courts around London and I began to get recognised. There were very few female criminal lawyers in the business and I was not a typical-looking lawyer. I was a young, sexy woman who wore short skirts, stilettos and low-cut blouses. It was a male-dominated business and I was astonished at how easy it was for me to manipulate them into getting my own way. It didn't take much, just talking to them flirtatiously or teasing them and playing hard to get was enough to turn them on and give me what I wanted.

It was obvious for all to see that I was getting preferential treatment. I manipulated the court clerks to delay my clients' cases if I was running late, or to put my case on first if I wanted to get away early.

I persuaded police sergeants to caution my clients instead of charging them and sometimes they would let them off completely if I agreed to go out to dinner with them. How shallow they were? I would walk into any police station or court room and know that it would only be a matter of seconds before a man would come up to ask me if I needed any help and, even though I didn't, I always pretended that I did.

"Oh, yes please. Er, where is Court 1?"

"Can I please go on last?"

"Can you walk me to the cell where my client is, please?"

I played the role of damsel in distress magnificently and got everything I wanted for my clients. I loved playing the bimbo and my clients loved me for it once they got over the initial shock of our first meeting. I looked like a young, inexperienced, bimbo tart and the frightened look on their faces was a picture.

"Oh, my God. I'm going to jail," one said.

I found it hilarious watching their initial reaction when they first clapped eyes on me, but once they saw my laid-back style, especially the way I strolled in and out of the court rooms like a queen bee, they began to have confidence in me. I may not have looked the part but I certainly got the job done.

My confident reputation was soon getting around the judicial system and a few weeks into the job I wondered what I would be like as an advocate.

I was soon to find out when one morning in Waltham Forest Magistrates Court I was approached by a criminal advocate who I had seen in court many times. I had watched him doing bail applications and hearings and I was in awe of him.

He was an incredible advocate and such a natural with his flair and articulate language. He was about thirty-six, tall with dark, spiky hair. He was not only handsome but there was something about him that I found attractive. He had a confident aura and was always dressed in smart suits which made him look as sexy as hell.

Sometimes I would catch his eye and he would smile but we never spoke until one day I was sitting outside a court room waiting for my case to be heard and he came over and asked if he could sit next to me.

"Of course," I smiled.

"I'm David Mills," he said as he handed me his business card.

"Annie Ross," I said smiling and shook his hand.

"Would you care to join me in the solicitors' cafeteria? I'd love to talk to you about something over coffee if you are free."

"OK," I said. I was nervous and couldn't think of anything else to say as I followed him to the cafeteria.

We sat at a corner table by the window.

"Well, young lady, thank you for meeting me," he said.

"You're welcome. Thanks for meeting me!"

"Coffee for the lady," he told the waitress. I liked that assertiveness. It turned me on. "Don't think I'm coming on to you but I couldn't help but notice you over the last few weeks, the way you swarm in like queen bee and take command of the court room and the way that you wrap police and the prosecution around your little finger. Do you realise the effect you have on people young lady? You are like a breath of fresh air and you ooze so much confidence."

"Oh, do I?" I said, pretending that I didn't know.

"You know you do. Don't pretend with me. You know you've got it going on, girl."

"Wow, I have been sussed," I joked. I found him so clever and assertive and that was good.

"Anyway," he continued, "I am looking for someone to help me. I am inundated with work and I could do with someone like you to take over some of my cases. I will pay you whatever you want. I'll give you a phone and lots of work. If you are interested, we can meet up again and discuss terms."

"I am interested," I said, "but you need to know that I've never done any advocacy but I can do all your clerking."

"That's great, but don't worry, I will teach you the advocacy. I am sure you will catch on to it in no time and will be great at it." He went on to explain how he worked but I just kept staring at his gorgeous mouth and blue eyes and didn't hear a word.

A week later, he was my new boss.

He was very intelligent and a complete gentleman but most of the time I wished he wasn't. He did not size me up as a sexual conquest, unlike other lawyers who regularly made sexual advances towards me. He was a true professional and treated me with great respect. He gave me lots of work and in return I manipulated my way through it for our joint financial gain.

The first few weeks I followed him around court and sat in on his cases. He strutted around like a peacock, giving the impression of a cat that had got the cream. I found it amusing watching people's faces as they tried to figure out what our relationship was and whether he had pulled or whether we were shagging. It was amusing to keep everyone guessing, especially knowing that nothing was going on.

I felt myself falling for David but he didn't seem to be giving me any romantic signs, until one day he invited me around to his place for dinner.

I was excited and knew that this was the night that he was going to make his move. I got my hair and nails done, wore a sexy little black number and drove myself to Tower Bridge, where he lived, smothered in my favourite Moschino perfume.

He greeted me at his front door with a huge smile and a kiss to my left cheek. I was so used to him being dressed in a suit and I found him even sexier in a casual white t-shirt and blue faded jeans.

"Wow, you look and smell gorgeous," he said. "Please come in."

"Thank you," I said while he took my coat. I felt like jumping on him there and then until I heard the words, "Let me introduce you to my boyfriend, Jason."

I nearly died on the spot and felt like a complete idiot when I saw a gorgeous, blond, blue-eyed man coming towards me with his hand out ready to shake hands.

"Hi Jason, lovely to meet you. How are you?" I said, with a huge fake smile on my face.

I sat through three agonising hours of dinner with two gorgeous men who were quite clearly in love with each other, having to pretend that I knew David was gay all along and feeling like a gooseberry while they canoodled in front of me all night.

They were both lovely hosts and by the end of the night I fancied Jason, too.

I drove home that night wondering how on earth I had missed the signs that David was gay, but as disappointed as I was, I laughed all the way home.

I rang Alexis to tell her what had happened and we laughed so much that I wet myself.

CHAPTER 28

The Advocate

My working relationship with David went from strength to strength and I had him to thank for my first-ever advocacy case.

I continued to watch him daily as he beat prosecutors into submission.

I felt the confidence to do one myself, but every time he asked me if I wanted to do the next case I would bottle out in fear, saying that I wasn't ready.

One morning in Walthamstow Magistrates Court he had a case that was adjourned to the afternoon and he asked me to wait around until the client turned up while he went to the nearby court to adjourn another case. Once the court reconvened after lunch, the client had still not turned up and I rang David to tell him.

He told me that he had just received a call from the client to say that his train was cancelled and he was not coming to the hearing. He continued to tell me that he was unable to get back to court to adjourn the case and that I had to adjourn the hearing myself.

As I heard these words, my heart started pumping faster and my body was overcome with panic. I could feel the blood rush to my head and I felt sick at the thought of appearing in front of three magistrates in a packed court room with everyone looking at me. I vaguely remember telling him that I didn't know what to do and could hear him giggling at the other end of the telephone.

I realised that he had set me up. He had no intention of coming back to adjourn the hearing. He had just wanted to throw me in at the deep end.

"Noooooo!" I screamed down the phone. "Don't do this to me, David."

"Please David. I'll do one another day when I've had time to prepare, but not today. I'm not ready."

"Trust me, Annie. This is the best way to do it, off the cuff with no preparation."

The horror set in as I realised he was not joking. He wanted me to adjourn the hearing and he was not going to be there.

I screamed down the phone in terror, "David, I can't do it. I mean it, I can't. You have to come back now."

I was yelling down the phone like a lunatic, pacing up and down the court corridor like a headless chicken, begging him to come back, but he was having none of it.

It became increasingly apparent that he was not coming back and I was going to have to do the adjournment.

He was still laughing at the other end of the phone.

"Listen," he said, "stop yelling and just listen to me. All you have to say is this:

Your Honours. I request an adjournment for my client. His train from Leeds has been cancelled and therefore he will not be able to attend today despite attempts to do so. I request that you give him the benefit of the doubt and extend his bail conditions to attend the next time on the grounds that he has always attended in the past and has never breached his bail. I request an adjournment with an application for bail."

I rummaged through my bag to find a pen, shouting down the phone at him "Wait and let me get a pen so I can write it down. Just a minute, OK. Say that again."

I wrote down the brief word for word and when he had finished, he said: "Annie, you are a qualified lawyer, you have a right of audience, you are a confident, brilliant young woman and I have every faith that you can do this. Believe in yourself! You can walk this easily. Besides, it's only an adjournment, for God's sake, not a full-blown trial."

All I could find to say was, "You bastard. I hate you."

I heard him laughing at the other end of the phone again and I said, "Oh shut up and stop taking the piss out of me."

"I can't believe that you just called your boss a bastard," he said and continued to laugh.

I paced up and down the corridor as I practised the words, like an actress rehearsing her lines. "Your Honours, I request an adjournment for my client ..." I must have repeated the whole thing at least ten times until I knew it off by heart and I was beginning to feel a little more confident that at least I was not going in completely cold.

My client's name was called by the usher. I straightened my shirt, and pushed my short skirt down a little bit closer to my knees. I held my folder tightly under my arm with my scribbled brief clipped to the top, so I could see it easily.

I opened the door and took a deep breath on seeing a large, packed, court room with all eyes looking at me. I walked swiftly down the centre aisle and it seemed to take forever, as the sound of my stilettos on the wooden floor pierced the silence in the waiting room.

"Oh my God, oh my God," was all I could think of as my heart pounded. I smiled to distract everyone from my pale face and the sweat that was pouring from my brow.

By the time I finally reached the front row I had control of my breathing. I placed my folder on the podium and took a deep breath.

"Hello, my name is Miss Ross and I am representing the defendant." So far, so good .

"Thank you, Miss Ross," said the clerk. "All be seated."

As the prosecution read the case to the magistrates, I did not hear a word. All I was doing was rehearsing the lines in my head until I finally saw the prosecutor sit down and heard the clerk say: "Thank you, Mr Williams."

"Miss Ross?"

I stood up, looked at the clerk and smiled at the magistrates.

"Your Honours, Leeds, train, bail, erm, benefit doubt, erm, late, never been late before ..." All the words came out jumbled, making no sense, pure gobbledegook and my mouth just churned out the words one after the other. "Attend! Today! Leeds! Bail adjournment, conditions, train, Leeds, bail, no breach ..." Complete meaningless garbage was coming out of my mouth in front of a packed court room all staring at me. I just wanted the floor to open up and swallow me.

I had an out-of-body experience where I could feel myself rising up from my body and hear my brain telling my mouth to "shut the fuck up, you fucking idiot!"

At this point, a guardian angel came to my rescue. The court clerk interrupted me calmly and elegantly said: "Miss Ross, would you like to ask the magistrates for an adjournment?"

"Yes, sir," I squeaked.

"Was your client's train from Leeds cancelled?"

"Yes, sir" I gulped.

"As he has never breached bail before, would you like the magistrates to give him the benefit of the doubt and extend his bail?"

"Yes, sir."

"Very well" He turned to the magistrates, requested the adjournment for one week ahead with bail granted to that day. A magistrate sanctioned the request as he looked at me and smiled.

"Miss Ross, we adjourn the matter to 24 January and grant your client bail to appear on that day. Thank you," the magistrate said.

"Thank you," I said.

I said a heartfelt thank you to the Clerk. He nodded and smiled. I swiftly gathered my papers together like a newsreader, closed my file, picked up my bag, turned around and rushed straight back up the aisle, towards everyone in the court room, tripping over my own feet, and not daring to look anyone in the eye.

I pushed the door open so hard to get out that it almost came off its hinges, then ran straight down the corridor, out of the building, across the grass, into the car park and into my car. This was my first criminal case and I had humiliated myself.

My mobile rang as I was still cringing with embarrassment. It was David and before I could speak, he said: "Well? Did you get the adjournment?"

"Yes, I did."

"Good girl. I knew you could do it. See you tomorrow."

"OK." And it was left it at that. I guessed that I did get the adjournment so there was little point telling him what a complete moron I'd been.

I got better at advocacy as time went on and I continued to work for David for a few more months, until I left to become a freelance advocate, and we remained good friends.

I made enough contacts at court to act as an agent and picked up four law firms as clients just by chatting to them in the court canteen.

They briefed me daily for the next day's work and whenever I was travelling, or in court or police stations, I diverted my mobile to the home number to avoid missing calls.

I warned Mum that if anyone called, she was to take a name and number or get them to call back after six o'clock.

One day I came home dying to go to the toilet and ran straight upstairs to the bathroom. Just as I had sat down the home phone rang and I called out to Mum to answer it: "If it is for me, ask them to wait two minutes."

"OK," she shouted back. "Hallo, yes," I heard her say. "I'm her mother. She is on the toilet. Please wait two minutes."

Oh God. I could not believe that she had just told them I was on the toilet. How unprofessional! I pulled up my knickers and ran down the stairs, giving Mum a dirty look on the way. I grabbed the phone and said: "Sorry, I have a Greek mother, what can I say?" hoping that I had salvaged my professionalism.

When I got off the phone, I shouted at Mum not to tell people I was on the toilet ever again. "Oh, ok," Mum said.

A few days later, I was in my room and the house phone rang. Before I could get to it, Mum answered it again.

"Hallo. Who is it? Yes, OK. Just a mini." Then she screamed at the top of her voice. "ANNA!!!! *THELOUN SE PASTO TILEPHONO*!!" ("THEY WANT YOU ON THE TELEPHONE!!")

I ran down the stairs giving Mum another one of my dirty looks as she handed me the phone."Hi, sorry about that. I have a Greek mother and she is a bit loud."

The voice on the other end replied, "No problem". He proceeded to give me the details for a bail application the next day.

As soon as I got off the phone, I barged into the kitchen and screamed at Mum:

"What the hell are you doing shouting to me like that? These are clients, don't you understand?"

"OK, OK," she said obliviously.

"Next time, don't say anything, just pick up the receiver and say, one moment please, OK? Nothing else. Do you understand?"

"*Entaxi.* (Okay.) Why are you shouting?" she said.

The final straw came when I came home after work one evening and asked if anyone had phoned for me and Mum said that someone had called.

"Well, who was it?" I asked.

"How do I know? Some man."

"What did he want?"

"I don't know. I didn't ask him."

"Why not?"

"O ma' God. You told me not to say anything."

"I didn't mean don't say anything at all, at least take their name and number. Didn't you say anything at all?" I asked.

"No," she replied. "They said can I speak to Miss Ross and I put the phone down on them just like you said."

I was fuming. This was not doing my business any good, so it was time to invest in an answer machine. I showed Mum how to use it.

"Don't touch anything. Just listen. If the voice on the other end of the phone is for me, don't do anything. If it is for you, just pick up the receiver and talk normally. That's all you have to do. Do you understand?"

"Of course. You think I'm stupi'?" she said.

The answer machine did the trick; I was getting my messages daily and business was booming.

I came home one afternoon and listened to my messages on the answer machine, as usual.

Bleep! The first message was from a client asking me to visit cells the following day at Holloway Police Station.

Bleep! The next message was for a bail application on Thursday.

Bleep! The next was about an ID parade on Tuesday.

Bleep! I heard: "... she doesn't come home till three in the morning, she uses this house like a hotel, she wears skirts up to her arse, her arse actually shows, she should be ashamed of herself, *en antrepete din masellan tis, eyinigken rezilin!* (she isn't ashamed of herself, she's becoming a laughing stock!)."

It was Mum's voice slagging me off to my sister – and my sister was agreeing. I turned up the volume so Mum would hear it and waited to see her face appear from behind the kitchen door:

"Oooo, is that me?" she laughed. "I didn't say anything. It wasn't me." she said

I had caught my own mother red-handed on tape, cussing to my sister about me and she still denied it.

CHAPTER 29

The Starlight

It was 1992 and I was looking the best I ever had. More weight loss had emphasised my breasts and made them look massive.

I began to notice that since becoming single I was viewed somewhat suspiciously by some married women who thought that, by virtue of me being single, I was some kind of desperado " gagging for it" and hung onto their husbands in fear that I was going to pounce on them or steal them away - like I would touch them with a barge pole. Ironically, some husbands also barred their women from seeing me in case I led them astray or, God forbid, encouraged them to dump them. These blatant displays of insecurities annoyed me so I avoided couples events and dinner parties and I started to build a circle of friends, with those from my childhood, Alexis, Stella and Mastra, being the main focus of my social life.

Jack was hardly ever in my thoughts apart from when I received letters from his lawyer about the forthcoming divorce. There was never any mention about him wanting to see George and this made my blood boil. When he didn't even send George a card on his third birthday or Christmas, I began to despise him.

Angel and Haris stayed in regular contact and not a week went by when they didn't ring to find out how we were and learn of George's progress.

On the day of the court hearing, Jack attempted to mislead the court by producing an affidavit with dishonest claims of poverty. As soon as I read his affidavit, I knew that he was going to make a fool of himself with his lying proclamations. He was a partner in a law firm and his girlfriend was a barrister so, not surprisingly, his sham was foiled by the judge who was about to order him to pay me a large financial settlement for George.

But Jack anticipated the order and surpassed himself when he faked a breakdown and collapsed in the court room claiming that he had a heart condition just before the judge made the order.

His family were concerned about his health but I wasn't fooled. I knew that he was lying and had no sympathy for him and the callous way he had abandoned George.

The hearing had to be adjourned and eventually, I settled out of court for a measly amount and a clean break, just to get him out of my life for good. He was a loser and I did not put it past him to have the audacity to make financial demands against me in the future.

I was tempted to put him through a full-blown hearing and watch him squirm in front of a judge, but I couldn't bear the thought of having to see his sorry, lying face reminding me of how stupid I had been for falling for his charms and marrying such a loser in the first place.

I did, however, keep every letter that Jack sent declining access to his son and saved them in a folder for George to read when he got older, just in case he decided one day to charm himself back into George's life with his fabricated sob stories.

The decree absolute came through and I was a divorced woman. I threw a party at the Abbey Taverna and celebrated my divorce, ironically in a room full of hen parties.

Alexis and I sipped champagne, tapped our glasses together and made a toast to our loser ex-husbands. "May they be as miserable as hell," I toasted and we laughed.

Before long it was Christmas 1993 and the whole extended family gathered at Mum's for Christmas day.

I found it hard getting through all the family festivities alone for the first time as a divorced woman, but watching George's little face beam with excitement as he ripped open his presents helped me get through the day. I got some bath towels and a table cloth from Mum and when I told her that I didn't have a house any more she said, "Save them for George for when he gets marri".

Instead of turkey we had a suckling pig and we missed The Queen's Speech and "Only Fools and Horses" because Dad insisted on watching the Greek news on the RIK channel all day with Uncle Nicholas. Mum and Aunty Marika slept on the couch as the rest of us played family fortunes using saucepans as buzzers.

On Boxing Day Maria took me with her to her office Christmas party, where she had recently got a job in an accountancy firm. She introduced me to a guy called Kiri and a girl called Tina, who were both single, and we hit it off straightaway. They invited me to go out with them on weekends and before long we were out every weekend.

Kiri was twenty-one years old, tall, dark with short cropped hair, immaculately dressed, and surprisingly open-minded for a Greek guy. He lived on his own in a flat in Enfield which ended up being our hang out.

Tina was a short, skinny girl of nineteen with masses of heavily gelled curly hair. She was not the brightest of sparks, she would be the first to admit that, but certainly knew how to have fun. She came from a very strict Greek family and she told me that she had to creep out of her bedroom window to be able to meet boys in secret.

She couldn't wait to introduce me to her parents as her new friend. She was convinced that they would be so impressed that their daughter had befriended an older lawyer that they would let her go out. It worked a treat. I was thirty-one, a lawyer and spoke fluent Greek, which made me very "suitable" for their daughter to go out socialising with.

When I picked Tina up from her house, she would come out wearing a long, conservative red anorak down to her ankles. She looked very respectable and sensible, as if she were going out to the theatre. But little did her parents know that as soon as she was in the car, the anorak would come off revealing the tiniest mini-skirt – resembling more a belt than a skirt.

We did not go to the theatre at all but to a nightclub called the Starlight Rooms in Enfield.

This is where the three of us hung out every Friday night and without fail Kiri and Tina would get rat-arsed within half an hour of us arriving. They would take to the dance floor paralytic, laughing hysterically, knocking everyone over and at the end of the night I took them home.

There was not a singles' joint that we did not frequent throughout 1992 to 1994 and we had VIP membership at most London night clubs. After memorable nights at China Whites and A'mbres, we often ended up having a burger in Chicago's in Muswell Hill until the early hours of the morning, as it was the only place near that was open twenty-four hours.

Our favourite hangout was a telephone dating bar in the West End called Caspers. It was a singles' bar where people checked out someone they liked and then phoned their table to chat with them. Our gang never followed the rules. We picked the ugliest boy or girl in the room and rang up pretending that we fancied them, just so that we could look at their faces when we took the piss out of them. We were so cruel but it made us laugh.

We laughed all the time and everywhere we went we always found something that put us into hysterical fits of laughter.

The three of us were inseparable and our fun-loving antics and sense of humour were infectious as everyone wanted to be in our gang. We became very popular on the Greek singles scene and we were invited everywhere. We were at every party, concert, Greek dinner and dances, barbeques and we were always the life and soul of the party.

In August 1994 we went on a holiday to Cyprus – which changed my life. It was the first time I had been back since 1975 when I had stayed in the tents with Youlla and I couldn't believe the transformation. The main towns of Larnaca and Limassol had been developed into tourist attractions, and the small fishing village of Ayia Napa had become one of the biggest club scenes in Europe. Long gone were the dirt roads, quaint villages and men on donkeys with their *vrages* (traditional costumes). They had been replaced with motorways, neon lights and McDonald's. The most noticeable change was the growing presence of "Gentlemen's Clubs". Groups of foreign artistes, primarily girls from Russia and Bulgaria, specifically imported by cabaret nightclub owners for "entertainment" in their clubs, were given work permits and visas by the Cypriot government to work in the clubs as dancers: cabaret-frequenting became men's favourite pastime. I remembered Dad's words all those years ago that Cyprus will never be the same again. He was right. Cyprus had become sleazy.

My family had also changed, as the new generation of children were now adults and I hardly knew them. Auntie Dimitra, Uncle Stavros and Auntie Kaliopi had passed away and it just wasn't the same anymore.

We stayed in an apartment in Limassol and the reason that my life changed was that I was introduced to shots.

I hated the taste of alcohol, but one night in Hollywood's bar in Limassol, a Cypriot waiter made us a drink called a Blow Job. It was a shot of Baileys, Tia Maria and runny cream on top served in a sherry glass. The cream sweetened it up and made it taste nice so I was able to drink it without heaving.

It was called a Blow Job because of the way you had to drink it. You had to put your hands behind your back, lift the small sherry glass up with your mouth and down it. With little control over the glass, inevitably some cream would trickle down either side of the mouth like cum, hence the name.

Being a lawyer and supposedly the sensible one of the trio, I was too embarrassed to order it by its name and refused to drink it in this provocative manner. I picked up the glass with my hand and sipped it slowly but after three shots felt them going straight to my head. The sudden change to my behaviour made such a noticeable difference that Kiri and Tina burst out laughing, calling me a lightweight.

I was oblivious to the fact that they had both stopped drinking so as to watch me make a fool of myself. After the fifth Blow Job, my inhibitions soon went out the window and I proceeded to perform an explicit sexual show for all to see.

I put my hands behind my back, bent over the glass revealing my cleavage, licked the cream slowly and seductively from the glass with my tongue before lifting it up to my mouth, downing it, deliberately spilling the cream down the side of my mouth and provocatively licked the running cream off my lips – as if I was licking cum from my mouth.

"How very lawyerish!" exclaimed Tina in a state of shock.

"Wow. You sexy cow. You are such a prick tease," laughed Kiri.

The more legless I got, the less embarrassed I got about ordering the Blow Job quietly. It became a loud shout from across the other side of the bar, "Oi, give me a Blow Job, darling."

I later extended my show to seductively lick the cream from Tina's cleavage and this became our party trick. We were driving men crazy with our "lesbian Blow Job show" and we became the biggest prick teasers in Limassol. We took the show to Ayia Napa and then back home to the Starlight Rooms in Enfield.

Every guy that watched our lesbian show got a hard on and I realised what a pulling tool it was to get guys. Forget the bling, the Chanel perfume, Jimmy Choo shoes and the Toni and Guy haircut, downing a Blow Job from a sherry glass and letting it run down my chin and cleavage was all it took to get men queuing.

I finally became liberated at the age of thirty-two.

I was doing things I would never have dreamed of doing before. I had been a respectful virgin daughter, dutiful wife, devoted mother, respectable lawyer and now a prick-teasing, piss-taking, loud drunken tart – and loved every minute of it. My attitude changed and I couldn't care less about what people thought about me .The prude inside me left and Jack genuinely became, "Jack who?"

It was common to find me and Tina rolling on the floor outside a pub somewhere, drunk off our faces and laughing so much that we were oblivious to people trampling all over us.

I came home one time at five in the morning and was trying to creep up the stairs so as not to wake up Mum but she heard and came out of her room just as I was going into mine.

She took one look at me, crossed herself and said: "*O Theos na se voithisei*" ("May God help you").

I went into my room and it was not until I looked in the mirror that I realised what Mum must have seen, which explained why she crossed herself. My hair was full of sick, my mascara was no longer on my lashes but all over my face, my white top was stained with drink, my tights were laddered and God knows where one of my earrings was.

It looked like I had just shagged someone behind a bush and I was sure that's what Mum must have thought too. I burst out laughing, holding my mouth so as not to wake up George.

Mum didn't speak to me for three days after that and would only look at me in disgust. I didn't even attempt to explain to her what had really gone on, but decided that I couldn't let her see me like that anymore. It was time for me to get my own place.

CHAPTER 30

Bob the Builder

I became the proud owner of a small mid-terraced three-bedroomed house in Enfield, about five minute's walk from my parents' house and George's school. It was the perfect location but needed total refurbishment and I discovered a talent for interior design.

A cousin recommended a builder called Prokopi and from the day he started I knew that I had made a big mistake in hiring a Greek builder. Not a day went by that we didn't argue. Whatever he was asked to do he said it could not be done my way, only his way.

The disputes started when I asked him to knock down two old unused fireplaces, which were taking up room in the lounge, and build a new centralised feature fireplace.

"People knock fireplaces down and you want to put one in. Why?" he asked.

"Because it's a nice feature and I want one," I replied.

"But it's not nice. It is dirty, it takes up too much room and it is dangerous."

"Why is it dangerous?" I asked curiously.

"Because you might set the house on fire," was his response.

"I'm not going to light up fireworks in it. I'm not stupid!"

"No, it can't be done," he said adamantly and I could feel myself getting agitated.

"And why can't it be done"?

"Well, the walls of these houses are not built for fires and the smoke will get in the room and could kill you."

I gave him a dagger-like look and could feel my blood boiling. I let rip:

"What a load of rubbish. Do you think I'm a fucking idiot just because I'm a woman? You may have noticed that this house has *two* fireplaces." I emphasised two with my fingers. "Not one fireplace but two and it has a flue with a chimney on top of the roof like every other house in this road so I know it can be done, so just do it."

He dug his heels in: "It can't be done."

"What you really mean to say is, you don't know how to do it? OK, well if you can't do it I will get a builder that can do it," and I started to walk out of the room.

"Don't be silly," he said. "I didn't say I can't do it, I just said it can't be done. Of course I can do it. Do you know who I am? I am Prokopi Paraskevas and I can do anything," and proceeded to knock the old fireplaces down with a sledge-hammer.

Another time, I went to work, leaving him to hinge a door under the stairs for an under-stairs cloakroom.

I had provided him with a pre-measured eight-panel door which fitted perfectly under the stairs. All he had to do was cut a small diagonal piece off the top left-hand corner to fit in line with the staircase. I came home to find that he had cut the top off the door, which was now four-feet high with a two-foot gap at the top. I took one look at it and exploded.

"What the fuck is that? What have you done to the door?"

"I cut it so it is straight at the top. All doors have to be straight at the top, not slanted."

"Are you mad?" I shouted. "You have just ruined a new door!"

"No, it's going to be fine". He said all smug "I am going to join a piece at the top to fill the gap."

"You are an idiot," I yelled. "You have just cut up a perfectly good door only to join a piece to the top of it when all you had to do was cut a tiny piece off in the corner to fit under the stairs."

"It's your fault," he responded, "you made a mistake and bought me a wrong-size door".

I told him very calmly and very slowly to go and buy a new door and fit it properly before I smacked him over the head with it. He then had the nerve to ask who was going to pay for it, but he soon got the message when I gave him a look like thunder and told him to "get the hell out of my sight".

His blunders didn't end there. He fixed twelve spindles to the staircase upside down and had to take them all out and fit them again; he concreted the kitchen floor three inches too high, resulting in him having to drill it all out with an industrial Kango, covering the house in debris; he built the new fireplace two feet smaller than the plan dimensions just to make a point of doing it "his way"; he painted all the wood instead of varnishing it and spent six days steaming off the paint; he forgot where he had left the electric cables for the wall lights so had to chisel off the newly plastered walls to locate them; but the final straw came when, in the middle of another argument with me, he reached out with both his hands and squeezed my tits.

I froze in horror for a second, then punched him in the face.

"What the fuck did you do that for?" he screamed, holding his bleeding nose. "Why did you hit me, what have I done?" he said stunned and then he had the audacity to deny it.

I yelled at him to get the fuck out of my house and never come back. I told him that I was going to deduct all the mistakes that he had made, from his money, and then double it for groping me and if he dared to complain I would report him to the police and to the *Parikiaki* newspaper.

Acting like a woman possessed, I picked up a hammer and he thought that I was about to crack him over the head with it, so he grabbed his toolbox and ran out the door.

He kept turning up at my house demanding his money and his hammer, and threatened to break my windows, but on his fourth appearance I kicked him in the balls and I never saw him again.

Mum was quick to come over and light up a whole load of *elian* (olive leaves) in her terracotta pot to bless the house room by room. She hung some religious icons all over my kitchen and soaked everything with her jar of Holy water which, she said, she bought especially for me from her trip to the Holy Land. She re-arranged my furniture and everything in the kitchen cupboards and, if that wasn't enough, when I was busy in the bedroom unpacking boxes, she dug up my lovely new lawn and planted some tomatoes and marrows.

"Why didn't you plant them at the side of the lawn instead of right in the middle?" I yelled.

"They need the sun to grow, stupi'," she said.

CHAPTER 31

Santorini

My new house became the new hangout.

George was now six and had his own bedroom but spent most of the time with my dad, with whom he had developed a huge bond, and they went everywhere together. They went to the *kafeneion* where George was taught how to play *Kongan* (Gin rummy) and *Tavli* (backgammon) and he became bilingual. They adored each other and it made me happy to see them enjoying themselves.

It was the early nineties and there was a property boom in London. To take advantage of the market, I set up my own conveyancing practice from home, and soon had so many clients that I didn't know what to do with them.

The money was rolling in and I invested in a property to rent and bought a new red BMW 3 series. I was buying new clothes every week and got a dramatic makeover by getting rid of my curly hair and going straight. I looked ten years' younger and became conscious that men turned their heads when I walked by. I was proud of myself and confident with my sexy new image, and decided that it was time to start dating again.

The first guy I dated was a Greek called Jonny. I met him at a restaurant while celebrating Stella's birthday.

I realised that he liked me when he changed seats with one of Stella's brothers who was sitting opposite. He had a receding hairline and was a little overweight, but looked quite distinguished and had a nice smile. I couldn't help noticing his Rolex watch, a huge gold sovereign ring and a thick gold chain around his neck. His success was apparent but it was his confidence that attracted me to him.

He tried to eavesdrop on my conversation with Stella and made the occasional remark. He asked questions about me and paid me lots of compliments – I liked that.

He told me he was a property developer and lived in Southgate. He asked for my number and if he could take me out to dinner the following evening. I said yes and before I knew it he was outside my house in his silver Mercedes picking me up.

He looked very smart in a grey suit and I wore a short, black dress with high, black strappy sandals. As he opened the car door to let me in he welcomed me with a kiss on the cheek and a rose. "What a gentleman," I said, "I am impressed!"

"Anything for a beautiful lady," he said.

"Thank you," I said, blushing.

He drove to an Italian restaurant called The Villa Rosa in Barnet. The conversation flowed easily and I enjoyed his company but didn't fancy him – hoping that I would in time. Unfortunately, I didn't and after a few weeks of dating him I started making excuses from being on my period to having a headache, so that I didn't have to sleep with him. I could see that he was beginning to lose patience and started to ask me some testing questions.

"Do you like me?"

"Yes, of course I like you"

"Yes, but do you find me sexually attractive?"

I felt uncomfortable about lying to him but the truth was that I didn't. I didn't feel I could tell him that because he had been so good to me.

He was taking me to top restaurants and bars, I had met his mum and his two daughters, so he was clearly serious but physically he just didn't do it for me. But I did not want to lose all the attention he was giving me and I felt bad about that.

One Sunday afternoon, we went to check out the inventory in one of the flats he was about to rent out and we ended up lying on the bed. He started to kiss me and as he got more excited he started to undo my trouser button. I moved his hand away, as usual, but this time he carried on. He forcefully took my hands and put them behind my back as he proceeded to undo my trousers. I started to get agitated and politely asked him again to stop but he ignored me.

"What the fuck are you doing, arsehole?" I shouted.

As quick as a flash, he let go of my hands and sat up.

"What's up with you?" he asked. "Do you know how lucky you are to have a man like me? You are divorced with a child. Who else is going to have you?"

"What did you say?" I said and could feel myself getting mad.

"I said, who is going to want a divorcee with a kid at your age?"

"What? Oh my God! I can't believe you just said that," I exploded. "You are divorced with two children, not one, so how can you say that about me?"

"I can say it because I'm a man and it's different for me."

The volcano in me suddenly rose up to my mouth and erupted:

"Oh really? Well, let me tell you something, you fat, bald, hairy, thick, inarticulate, arrogant, pretentious medallion man. I find you repulsive and I'm not surprised that your wife left you. You think that just because you have money and show off your Rolex you can have anyone you want?"

"Yes, I can. I can get a younger, slimmer girl with no baggage."

"Well, why haven't you then? I don't see her!" I screamed, looking around the room. "Where is she then? This young girl you can get, you pervert!"

I stood up, straightened up my clothes, got my phone out of my bag and started to call for a cab.

"Don't," he said. "I'll take you later."

"I want to go now" I said.

"OK, I will take you now."

"Good," and I walked to the door.

He tried to make conversation as he drove me home but I just stared out of the window. He put his hand on my leg but I quickly pushed it away and gave him a look like thunder, but he giggled as though everything was normal.

"Come on, babe! Stop the drama. You are making an issue out of nothing," he laughed.

I was fuming inside and wanted to tell him to stop the car and fuck off, but held it in so I could get home. The journey seemed to be taking forever and I was sure that he was taking a longer route than usual and slowing down at traffic lights to catch them red. I wanted to smash him in the mouth but controlled myself.

When we eventually arrived at my house, I opened the door before he had even stopped the car. He turned off the ignition and was about to undo his seatbelt when I yelled : "Do you actually think that you are coming in? Don't you dare set foot out of the car. Fuck off and don't ever call me again, wanker."

I slammed the door and went into my house. I looked through the window to see if he had gone and saw him driving slowly away. I suspected that he was waiting for me to call him and beg him to come back. Like hell I was.

A few minutes later, he rang me and I had made up my mind to ignore him but was curious to hear what he had to say.

"What?" I asked.

"I wanted to tell you that you have made a big mistake," he said. "Nobody says goodbye to me and does not regret it later. I'm the catch here and it's your loss, lady."

I laughed. "You make me laugh, you loser. You flash your £50 notes around and you still live with your mum. What a great catch you are."

"That's just temporary," he said defensively, "I have three flats and I could live in any one of them if I wanted."

"No, please," I said "stay with your mummy so that she can cook and clean for you until you find your skinny young slave girl with no baggage to do it for you. Byeeeee!"

I hung up on him before he could say anything else and he rang back but I kept cutting him off so that he couldn't leave a message. He kept calling me for about a week but finally got the message and stopped.

Jonny was my first encounter of dating a Greek Cypriot man and I was not impressed. I was astonished, that such Neanderthal mentality toward women still existed in Greek men in the '90s.

I needed a holiday to get away. My cousin Thekla, in Los Angeles, had set up her own travel agency and when she rang me asking to go with her to visit some top hotels in Mykonos and Santorini to check out the accommodation for her American clients, and it was all complimentary, how could I refuse?

We met in Athens and jumped up and down hugging each other like excited children. We flew to Santorini and, as we caught up on all our news, the small propeller plane landed on the island. We were picked up by a limo to take us to the hotel in Oia. After a few miles the limo stopped on a narrow road half-way up a mountain and the driver got the suitcases out of the car.

We were standing in the middle of nowhere and couldn't see a hotel in sight.

"Why have you dropped us off here? Where is the hotel?" Thekla asked the driver.

"Someone will be along in a minute," he said and drove away.

We stood there puzzled and a bit concerned, but within moments a little man appeared pulling two donkeys.

"You have got to be kidding me!" said Thekla as she stared at the donkey in horror.

The old man picked up the suitcases and attached them either side of the donkeys. He then produced a small box and asked us to step onto the donkey. We were wearing short dresses and high-heeled shoes and as we got on the donkeys, we exposed our underwear, much to the old man's delight who kept looking at our knickers all the way up the white painted mountain. As I watched Thekla in front of me bouncing up and down with her legs sticking out from the donkey, clutching onto the mane for dear life, I laughed so much I wet myself.

Thekla was not impressed, but as we reached the top of the mountain and saw the magnificent view of the sea and the most amazing orange sunset, the donkeys and the sore bums were soon forgotten.

The hotel was set in a cave and was very quiet and peaceful – well, it was until we arrived. We were the only two single girls among loved-up couples and newlyweds, so it did not go down very well when we kept constantly laughing and talking loudly, disrupting the couples' quality time together.

It turned out that we were the only single girls in the whole area, so you can imagine the attention we received from the Greeks when we walked around in our shorts and bikini tops. We had an entourage of men everywhere we went and were treated to everything. It was a good job that we were only there for four days because things were brewing up with the local men. They started to cotton on to the fact that we were prick teasers, leading them on and getting nothing back in return. We lied about the day we were leaving the island and secretly got a taxi to the port before anyone got a whiff of our departure and boarded the boat to Mykonos.

We waved goodbye to Santorini and laughed as we reconstructed our ride on the donkeys, wondering whatever happened to the old man after his eyeful of our knickers.

"I bet he had a heart attack," said Thekla.

"I bet he had a stroke," I said and we laughed, but our smiles were soon wiped off our faces as the boat rocked from side to side on the choppy water and we both started to feel sick. As the boat violently hurled itself first to one side and then the other, my guts were in my mouth and I could see that Thekla had come off her seat and was on the floor gasping for air.

I pulled her up and dragged her to the outside deck where most of the other passengers had already made their way. We squeezed between two men on the side of the boat with our heads hanging overboard, taking deep breaths to avoid throwing up.

The boat tilted sharply to the left and threw me to the floor and I held Thekla's trouser belt to prevent her from falling overboard. The wind was howling and the gushing water soaked us but it was no time to worry about the state of our hair. As I hung tightly onto Thekla's belt to prevent myself rolling down the deck, I saw Thekla throw up over the edge and, at that precise moment, a gust of wind blew in our direction and blew her sick over the face of the man standing next to her. Seeing that, made me throw up all over my clothes and the man's shoes. It was a nightmare from hell.

By the time we got off the boat, Thekla was spaced out like a drug addict and I was covered in sick and smelt like a skunk.

When we got off the boat, we were greeted by another limo, but when the chauffeur saw the state of us, he refused to allow us in the car and hailed a taxi for us instead.

It took a few days for us to find our bearings and recover from our journey and, before I knew it, I was on my way home, just in time for Vasili's wedding to his English girlfriend Tracey.

Mum wore black and got through a box of tissues, as she poured her heart out to Auntie Marika at the reception. "I have one divorced daughter who has gone mad and now that *Englessa poutana* has put a curse on my Vasili. I might as well kill myself and be done with it," she cried.

CHAPTER 32

The Red Jacket

It felt great to be back at the Starlight Rooms with Tina again.

We jumped the queue as usual, knowing that the bouncer would let us through and were greeted by the manager who was always pleased to see us.

Over time we had developed friendships with crowds of guys who bought us drinks every week. Tina and I banged our glasses together, downed our drinks and said simultaneously "Cheers, oops see you tomorrow," pre-empting a drunken night ahead.

As the seventies and eighties hits were being churned out by the resident DJ, I would make my rounds to see who was about. I would stop and chat with regulars and have the occasional dance, especially if "Tease Me" was played. When this song came on, Tina and I would both make our way to the middle of the dance floor to strut our stuff.

The lesbian Blow Job routine was bad enough but our lesbian gyrating dance number was our second party piece and always caused a scene. We would gyrate on the dance floor dancing crotch to crotch, leaning backwards and then forwards into each other's tits, then open our legs and get as far down in between them as possible, making sure that we revealed a glimpse of our knickers. From the corner of my eye I would glimpse the men standing stock still with their mouths gaping, staring at us.

At the end we would get a round of applause. Men stopped us as we left the dance floor to offer us drinks. If the men were good looking we would accept but if they were ugly we would barge straight past them like stuck up cows.

Tina and I ruled the Starlight Rooms. At the end of the night we would compare phone numbers we'd been given and would laugh hysterically as they were thrown out of the car window.

Occasionally we arranged to go on double dates but invariably ended up laughing so much that the guys would get pissed off, which made us laugh even more.

In a restaurant one time we made an excuse to powder our noses so that could have a good laugh in the toilet, but we spotted a back door open and we walked straight out, into the car park, got in the car and drove off. Both the guys turned up at the Starlight Rooms the following week and we spent the whole evening ducking and diving trying to avoid them.

I was doing my rounds one night when I ended up in the foyer talking with another regular called Stavros. From the corner of my eye, I spotted a guy in a red jacket. I did a double take and zoomed in for a better look.

He was tall with short, black hair, dark, and a gorgeous wide smile, with perfectly chiselled cheek bones. I had not seen such a good looking guy for ages. He was just my type: smartly dressed in black suit trousers, white shirt, a tie and red jacket. He stood out by a mile and as I stared at him he turned his head around and looked straight at me. I quickly turned my head away and carried on speaking to Stavros. I moved my head slightly to the right to catch a glimpse of him again and he did the same and caught me looking at him. He smiled to acknowledge me. I smiled back, hoping that he would come over and talk to me. Tina came over instead.

"Annie, where have you been?" she asked. "I've been looking everywhere for you."

"I'll leave you girls to it," said Stav and left.

"I'm here and I'm not budging," I said gesturing my eyes towards the hunk's direction.

Tina looked around and soon spotted him.

"Ah," she said. "Red jacket?"

"Yep," I replied.

"Wow, I'm staying here too," she said and he looked over again.

I noticed that Stavros had gone over to him and when they finished talking red jacket started walking towards me. "Oh my God," I said to Tina "Shit, he's coming over. *Daraxe!* (Move!)." She stepped sideways three times, making it embarrassingly obvious that I had asked her to scarper as she disappeared into the crowd.

Suddenly I, and red jacket were face to face and for a moment it seemed that we were alone: no music, no people, no noise, no nothing, just him and me one-foot apart. We just smiled and stared into each other's eyes as my heart thumped inside my ribcage.

"Hi, Annie," he said.

"Hi. Did Stavros tell you my name?"

"Yes. I'm Mario."

"Hi, Mario."

"I know all about you," he said.

"Oh yeah? What do you know?"

"I know everything I need to know." He then lifted up his right hand and placed it at the top of my chest just above my heart. "I can feel your heart beating fast."

Normally I would whack someone across the face if he came anywhere near my tits, but I stood there, frozen with his hand on my chest as he felt my heart pulsing.

"Oh, is it? I can't feel anything," I said coolly.

"Yeah, right," he said laughing. "You're very hot, too."

"Yes, I know," I said boasting.

"No. I mean you are hot, as in temperature."

"Yes, I know what you meant," I said. He removed his hand.

"You're funny, too." he said.

"I'm not just a pretty face, you know".

"Mmm, I can see that."

I really don't know where all the cool lines were coming from but he was even better looking and sexier close up.

I asked him what he knew about me. He said he knew that my name was Annie Ross and that I was thirty-three, Greek, divorced, a lawyer, had a six-year-old child and lived in Enfield.

"So, what about you?" I asked.

"What about me?" he smiled.

"What did you say your name was again?" I laughed.

"Ha ha. Funny," he said. "Mario. Remember it. You'll be screaming it later."

"Ha, ha. Very funny,"

"Sorry, bad joke," he said.

"I've heard it a million times".

"Oops. I'd better watch what I say then."

"Yes, you'd better," I felt in control.

"I can see that I can't mess about with you."

"You can try but you won't get far," I said with a serious face. "So, about you ...?"

"OK," he said. "I'm thirty-five, I'm an accountant and I live in Clapham."

"Are you a turf accountant?" I joked grinning.

"Oh, you are funny, Miss Ross. No. I am a chartered accountant. I've never been married and have no children."

"Why? What's wrong with you?" I asked cheekily.

"Nothing. I have sense."

"You're right there," I laughed. "Any girlfriend?"

"Nope."

"Well, I don't believe you."

"You should because it's true."

"Well, I still don't believe you."

"God, you're hard," he said.

"Not as hard as you," I said suggestively, looking down at his crotch."Oh my God! I can't believe I just said that," I said. "I'm so sorry" and pretended to cover my mouth in shame.

We both laughed. "That makes us even for the screaming joke earlier," he said.

"Yes, it does," and we continued to laugh.

Me and Mario carried on talking for ages, completely oblivious to everyone around us and the time. The foyer was getting busier as people were starting to leave and queuing for their coats.

"Well, when are you going to give me your telephone number?" he asked.

"When you ask me for it," I replied.

"OK. Give it to me bitch," he said laughing.

"OK, you bastard." We teased and continued to banter with each other and the humour seemed to flow. I fancied him like crazy.

I gave him my number which he put in his phone. "I'll call you tomorrow."

"I know you will," I said.

"Mmm, arrogant too. I like it." He took my hand and kissed me on the cheek. "Goodbye, Annie. Speak to you tomorrow."

"Goodbye, Frankie," I said pretending to forget his name.

"Cow," he said and left.

When he had gone, I wanted to jump up and down and shout "Wow! Wow! Wow!" but managed to stay cool. Tina appeared suddenly from nowhere.

"Oh my God," she said. "I've been watching you two – he's lovely. Well?"

"Tina, I don't know where to start. Quick, let's get our jackets. I need to get some air. I'm suffocating in here."

We grabbed our jackets and went to the car. I tried to tell her the whole conversation I'd had with Mario but I couldn't remember any of it, I was in such a daze.

I still had a smile on my face at 2am when I crawled into bed. Suddenly my mobile rang. "Hello-o-o-o ..." I said slowly.

"Hello Miss Ross. Keep tomorrow night free. I'm taking you out."

"Let me just check my diary to see if I can fit you in."

"I do the jokes, please."

"Ha, ha. OK. I will let you. What time?"

"I'll pick you up at 8pm."

"OK. You've got a date."

"No, *you've* got a date," he said.

"No, *you've* got a date," I said.

"OK, Miss Ross. I have a date."

"Good boy."

"See you tomorrow. Text me your address. Goodnight, gorgeous."

"Good night, Freddie."

"Piss off."

"Mwah. Goodnight sweetie." I put the phone down, switched off the light and fell asleep with a smile on my face.

Next day I couldn't wait for the evening to come. At 3pm my phone rang with an anonymous number and I got excited.

"Hello," I said in a seductive voice.

"Hi, Annie. It's Jonny."

"What the hell do you want?"I asked.

"I wondered if you were free one night. I'd like to take you out for a meal."

"Why? Haven't you found your skinny, young bimbo with no baggage yet?"

"Stop it, Annie. You know I didn't mean that."

"Oh, really? Well, sorry. I'm not free."

"What about next week?" he asked.

"No, I'm not free. Ever. I'm seeing someone else."

"Well, that was quick."

"Well I guess that makes me the catch then, doesn't it?" I cawed.

"Blimey. You don't forget anything, do you Miss Lawyer?"

"No, I don't. Anyway, I am seeing a tall, dark, slim guy with lots of black hair who is single and has no baggage. He's also fantastic in bed so please don't ring me again. And I hope you find your bimbo."

"You are a bitch!" he said viciously.

"I know. But it's *the* bitch, to you. Bye." I hung up on him and threw the phone onto the bed. The audacity of the man! It was eight o'clock and I kept looking at my watch. I was happy with the way I looked and pulled my top down to reveal a bit more cleavage. I wore a short, black Lycra skirt, closed stiletto shoes, a black camisole and black jacket. My phone rang and this time it was Mario. "Hi," I said.

"Hello. I'm outside."

"OK, I'll be out in a sec."

I took some deep breaths, straightened my skirt and opened the front door. There he was in a red XR3i. I closed the front door and trotted to his car. I sat down in the seat and started nervously fiddling around with the seatbelt while he waited for me to finish.

"OK, I'm done," I said.

"Hi, Miss Ross." He leaned over and pecked me on the lips. I have a present for you." He produced a CD from the inside pocket on his door. It was called "I Swear" by All-4-One and he had signed it: *To Annie, Love Mario xx*

I was so touched! "I heard this song," he said, "and it reminded me of you so I had to get it for you today. I mean every word it says and I just want you to believe me. OK?"

"Wow, OK. Thank you. Please play it," I said.

"Are you sure you want to hear it here now with me here?" he asked.

"Well, yes."

He took it out of the case and put it in the CD player as he started driving.

"I swear, by the moon and the stars in the sky, I'll be there, forever in love, til death do us part, I love you with every beat of my heart, I swear ..."

The words touched me and soon tears were rolling down my cheeks. He stopped the car and reached out and held me. He wiped the tears from my eyes and then kissed them. "Oh, baby, don't cry. I mean it. You've got me now. I will always be here to look after you. I swear."

I never thought that I could feel this way again after Jack but this was better. The lyrics of the song, the music, his arms around me all felt right. My heart was complete and at peace once more and this was the reason for my tears.

CHAPTER 33

Next!

For the months that followed Mario and I were inseparable. He showered me with affection and I wasn't going out much because I wanted to be home with him. When I did go out, he would turn up unexpectedly to surprise me and I was flattered by that. Finally I realised that there was a purpose in Jack leaving me and that was because I was destined for someone better. Mario showed me that Cypriot men were more passionate and family orientated.

On my birthday, Mario took me out for dinner to a restaurant in the West End. While we were eating, he stood up, got down on one knee and produced a small box from his pocket. My heart missed a beat as he handed it to me and asked me to open it.

"Oh, my God," I gasped. "Is that what I think it is?"

"Please open it, baby."

My eyes started to fill up and I began to choke. As I slowly opened the case, a musical rendition of "Happy Birthday" began to play. It was a music box. He saw the disappointment appear on my face and burst out laughing. "Happy birthday, baby," he said.

"You fucking bastard," I said as I slammed the box and threw it at him – it hit him straight in the eye.

"Ouch, that hurt."

"Good, you bastard." He loved to wind me up. He then took off his ring from his finger and put it on the second finger of my left hand.

"There. I want you to wear my ring to show that you are mine." That felt good and I never took it off.

On Valentine's Day Mario took me to a Chinese restaurant in China Town. As we finished the first course, his phone rang and I heard him say: "Oh my God. OK. I'll be right there."

He got up from the table. "I'm so sorry, baby. I have to go. That was my sister. My cousin Antros has just had a car crash and I have to get to the hospital."

"I'm sorry baby. Of course, go now." He gave me some money to pay the bill and for a taxi home, saying he would call later. I never heard from him that night and I was concerned about him. His mobile was switched off and he finally called at eight in the morning. He said he had been at the hospital all night and that his cousin was now out of a coma. He asked if he could come around. He said he was really tired and just wanted to sleep. "Of course," I said. "I have no work today."

He came over and seemed quite distraught. Mario slept while I caught up on my legal work. When he woke up, he said: "Get ready, darling. I'm taking you out for dinner to make up for last night." We went to a Greek restaurant, Vrisaki, and he was so attentive but I could see that he was still anxious about his cousin. As we were driving back from the restaurant he put his foot down on the accelerator and sped down the dual carriageway of the A10, well exceeding the speed limit. He was swaying the car from side to side changing from one lane to another and he jumped a red light.

"Oh, my God! What the hell are you doing darling? Slow down," I screamed as I held onto my seat with both hands.

Looking behind, I saw a light blue Ford Escort also switching between lanes and it seemed to be following us. We were in a high-speed chase along a dual carriageway doing ninety miles an hour in a forty mile an hour zone.

"Stop," I screamed. "What the hell is going on?" He told me not to worry. "It's OK. They are just loan sharks and I owe them some money. I'm so sorry, baby, but I'll explain later when we get home. I promise."

We came close to hitting two cars on the road but he turned off onto a side road and swerved the car to safety. He drove for about half a mile at normal speed and then stopped the car, breathed a sigh of relief and put his head on the steering wheel. I looked at him in shock.

I was angry and shaken and insisted on an explanation but he said "I'm drained and I don't want to talk about it right now."

"Mario, please tell me."

"Baby, I'm really sorry."

"So tell me what the hell that was all about."

"I told you. I owe them money. They are loan sharks."

"Why didn't you stop and just pay them some money?"

"I don't want to involve you in this. I don't want them to know that I am seeing you. They are dangerous people. Don't worry. I will pay them some of the money tomorrow and get them out of the way."

"How much do you owe them?"

"Not much, babe. Seriously, forget about it."

"How can I forget?" I said "You have just involved me in a high-speed car chase. Please take me home."

"Whatever," he said

"I hope you're not annoyed at me?" I asked.

"Look, I'm not annoyed at you. Just leave me alone. I am taking you home, all right?"

As he pulled up outside my house, he kept the engine running. "Aren't you coming in?" I asked.

"No. I'll see you later."

"I thought you were going to explain everything to me?"

"There's nothing more to explain. I've told you."

"No, you haven't," I said getting annoyed.

"Babe, just go home and I'll speak to you later, OK?" and without a kiss, he drove away. I sat on my settee and tried to reflect on what had just happened. He called me later in the evening but he would not talk about the chase. I assumed that he was in some kind of debt and was too embarrassed to talk about it, so let it be.

As the months went by, he became a rock to me.

I introduced him to George and they were great together. They played football in the garden – George loved football so took an instant liking to Mario. Sometimes I let Mario take him to the park and George would always come home covered in mud and with an ice-cream. George loved it and followed Mario around everywhere he went. It was so lovely to see him happy and my heart was at peace. I was with a guy I absolutely adored and he was making my kid really happy too. George so deserved that.

This was it for me. I experienced a burning desire to be with him. That's what love meant to me. I was comfortable with the relationship and started to introduce him to my family and friends. He introduced me to his family too and I truly believed that one day we would get married. Until one Thursday afternoon my mobile rang:

"Hello, who is this?" asked a woman's voice.

"This is Annie. Who is this?"

"Are you Mario's girlfriend?"

"Yes, I am. Who are you?"

"You don't know me but I'm his girlfriend too."

"What? Is your name Sophia?" I asked.

"Yes. How do you know me?" she asked.

"Mario told me all about you. You are the ex-girlfriend who stalks him."

"That's what he tells all of the girls," she said.

"All of the girls?"

"Yes. We are not the only ones he is seeing. He is seeing at least two other women that I know of."

"You're lying. Leave us alone."

"No, Annie please, don't hang up. I can prove it to you. I have a blue Escort. A few months ago, I chased him down a dual carriageway and he had a girl in the car. I think that might have been you."

I sat down. "Yes, it was me. He told me it was a loan shark chasing him."

"Well, it wasn't. It was me, and on Valentine's Day he was supposed to take me out and he turned up really late because he had to visit his cousin in hospital, I knew he was lying, though. He was probably with you."

"Yes, he was."

"Seriously, Annie. I'm not lying to you. I've caught him out. Please meet me and I will confront him with you. You will see that I am telling the truth."

I could feel myself seething slowly as the truth started to sink in. It was all making sense: the car chase, Valentine's Day. My heart sank to the floor and the sick feeling quickly changed to rage. But I remained cool.

I met Sophia in the Fox pub in Palmers Green. As I drove into the car park, I saw a blue Escort and she was waiting for me.

"Hi, Annie."

"Hi, Sophia."

I got in Sophia's car and she drove us to Clapham, discussing Mario all the way. She said that she had been seeing him for five years and that she had caught him out seven times.

"Why do you keep taking him back?" I asked. "You're the idiot."

"I love him," she simply said.

"No wonder he cheats on you," I said. "You let him walk all over you."

"I know. I can't help it. I am sure he will do the same to you. He has this hold on women and they always take him back."

"Really? Well, not this woman. You just watch me."

"Wow, you're strong," she replied. "But don't you see? He will get around you with flowers, text messages and he will win you round again, he always does."

As we approached his flat, Sophia phoned him. "Hello, darling. I'm coming round to yours. Are you home? I'll be there in five minutes."

"Good. He is home and he doesn't suspect a thing," she said.

I remained speechless but couldn't wait to see his face when he got caught out. Sophia parked the car around the corner so he didn't see us from the window. She phoned Mario to come down and said, she had a box which she needed his help to take out of the car. I got out and waited by the kerb and, within a few seconds, he walked around the corner. He saw Sophia and was about to kiss her when he spotted me. His face was a picture; it was like he had seen a ghost. He ran back the way he came, got into his car and drove off.

No sooner had I got home my mobile rang. It was him. I was not surprised that he tried to call. No doubt he wanted to explain, but I didn't want to hear his bullshit so cut him off.

He was no longer a gorgeous, intelligent, funny man who I would have married. He was a fake and a phoney and I instantly felt nothing for him.

"And there I was thinking that Cypriot men were more passionate and family-orientated," I complained to Alexis over the phone. "Like hell they are. They are more passionate about their dicks more like. At least Jack went off with one woman at a time."

This was the first time that I had tested my emotions since Jack and I realised that I had become heartless, someone who was able to switch off her emotions in an instant. From that moment on I became fearless, knowing that I could never get hurt again. This strength was to become my biggest asset.

Mario did not go away easily. He rang constantly but I kept cutting him off. The only pain I experienced was when George asked "Where's Mario Mummy? I want to play Nintendo," and I hated Mario for that.

I managed to avoid him for weeks but eventually one Friday night at the Starlight Rooms I was talking to a group of friends and saw him from the corner of my eye. He was trying to get into my line of vision but I ignored him and never once met his eye. I made sure that I was surrounded by guys so as not to give him the opportunity to come over to me.

To really put the boot in, I asked the DJ to play our song, "I Swear", and made sure that he saw me mimicking putting my fingers down my throat. He waited until Tina and I went onto the dance floor and as we danced to Bobby Brown's "Two Can Play That Game", he came and stood a foot away from me, watching me like a lost, little lost puppy. This was his attempt to win me over, thinking I would feel sorry for him and be flattered by his efforts. Even Tina was taken in by him.

"Annie, I feel sorry for him. Please go and talk to him. He looks like he is really sorry."

I gave her a stern look and said, "*Na tou sheso!*" ("I would rather shit on him!") and I took off the ring he had given me and threw it to the floor by his feet.

"I admire you, girl," Tina said. "You are really strong. That guy is completely in love with you and he has just humiliated himself for you."

"Tina. The only thing that guy is in love with is his ego. I will never let any man hurt me again," I said.

As I got my coat from the foyer, Mario stood in my way trying to block my path, but I walked straight past him like he was nothing. He stopped Tina who was behind me, opened her left hand and put the ring in it.

"Tell Annie goodbye, I'm sorry and I love her," he said.

It moved me when Tina told me what he had done. Tina gave me the ring and I stared at it for a few seconds before throwing it in the glove compartment.

"Next," I said.

Poor Alexis got the brunt of it again.

"No wonder Greek men have a reputation for being sleazy gigolos" laughed Alexis.

"It amazes me how men complain that there are no decent girls any more. What decent girl is going to want a coward loser like Jack, a womanising gigolo like Mario or a Neanderthal, mummy's boy like Jonny? They need to wake up and smell the coffee. Bastards," I said.

CHAPTER 34

In with the New

My new motto throughout the nineties became, "Treat them mean, keep them keen."

By going out with Mario and Jack, I had heard every lie and excuse under the sun. I had lived through a high-speed car chase, been showered with flowers, gifts and love letters on my windscreen, dedicated music, given love notes and had whirlwind romances. How could I possibly believe or trust a man ever again?

I now got great pleasure in winding-up men and jumped at any opportunity to turn them on and dump them, especially the arrogant show-offs who thought they were God's gift to women. I loved knocking them off their perches and outwitting their chat-up lines with lawyerish interrogations and banter.

I got called a minger, lesbian, bitter and twisted divorcee, a stuck-up cow and my favourite was a cold, heartless, vicious bitch – I loved it. "I'm *the* bitch to you," I would say in reply to their taunts and laughed in their faces.

Tina started dating a guy from work and was not going out as much, although we still spoke daily on the phone. Kiri also started dating a girl and was otherwise detained – it wasn't the same without them around.

With Tina and Kiri now off the singles scene I started spending more time with Alexis and Stella. Stella had started working for a national newspaper and got to go to some great events. On many occasions she would be given VIP passes and take me with her.

We were living the high life, attending book launches and film premieres, music festivals and concerts, PFA Footballer of the Year events, and frequented top hotels and restaurants.

One Saturday night, Stella, Tina and I went to the Apollo Greek restaurant in Holloway. I got chatting to a girl sitting on the next table, who said her name was Frosso, and went on to say that she didn't have any single friends to go out with, because most of her friends were married or had boyfriends. I felt sorry for her: "I have lots of single friends and cousins and there's room for you too." I introduced her to my crowd and invited her out with us.

She was a pretty girl with long, dark brown hair and wore her clothes two sizes too small. She was not very streetwise, but she was a nice girl and it wasn't long before Frosso was a regular in the crowd.

It was summer and I invited Frosso on holiday with me and Alexis to Ayia Napa. I booked a suite in the Gresham Bay Hotel and couldn't wait to hit the pool and vegetate for the next two weeks. It was quite an adventure having three single girls on holiday together and not a day went by when one or more of us did not get chatted up. The late 1990s in Cyprus brought with it a growing tourism of women visiting the island. Cypriot men "on the prowl" for sex turned to the more promiscuous tourists as their own women were inhibited and sexual harassment became rife in the streets. I found it hilarious watching the Cypriots with their curly long hair, hairy chests and flip-flops using their broken English to lure women into bed. Sadly, Cyprus had become all about sex.

Frosso loved the attention from the Cypriot men, whereas Alexis and I found it an intrusion when our sunbathing was disrupted by their bullshit Greek, cheesy chat-up lines, with their sleazy Greek accents.

"Er, me and you ... jiggy-jiggy?" asked one shirtless, afro-haired Cypriot man standing above me with his hairy gorilla-like chest, gyrating his groin from side to side and swinging his worry beads.

Not realising that we were Greek, I lifted up my sunglasses from my face, took one look at him with beady eyes and said in Greek, "*Fihe po thame je pihene stin mana sou*" ("Go away from here and go back to your mummy").

He stepped back startled. "Oh I'm sorry, I thought you were English," he said and his friends ridiculed him as he walked away.

"Aww, he was really cute," said Frosso. Alexis and I looked at each other wondering if she was joking. In fact the whole fortnight turned out to be about Frosso. She flirted with anyone who wore trousers and gave her a bit of attention. With her tight clothing revealing her stomach bulges, she would blink her eyelashes when a guy introduced himself to her and introduced herself back as "Frosso, with the lovely eyes." Me and Alexis cringed.

At dinner, Frosso giggled like a schoolgirl and blatantly flirted with all the waiters who gave her attention but if they turned their attention to anyone else, she would get all irritable and say she was bored and would want to leave.

I had a great chat-up line when a guy asked me what I did for a living: "I solicit."

This left them wondering whether I was a solicitor or a prostitute. It was an ice-breaker with men who found it rather amusing and sexy. Frosso noticed that it created attention, so she started saying it too, regardless of the fact that she was a nail technician.

Alexis and I named her "Gori girl". This is the name that we gave to a fast-growing population of simple girls, originating usually from Palmers Green, whose ambitions and interests extended no further than the state of their hair, nails and clothes and finding a man to marry. I was slowly losing patience with her.

Back in London, Frosso continued her desperate, flirtatious ways and carried on putting her foot in everything with her stupid comments. She then started to copy my look, my hair and my clothes, and she was beginning to be an irritating thorn in the side.

When she wasn't around, people called her my sidekick or my shadow, which became her nickname for a while until it was replaced by "bimbo".

Even though she was irritating, I felt sorry for her and generally had a good time when we were out together, so I let it go and took her copying as a compliment.

One Saturday afternoon George and I were out having lunch at the Orange Tree in Whetstone when I got a call from Mum:

"O ma' God, please come round, something terrible has happened. Please come now," Mum screamed down the phone. Before I could ask her anything she hung up. I panicked and tried to call her back but there was no answer. We left our food, jumped in the car and quickly drove to Mum's.

When we got there, I opened the door and Mum was in the garden with her wellies on and holding a trowel.

"Oh, hello darli, where is George?"

"Why don't you answer your bloody phone?"

"I was in the garden. Can't you see? I can't hear from here. I haven't got big ears you know."

"Mum. What's happened that is so terrible?"

"Ah. Let me show you," she said walking to the kitchen. "Look. I found a hole under the kitchen cupboard and a mouse came in and ate all my *bourkouri* (cous cous) the basta'."

"You made me leave my food and rush over here like a lunatic, so that you can tell me about a stupid mouse?"

"No. I wanted you to come and block up the hole with some of that polyfiller of yours but don't worry, your father put some poison down there and a mousetrap and it's dead now. Look. Here it is," she said showing me the dead mouse in the trap.

"And that is so terrible that it couldn't wait?"

"Of course it's terrible, it ate my *bourkouri.* Anyway, where is that lovely grandson of mine? I miss him. *Ahabi mou*! (My love!)

CHAPTER 35

New York

It was 1999 and I was having the time of my life, sharing my success with my friends. One Thursday night I was in a bar called P'zazz listening to Westlife's "Flying Without Wings" and got talking to a lady called Lydia who looked fed-up. We chatted all night and were laughing at ourselves for being the oldest people in the bar and getting tone deaf at the noise levels of the live band, so we left and went out for a quiet bite to eat.

It transpired that Lydia worked for a company that housed asylum seekers and she said that she had been awarded a lucrative contract but had no money to set it up and was looking for investors. I told her that I had some spare cash that I might be interested in investing if she sent me a business proposal. This was the beginning of what turned out to be a very successful and lucrative business venture.

We became business partners and within six months our contract was extended and we established a company to run it. I was now a company director.

I gave up my conveyancing practice to manage the operations of our new company, housing young males from Kosovo, and Lydia took an administrative role.

Within months, we were on our third hostel and money was flooding in. I could not believe how fortunate I was and all because I was in the right place at the right time one boring Thursday night in P'zazz.

Before long, I changed my car to a convertible Mercedes Sport and treated myself to a gated, luxury penthouse apartment in one of the most desirable locations in North London. Haris and Angel came to visit and congratulated me on my new penthouse and success.

"I'm successful because I don't have a man in my life to hold me back," I said.

"It is admirable the way you have made something of yourself without anybody's help, whereas that loser ex-husband of yours is still in rented accommodation and struggles to make ends meet," said Haris. "By the way", he added "did I mention that he left his girlfriend at the altar because she ran up thousands of pounds of debts behind his back?" Angel and I laughed.

"The best thing he ever did was leave me," I said.

It was time to celebrate my new status with another holiday.

I called Thekla in LA who said it was great timing, as she was exhausted and needed a break.

We arranged to meet in New York City. It was my first time there and was so excited about seeing it.

I arrived at JFK airport and expected Thekla to pick me up as she was due to land from Los Angeles an hour before me. When I came out of arrivals there was no sign of her. I switched on my mobile to call her but it rang before I could dial the number. "Annie it's Thekla."

"Where are you hiding you cow?" I asked, looking around to see her.

"Annie listen, something happened at work today and I missed my flight, so I won't be coming now until tomorrow evening."

"What?" I said. "Are you kidding me?"

"No Annie, honestly. Listen, get a cab to the Waldorf Astoria Hotel, that's where you are staying. It's a beautiful hotel and I am sure that you can find something to do until I get there."

"OK, it's a bit scary on my own but I'm sure it won't be a

problem. I'm really looking forward to it. I will chat to you later when I've settled in."

I took a yellow cab, which in itself was exciting. As expected, the driver was very friendly and chatty and had a deep Bronx accent, which is where he said he came from.

"First time in New York?"

"Yes, actually it is."

"Alone?"

"Yes, for tonight anyway. My cousin is joining me tomorrow."

"Wow, you have a great accent lady. I'd watch these New York guys, they just love the English."

"Oh good," I said. "I'm looking forward to meeting them all," which made him laugh.

I could not get over the breathtaking view as the cab crossed over Manhattan Bridge. New York was everything that I had ever imagined and was in awe of the huge skyscrapers.

The driver dropped me off at the hotel and as I got out of the car I could not hear myself speak. I was deafened by the noise of the loud congestion of traffic and all the hooting that was going on – but loved it.

The lobby of the Waldorf was traditional and magnificent. As I walked to the reception I had a huge smile on my face as I took it all in. I checked in, unpacked and decided to sit in the foyer and people-watch to see what the night might bring. I was sitting smiling at everyone for about half an hour when the bellboy came up to me and said: "I have a note for you, ma'am."

"For me? Oh, how exciting," I said. "Thank you."

I thought it was from Thekla but when I opened it and read: "*Would you care to join me for a drink at the bar?*"

I looked around and the bellboy pointed to a guy leaning up against the reception desk. He was about five-feet-ten-inches, had shoulder-length, black hair with shades pushed up onto his head, wearing blue jeans and a white t-shirt. He was just my type. "Mmmmm," I thought.

I looked at him and he smiled, so I smiled back and he started to walk over. He put his hand out and said: "Hi, I'm Bruce Jon."

"Hi," I responded, shaking his hand, "I'm Annie Ross."

"Would you mind joining me for that drink?" he asked.

"I wouldn't mind at all, I could do with the company. Thank you," I said coyly and we walked to the bar together.

The table was reserved and it was tucked away in the corner. The barman immediately came over to take our order and I couldn't help noticing that he knew his name.

"The usual, Mr Jon?"

"Yes, and champagne for the lady," he answered.

"Oh no, please. Not for me," I said. "Could I just have a glass of still water, please?"

Bruce looked at me surprised and said to the barman, "Whatever the lady wants."

He then ordered two glasses of orange juice "for the gentlemen over there" and pointed at two men standing at the bar in black suits.

"Ahh, that's nice of you," I said. "Do you know them?"

"Yes. They work for me."

"Oh really? Do you own the bar then?"

"No," he said and grinned.

We sat down and he said: "I spotted you as soon as you walked into the reception. I could not help noticing that beautiful smile. What's your story Annie?"

"Do you have all year?" I asked.

"I have a lifetime," he replied.

"Ha. That's a good line. I want to use that one," I laughed.

He laughed. I started telling him about my Cypriot upbringing and just when I got to the bit when I poured the drink over Jack's head I stopped and said: "Enough about me. I'm bored now. How about you? What's your story Bruce?"

He started laughing. "Don't you know?" he asked.

"Don't I know what?"

He looked at me, moved his head closer to mine, moved my hair out of my face and kissed me briefly on the lips.

"I have been meaning to do that. I hope you don't mind?" he asked.

"Erm no. Do I look as though I mind"?

He was scruffy and rough-looking with new stubble and ripped jeans but he had a cute bum and lovely piercing brown eyes that hypnotised me when he looked at me.

"So, where were we?" he asked.

"We were at the bit when I asked you about your story."

"OK. Well. Do you know who I am?"

"Yes. You're name is Bruce Jon, you already told me."

"You really don't know who I am do you?"

"What? Are you telling me now that's not your name?"

"No. That's not what I'm saying. I am who I said." He grinned. "Do you like rock music?"

"No, not really. It's a bit loud."

"You're kidding me right?"

"No really. I'm more into pop."

"OK," he said and continued to grin. "Are you for real?"

"What do you mean?"

"OK, Annie. I am a rock musician and producer."

"Wow, how interesting. Have you done any records?"

He laughed out loud and said "You are wonderful, do you know that? Erm. Yes, I have four Gold discs."

"Wow, you must be good then!"

He laughed again and just at that moment a camera flash went off and one of the men dressed in black ran out of the door and gave chase.

"What's that all about?" I asked.

"Paparazzi."

The man returned a few minutes later shaking his head at Bruce who got up and said: "Annie, I'm sorry I have to get out of here."

"Aww, that's a shame but it was lovely meeting you."

"Would you please join me in my room?"

"Oh no! Sorry. I really don't know you."

"I completely understand but please just for a while. I really would like to get to know you more."

I gave him a dirty look and said "Hey. I'm not like that."

"Oh Jesus," he said," I didn't mean it like that sweetheart. Please believe me. I just really like your company and would like to talk to you some more. I just can't stay here that's all."

"Why can't we stay here? It's nice."

"Annie, there's going to be paparazzi surrounding this place soon and I really have to go," he said anxiously.

The two men in black stood behind him as if to shield him and guided him out of the bar towards the lift. Only at that moment did I register that the guys were bodyguards and realised that he must be famous.

"Please Annie, just half an hour. I will get one of my guys to walk you back to your room later. I promise you will be safe."

I was intrigued and genuinely felt that he wanted to chat so, against my better judgement, I went with them in the lift.

When he opened the door to his room I could not believe my eyes. It was a suite with a huge entrance hall leading into a massive lounge full of traditional furniture on a beautiful red Chinese rug. The view was breathtaking and I couldn't stop looking out of the window. He cracked open a bottle of champagne and poured himself a glass and poured me some chilled water. We sat on one of the many couches and he began to talk about his life. He said he was a famous rock star and a music producer, even though I had never heard of him. He said he was thirty-five and never married because he had never fallen in love. I really liked him but didn't believe a word he was saying and told him so.

"Why would I lie to you?" he asked.

"Because you're a man and that's what men do. It is their job!" I replied.

He laughed, "Boy, you're one tough cookie."

"Yep. I am," I said, feeling very proud of myself.

"I can't believe that you have never heard of me!"

"Well, I've heard of Bruce Springsteen and John Bon Jovi but not you, so you can't be all that famous."

He laughed again. "Do you know," he said, "no one makes me laugh like you do. You are so pure. I like it and I love your accent."

So there I was in a magnificent suite in the Waldorf Astoria Hotel with someone who reckoned he was a rock star with two bodyguards outside and what did I do?

"Anyway Bruce," I said, "I'm really tired and I have to get some sleep. I want to catch the tour bus early in the morning so that I can do the uptown and downtown tours before my cousin arrives tomorrow night."

He looked at me in disbelief.

"Please stay here with me. I have three bedrooms. It's a lovely suite and I would love you to share it with me. I want to know more about you and I can get the butler to bring us breakfast in the morning. I don't have to be in the studio till ten."

"Seriously, thank you. I am flattered but I can't. I just don't feel right about it but I tell you what, if you are free tomorrow evening I can see you after my tour before my cousin arrives."

He laughed out loud.

"Do you know what Annie? I'm the one who usually tells women that I will see them after my tour. I've never had a woman tell me that she will see me after her tour. I feel used," and he continued to laugh hysterically.

"Good. Now you know how it feels, Mr Rock Star."

"OK. Are you serious about coming tomorrow?"

"Yes. Of course. I would love to get to know you more too but tonight I am tired and have jetlag and I really need some sleep."

"OK. I will hold you to that," he said and as I stood up to leave he pulled me towards him and kissed me gently. He was lovely and my heart missed a beat. I really wanted to stay but deep down I didn't believe him. I didn't want him to think I was easy and figured that if he were genuine he would wait one more day.

"I will get my guy to walk you to your room."

"Wow," I said, "I've never had my own personal body guard before. I like it," and we both laughed.

Next morning Thekla woke me up with a call.

"Morning cuz," she said, "a little change of plan. I can't come to New York now so I have booked you on a first-class flight to LA but it leaves JFK in three hours' time so get yourself ready and get to the airport quick and I will pick you up this end."

"What! Oh my God you stupid cow, you're cutting it fine. You could have given me a bit more notice. OK. See you in a few hours."

I was in my element sitting in my first-class seat. There were only ten seats in a pyramid shape and I was seated in the one right at the front with nothing but a panoramic view in front of me.

As the plane was getting ready to take off I was smiling to myself and thought of poor Bruce who was going to find out that I had checked out and would have wondered what on earth had happened to me. I felt quite bad but then did wonder whether he really was a famous rock star and what it would have been like if we'd met again. If he was telling the truth and he really did like me then I had just blown it.

I got my freshly squeezed orange juice from the air stewardess and as I thanked her a man appeared from behind my seat, startling me.

"Hello. My name is Sheik Muhamed."

"Oh hello," I said, "You frightened me. Where did you spring up from?"

"I am sitting behind you and couldn't help but notice you, so I just had to come and say hello."

"Oh. That's nice of you. Hi, I'm Annie," and shook his hand.

"I'm honoured to meet you," he said.

He was a fair-haired man with big brown eyes and he was very smartly dressed in a beige suit, white shirt and the most amazing S-shaped cuff links that shone like diamonds.

"I just wanted to tell you that you are the most beautiful woman I have ever seen," – I nearly choked on my orange juice.

"What? Don't be so ridiculous," I said, pissed off at his bullshit.

He looked at me all taken aback and said: "I'm not being ridiculous, I mean it. You have the most amazing green eyes. They are hypnotic. In my country a woman with green eyes is blessed."

I looked at him with a half dirty look, like I didn't believe a word he was telling me.

"So where is your country exactly?" I asked.

"Saudi Arabia."

"So what are you doing in LA?"

"I have business here."

"And what business do you do?"

"I am a sheik and I have many businesses but my main one is art. I am an art dealer."

"Oh that's interesting," I said just to be polite.

"Do you mind if I sit here?" he asked and before I could say anything he crouched down on the floor next to my chair.

"So what do you do if you don't mind me asking?" he asked.

"I'm a lawyer."

"I am proud of you," he said "This is very unusual for a woman. Women in my country do not get education."

"Well it's unusual where I come from too but more women are going to university now."

"Are you English?" he asked.

"Well yes, but to Cypriot parents."

"I knew it. I could tell that you had some Mediterranean blood in you from your eyes."

"You make me laugh. You're such a charmer, bet you charm the pants off all the women in your country, being a sheik. Are you really a sheik?"

"Yes I really am."

"Well you don't look like one to me. Where's your sheik outfit?" I said sarcastically.

"My family are westernised and I am free to wear what I choose. Have you been to Dubai?"

"No I haven't yet but I would love to go one day."

"Please let me take you. I have a palace there."

I laughed, "A palace. You make me laugh."

"I'm serious. I do have a palace there."

"I thought you said you live in Saudi Arabia."

"I do but I live in Dubai too."

"So how many wives do you have?"

"I don't have any wives. I told you my family are not traditionalists."

"Oh come on. I bet they want you to marry some Saudi Arabian princess!"

"Yes, they do but I can marry who I like if I want. You never know I might even marry a Cypriot girl called Annie."

"Oh haha, you are so full of it. Well my mum wants me to marry a nice Cypriot boy."

"You are breaking my heart."

"You should be an actor not an artist," I laughed.

"Why don't you like me?"

"Who said I don't like you?"

"But you keep ridiculing me and I'm trying to have a serious conversation with you."

"Oops, sorry. OK. Let's do serious. Go ahead I'm listening."

"Well I know that I have only just met you but I have this feeling in my heart which I never felt before. It is like you have hypnotised me. I don't want us to leave the plane as strangers. I want you to agree to let me take you out in Los Angeles. You need to know that I am serious about you. I want you to see what kind of life I can give you. You will never be short of anything. You will live like a queen. I will lavish you with gifts and my love."

As he was giving me his speech all I could think was "boy this guy is good". I had thought that Mario was good but this one was an Oscar-winning performer. I deduced that this was some kind of Arabic chat-up line and I found him amusing.

"You are hilarious," I said. "You are so full of it."

"There you go again." You are ridiculing me. Why don't you believe what I am telling you. I love you."

"What! You're mad. I've just realised now that you must be from a lunatic asylum. That explains everything."

He got up, gave me a piercing look and walked back to his seat. At last. I thought, peace and quiet. What a nutter.

I pressed the button on my seat to recline it and fell asleep.

I woke up a few hours later and looked at my watch and saw that there were still two hours to go. The stewardess brought me a menu and I chose my food. "Look at the Cypriot girl now in first class," I thought. Just as I finished eating the sheik appeared again.

"I'm sorry. Please accept my apology," he said.

"For what?"

"I should not have walked off like that. It was juvenile and I'm sorry."

"Don't worry about it," I said.

"I'm just not used to be spoken to like that," he said "but I have thought about it and I understand that we are from different cultures and I have to accept that you are different from me. This is why I like you."

I looked at him and smiled. "Look, sheik. I am sure you are very nice but I can't get used to your forthrightness. You speak your mind but, no offence, I find what you say very hard to believe. I am not used to that in England."

"I know this. I noticed this when I studied in Oxford."

"You went to Oxford"?

"Yes I studied philosophy and mathematics."

"And you ended up an art collector?"

"Yes. So please, what is your answer?"

"To what"?

"Will you let me take you out? I will be in Los Angeles for three days and then I fly back to Dubai. If you are impressed with me in Los Angeles then you can come back with me to Dubai."

"You are crazy. I have a job and a son at home. How could I go to Dubai?"

"You bring him with you and you don't need to work."

"Right. I'm sure that your parents will be delighted to have a Greek divorcee with a child in your life. They will hate me."

"No! I am a sheik. I will marry who I like."

"Well I don't want to be one of many wives. I'm no good at sharing."

"I only want one wife. I only want you. Please. Give me your number," and he handed me a pen and a small piece of paper. I wrote down my number with two wrong digits and handed it to him.

"There you go. Now can you leave me alone?"

"Thank you," he said. "Yes, now I will leave you alone."

"Thank you," I said and smiled at him.

The plane landed in Los Angeles airport and I was waiting at the carousel for my luggage when the sheik came up to me again. "Annie. I will call you tonight and I want to see you tomorrow. Please make yourself available for me," and he lifted my hand and kissed it.

Thekla greeted me at arrivals.

"You will never believe what happened to me in New York and on the plane here."

As I was telling her the story I saw two black limos and an entourage of security pass me by and drive into the distance.

"Oh my God Thekla, maybe he really was a sheik and I gave him a wrong number."

As we were driving home Thekla said: "There was this woman in the paper this morning with that millionaire rock star Bruce Jon and I could have sworn it was you. She really looked like you."

"Oh my God," I said "I'm gutted."

CHAPTER 36

The Millennium

I was thirty-seven years old and was on top of the world in my stunning penthouse apartment. I was rich and looked the best ever. I was the queen bee and centre of attention – everyone wanted to be my friend. I was happy, George was happy and no-one could have wished for a better life as we were about to embrace a new millennium.

My new penthouse was walking distance to a great country pub called the Cock and Dragon, which was very popular with the Greek singles. This is where I spent most of my time moaning to my friends that I could have been with a rock star or a sheik if I hadn't been such a cow to men. So my New Year's resolution was to be a bit more trusting and give men a chance.

Millennium New Year's Eve was fast approaching and we bought tickets for a Greek dinner and dance in an old, white mansion house in Park Lane, which had been converted into a banqueting hall and was a great setting for New Year's Eve.

I had bought a long, tight-fitting burgundy, Spanish-style dress on my trip to LA which made my figure look in peak condition, all tits and arse, and I was excited about wearing it at the party.

All my friends were going to be there: Alexis, Frosso and Stella with her two brothers and three of their friends. Even Tina and Kiri were going and I couldn't wait to see them again.

Taxis were organised to take me and the girls to the venue and the boys were making their own way there. Frosso turned up first at my flat and when she took her coat off she was wearing a burgundy Spanish-style dress just like mine – I was livid. I gave her a look like thunder but she was oblivious. But when she took out her perfume from her bag and I saw that it was the same I wore, Moschino, I had to say something.

"For fuck's sake, Frosso, are you going to be wearing my knickers next? Can you stop fucking copying me? It's not funny anymore."

I arrived at the venue fuming and headed straight for the champagne reception. I downed the first glass and went for a second and downed that one too. I hated the taste of champagne so by downing it I didn't taste it for long. The retching of my face after each glass was a dead giveaway and after the third glass I felt the blood rushing to my head.

"Oops!" I said and giggled.

I toasted the woman standing next to me and said, "See you tomorrow" and laughed.

I had only been there fifteen minutes and was already pissed. The foyer was packed with people mingling majestically with each other, as they made polite conversation – while I was having a conversation with a champagne glass.

I saw Alexis look at me from the corner of my eye and she came over. She took the glass from me and said: "Slow down, Annie."

"OK," I said smiling and grabbed a fifth glass from a passing waiter without Alexis seeing me and I downed it. I was having fun in my own little world.

I followed Alexis to our table and sat down on a chair near the dance floor.

I looked around the room and saw the boys looking dapper in their smart suits and the girls in their beautiful dresses – apart from Frosso who I gave a dirty look to and tutted.

I focused my eyes on the white and silver decorations and the lovely flowers and candles. "Mm, how romantic," I said cynically and picked up someone's drink from the table and downed that too. It was disgusting, God knows what was in it but I laughed at myself because no-one had seen me do it. I started chuckling loudly and as the rest of my table sat down they looked at me and wondered what was so amusing.

Charlie, one of Stella's brother's friends whom I had seen a couple of times before in the Cock and Dragon, bent over me and asked what I was laughing at.

"Shush," I said, putting my finger to my mouth. "Don't tell anyone, I'll tell you later."

"OK," he said and laughed with me, putting his finger over his mouth too.

The rest of the evening was a blur. I remember waking up at the table and everyone was eating and music was playing in the background, as the band had gone to eat.

My ears pricked up when I heard one of my favourite tunes of the time, "Bailamos" by Enrique Iglesias, start to play. I could not resist dancing to it at the best of times let alone when drunk. I shot up on my feet and gyrated to the dance floor, swinging my hips from side to side in time with the music and was dancing on my own having the whole dance floor to myself.

I had a glass of champagne in my hand – God knows where I picked that up from!

I could see people looking at me and laughing, and my friends were in hysterics. As I danced round and round in a circle I raised my glass intermittently and they all raised their glasses back and shouted out "cheers". The raising of the glasses and the cheers soon developed into clapping as they cheered me on. The more they cheered, the more encouraged I felt and the more provocatively I danced and the more claps and cheers I got from around the venue.

I was showing off and was on a complete high. Everyone started chanting: "Annie, Annie, Annie!" I started laughing so much that I spilled champagne on the floor and then slipped on it – somehow managing to keep my balance like a gymnast on a beam with my arms outstretched, rocking from side to side, trying not to fall over. The music finally stopped and I got a standing ovation. I bowed regimentally four times once in each direction of the room, with my hair swinging all over my face, and plonked myself onto my chair. I gave one final grin to the crowd on my table and collapsed into my plate of food.

I don't know how long I was out for, but I remembered coming around and feeling queasy. I opened my eyes and saw the dance floor full of people dancing. I stood up and determinedly like a solider, marched towards the foyer where I had remembered seeing the toilet sign earlier. I marched like the changing of the guards, one step after another until I found the Ladies. I laughed when I saw Alexis and Stella in there fixing their hair, and they burst out laughing when they saw me walk in. "Are you still with us, Shakira?" said Alexis.

"Ha, ha, yes," I nodded vigorously. I grabbed Alexis' lipstick as she was putting it into her bag and I spread it all over my lips and half my chin, then gave it back to her. As they left the toilets, one of them called out: "See you in a bit Annie!"

I kissed the mirror to wipe the excess gloss off my mouth and made my way back into the foyer.

Charlie came running over to me in a drunken stupor and told me that he had just burst a kid's balloon and he wanted to hide behind me. He was as drunk as I was and I thought: "At last, someone on my level."

I held my arms out wide while he hid behind my arse as if nobody could see him. We were acting like children who were up to no good. We kept shushing each other and looking around like two bandits on the run. He grabbed my hand and said: "Quick! Quick! I've found a hiding place!"

He pulled me up the main staircase to the top, where there was a tiny hidden landing. He was in control, which turned me on, and holding his hand felt good. We sat at the top of the secret landing and from there could see everyone coming and going, as we hid behind the banisters.

We watched our friends one by one as they came in and out of the lobby looking for us but they could not see us and this put us into hysterics, holding our mouths so as not to give ourselves away. Not once did anyone look up. We stayed there for ages, giggling like hyenas, until I heard the band announce that there were five minutes to go till countdown.

"Everybody get your champagne ready for the countdown!" called out the band leader. We could see our friends frantically looking for us but did not care as we let them carry on searching, like two naughty children hiding from their parents.

The countdown began 5, 4, 3, 2, 1, Happy New Year!

The champagne corks popped and the party poppers banged, then the fireworks started outside, blending in with the sound of the cymbals and the excitable screams of two hundred people.

Charlie turned to look at me and I turned to look at him, and our mouths automatically plonked themselves together.

Our lips fitted together naturally and we kissed for ages and couldn't stop. I was enjoying it too much and we were both oblivious to anything that was going on around us. The shouting, the music, the fireworks all seemed to be a million miles away. It was just me and him.

"Wow," I finally said. "What a start to the new millennium." If I had planned it that way it would not have worked out as well. It was spontaneous and exciting, and felt so good.

We would have kissed all night if we hadn't been interrupted by the sound of Frosso's voice screeching out: "What are you guys doing?"

I opened one of my eyes while I was still kissing Charlie and saw her face looking like thunder.

Our mouths parted for a moment as Charlie said: "Happy New Year!" to her and plonked his lips back onto mine and continued to kiss, completely ignoring her.

I really didn't care to ask at that moment what her problem was. I just wanted to kiss Charlie and he wanted to kiss me.

Finally our lips parted.

"Wow," he said, "that was so good." He licked his lips.

"Yep, I know," I replied, licking mine.

"What was that face all about?" he asked referring to Frosso.

"I've absolutely no idea, maybe she fancies you," I said.

"Yuk! She's gross."

"Maybe she thinks you like her then," I said.

"Well, I don't know where she got that idea from. I wouldn't touch her with a barge pole. She's fat and ugly."

"She isn't that bad"

"Oh, yes she is. Well, I don't like her. I like you."

"Mmm, and I like you back." We kissed again.

I spent the whole of millennium night sitting at the top of that landing kissing a gorgeous, young, hunky guy. A very memorable millennium indeed.

The party was over and it was time to leave. Stella came up the stairs to tell us that everyone was leaving and the cabs were outside. She also told us to be on our guard because we had been the talking point of the entire evening.

"Why?" I asked.

"Because Frosso is angry at both of you."

"What!" I exclaimed. "Why? Just because we got off with each other?"

"Don't worry," said Charlie. "It sounds like she's jealous."

"How pathetic!" I said and felt myself sobering up.

Nobody was going to wipe the smile off my face. I felt like the cat that got the cream, my only thought all the way home was whether I should invite Charlie to stay at my place – it was millennium after all.

It turned out that I didn't have to ask him. When the cab pulled up outside my flat, he got out, paid the cab and smiled at me. I smiled back approvingly. The rest is history.

My millennium eve 2000 was memorable. I was thirty-seven and he was twenty-five. I knew that it was going to be a one-night stand so made the most of it.

The night after the party Stella rang to invite me for drinks at her house in the evening. “Everyone’s coming,” she said. I was eating some *vasilopitta* (New Year cake) with Auntie Florou when, out of the blue, Frosso blurted out in tears, “How could you do that to me? How could you get off with Charlie when you knew I really liked him? It’s disgusting the way you acted last night.”

I was gobsmacked and nearly choked on my cake.

“I beg your pardon?” I asked. “What do you mean exactly?”

“You deliberately seduced Charlie away from me. You never let anyone else get attention. It’s always about you and you never have any regard for anyone else’s feelings.”

I could feel myself getting angry. I had bitten my tongue when Frosso had irritated me with her stupid comments and childish strops in Cyprus, and I even held back when she started to copy my look but this was the last straw and I let rip, stopping her in her tracks.

“Hold on a minute you stupid, fat cow, I didn’t know that Charlie liked me until last night and you didn’t even know him until last night, so how did I deliberately seduce him away from you? How dare you make me out to be a bitch in front of my family who, by the way, I introduced you to. I have carried you around with me for all these years, introduced you to my friends and family and even guys, taken you on holiday with me, put up with all your stupid desperate remarks and defended you when others called you “bimbo” behind your back, you ungrateful little cow.”

She starting sobbing and I could see she was faking it to get attention from everyone in the room.

“Oh and by the way, Charlie thinks you are gross and wouldn’t even touch you with a barge pole.”

Frosso called me a vicious liar.

“I have just realised that this isn’t about me snogging a guy at a New Year’s Eve party” I said, “it’s about you being jealous and spiteful and I don’t want people like that around me. You have just shown me that you are no true friend of mine because if it had been the other way around and you had got off with Charlie, I would have been happy for you. I don't trust you around me anymore and our friendship is over so why don't you fuck off and go and make your own friends." Frosso just cried.

I was gutted that a friend could be so two-faced, pretending to be a friend when all along she was jealous of my popularity and used me for a social life. I remembered Angel's words when I left Birmingham and from that moment on I brutally cut Frosso off and became very wary as to who I introduced in my life as a friend.

Charlie and I met up again a few times. We were physically and passionately attracted to each other and it suited us both to have this spontaneous secret "arrangement".

I saved him in my phone as "Ginola", so that if he ever rang no-one would know it was him and he saved me as "*Koukla*" (doll). We used to text each other from the same room, at either end of our favourite bar, Harley's, and then creep into the toilets or into the car for a snog. It was so exciting. We even managed to sneak away to Cannes for a week's holiday and nobody had a clue that we were seeing each other.

The one-night stand had become a six-month affair and I was beginning to develop feelings for him. He felt the same way and we were finding it hard to keep our relationship secret from our friends.

We wanted everyone to know about us but didn't want to admit that we had been lying to them for six months, so we came up with a plan that Charlie would pretend to ask me out at Harley's on Friday night and I was to pretend to accept. It was an Oscar-winning performance by both of us. When Harley's closed Charlie came to my flat as he always did but this time we didn't have to hide from our friends and that felt good.

Charlie left next morning and I was driving to my parents' house to pick up George when my mobile rang.

"Hello, Annie. It's Mario. Please don't hang up."

I was taken aback and didn't know what to say. "What do

you want?" I asked after a few moments of deadly silence.

"I just wanted to say hi and see if you are OK."

"I'm fine," I said abruptly.

"Annie, please don't be angry with me. I am truly sorry and I can't stop thinking about you."

"I'm not angry. I stopped being angry with you a long time ago. I'm over it and I'm over you."

"Have you met someone else?" he asked quietly.

"Yes, I have and I'm really happy."

"Oh," he said choking. "I'm really pleased for you, Annie, I really am."

"Thank you."

"Erm, can I call you sometimes, as friends?"

"I don't see the point."

"Please, Annie, I miss our chats. I miss you."

"Well, you should have thought of that when you cheated on me." I had to get that in. "Anyway, I'm seeing someone so it won't be fair on him."

"I will be discreet. Only as friends, I promise. Please?" he pleaded.

"OK, OK, as friends."

"Thanks, Annie. Nobody has had the guts to dump me before the way you did and you made me see that I was an idiot."

"Well, good, at least you learnt from it. Anyway, I've got to go."

"Oh, OK. Speak to you soon."

I put the phone down wondering why I just didn't tell him to get lost, then realised that I still had a soft spot for him.

CHAPTER 37

The Christmas Party

I was driving around in my flash convertible, wearing sunglasses and a huge smile, having just met up with Charlie for lunch. My telephone rang and a man with a Greek accent said:

"Hello, is that Annie?"

"Speaking."

"Oh, hallo Annie. My name is Bambos. You don't know me but I know about you."

"Oh yeah. What do you know about me?" I asked.

"I understand that you are in the hostel business and have recently obtained a lucrative contract. I own a property agency called Acropolis Alpha and wondered if we can do some work together. I want to invite you for lunch so that we can meet and talk. I have a proposition for you." I was intrigued.

We met in an Italian restaurant called Nolitos the next day. He was a tall, dark, handsome, middle-aged Cypriot man, immaculately dressed and he greeted me with a handshake and a peck on the cheek.

It was raining heavily and he strolled into the foyer with sunglasses on and acted like he owned the place, handing over his dripping brolly to a passing waitress. "Here," he said to her. "My name is Bambos and I have reserved the best table in the restaurant."

Then he took another look at the pretty blond waitress and added, "I'm a director. Here's my card," and he took out a wad of money and gave her a score along with his business card, touching her hand as he did it.

We sat at a corner table and before I could even look at the menu he ordered for me. An other woman may have been impressed by that but I wasn't, especially since he had ordered nothing that I liked. He had picked the most expensive things on the menu just to impress me. I hated caviar and oysters and well-done fillet steak. I liked mine rare but I guess it was the thought that counts. He acted as though he were God's gift to women, what with his arrogant gestures, flirting with me and all the waitresses, which, I'm sure was his attempt to lure me into joining his company.

The business proposition, however, was a good one. He wanted me to tender for a National Housing contract in return for a top salary and a share of the profits.

"To show you that I am honourable," he said, "my company wants to fly you to Cyprus to stay in a suite in one of the top hotels in Cyprus." It sounded like a bribe but, hey, how could I refuse a free holiday?

Two weeks later I found myself on a first-class flight to Cyprus and was greeted at the airport by a chauffeur in a smart, grey suit and cap standing conspicuously in the foyer.

I was well impressed. The chauffeur took my luggage and walked me to a waiting black limo.

All eyes were on me from the moment the chauffeur greeted me until we got to the limo. This VIP greeting was unusual for Cypriots, and people stood to watch and wonder who I was, as the black-tinted windows shut tight and I stepped into the air-conditioned cream interior to be met with a bottle of champagne on ice.

I felt like a celebrity.

Thirty minutes later I arrived at the Four Seasons Hotel in Limassol. The formalities of checking in were dispensed with as soon as my name was mentioned and I was led straight to a ground-floor suite.

I had my own housekeeper, called Aliki, who unzipped my case and hung up my clothes. I was shown the complimentary mini bar and how to work the jacuzzi, and, if that wasn't enough, the patio doors were opened, revealing my very own private swimming pool and hot tub.

Once Aliki left I jumped up and down on the bed laughing like a hyena and shouting: "Yes! Yes! Yes!" I picked up the phone and rang Alexis, who said "You jammy cow."

The hotel treatment worked and I decided to accept the position with Acropolis Alpha.

I put on my short skirt, white blouse, tight black jacket and stilettos, got into my convertible and drove to the offices in Barnet for my first day at work.

I introduced myself at reception, who immediately pointed to a glass office a few feet away, where I saw the directors sitting. Bambos greeted me first and then introduced me to his partner, Kostas. He was a short man about sixty-years old with a high, receding hairline, thick glasses and a big pot belly. He had a lovely warm smile and I noticed that he had a strong Greek accent when he said: "Oh, hello Annie. Welcome to Acropolis Alpha, the third biggest AA in the country. First there is Automobile Association then there is Alcoholics Anonymous and then there is Acropolis Alpha."

I found it amusing and laughed, "That's a good one, Kostas. You are funny."

He looked at me all perplexed and said, "Why is it funny? It is true."

We sat down and introduced ourselves properly before we discussed the business plan. Kostas said that he was married to a "lovely, fat, Greek lady who is the best cook in the world" He also said that he had six sons and he couldn't wait to retire. Bambos said that he was single and never married primarily because he never met a woman who could tolerate his gambling addiction. "My only true love is the casino," he said. I then handed them a brief that I had prepared, detailing all the things I required in order to complete the tender.

Kostas said: "Anything you need, you shall have, just ask."

He gave me a tour of the building and introduced me to the rest of the personnel and, after all the introductions, I was shown to my desk which was right outside their office.

"I moved somebody to the top floor so that you could have the prime location outside my office," said Kostas.

"Thank you. I'm honoured."

I soon got stuck into drafting the tender for the National Council contract. I had three weeks to draft it and it did not take me long to figure out that Acropolis Alpha were a cowboy outfit who dealt with everything *ad hoc*, in typical Cypriot style. People just walked in and out without appointments, interrupting meetings and shouting at the top of their voices. Not surprisingly, there were no policies or procedures in place so I had to draft them all from scratch.

Everyone was helpful and co-operative, apart from the guy that had been moved to the top floor to make way for me. His name was Fanos and he was Bambos' brother. He was the Procurement and Finance Manager and was far from helpful. I requested information from him to enable me to draft the policies on at least three occasions but it was not forthcoming.

He prevented me from looking at his files and insisted that he only let me see the ones that he wanted and even then under supervision. I reported this to the bosses who summoned him to their office and he explained that he was so short-staffed that he was stressed out. I could tell that he was lying from the way he mumbled his words – I had seen it before with Mario.

Not only did the directors believe his manipulative sob story, but they sympathised with him too and promised to recruit more help for his department.

He winked at me as he left the room and shut the door behind him. He had taken them for a ride but it was not my position to say anything about a member of staff who had obviously been there many years and was the brother of one of the directors.

However, I had clocked him and knew that he could not be trusted.

I had four days left to submit the tender, had no procurement policy and was running out of time, thanks to Fanos.

"His nose has been put out of joint by being moved upstairs," said the receptionist, "and as the new girl on the block you have taken away his limelight too, but don't worry, he'll get over it."

"Men!" I exclaimed and we both laughed.

On the last day of the deadline, some staff offered to stay late and help bind the document until it was finished. Fanos however said, "I am not willing to take orders from the new girl."

Next morning, I personally delivered the tender to the National Council building in Euston and when I got back to the office, I overheard Bambos boasting over the telephone to some entrepreneur in Cyprus, that we had won the contract already and he was giving it large that Acropolis Alpha was getting so big, that he had had to create an in-house legal department to deal with the influx of work. I took it that he was referring to me and I was beginning to wonder that maybe I had made a mistake in joining a Greek Cypriot company.

There was a fortnight to wait before we would hear whether we were short-listed, so I booked a well-earned holiday for me and Charlie. But before I could fly anywhere I had to attend the office Christmas party.

I wore my burgundy, Spanish dress that I had worn to the millennium party a year earlier. The directors hired Sirtaki, a Greek restaurant, and invited all their VIP clients and top executives from the Laiki and the Cyprus Popular Banks.

Each director took it in turns to parade me around the room and introduce me as their in-house solicitor and I hated that.

"We are the only Cypriot company in the world that has an in-house legal department," boasted Kostas to one of the guests and I looked at him and cringed.

The drinks flowed and the Greek band were in full swing.

I had a few shots of peach schnapps and, before I knew it, the in-house solicitor was on the floor with her dress rolled up the side of her legs showing her black lace frilly knickers and dancing to "Oops Upside Your Head" between two strapping young men who were rubbing their crotches up against me.

Bambos and Kostas were getting humiliated with my spectacle, especially as they had gone around singing my praises to everyone and I was soon put in a cab and sent home.

Christmas day and Boxing Day were spent with George and the family. The next day I was on a plane to the Bahamas with Charlie.

Charlie and I had been seeing each other for nearly a year and were at the stage where each knew how the other felt and thought. We would say the same things at the same time and pick a meal off of the menu that we knew the other would like. We clicked emotionally and it felt great.

We checked in late at the American Airlines desk and, despite my protests, ended up sitting twenty rows apart for the eleven-hour flight.

I sat near the front of the plane and Charlie sat at the rear, and I kept looking around anxiously to see if we could swap seats with anyone.

A male steward suddenly appeared in front of me and told me to get my hand luggage and follow him. I told him that I was with my boyfriend and he asked me to go fetch him too. The next thing we know we were both sitting in first class.

"I'm not budging from my throne," I said to Charlie, all smug as I strapped myself into the huge leather seat. He kissed me and told me that I was so jammy: "You always bring me luck babe."

We checked in at Sandals and it was the most idyllic location that I had ever stayed in. It was quiet and secluded and our bungalow was on the sea shore. Although it was in the thick of winter, we danced barefoot on the pure white sand under the stars and I felt at that moment that I may have found my soul mate.

Our five days in Paradise flew by quicker than expected and we boarded a plane to New York City. I had always wanted to spend New Year's Eve in Times Square and so had Charlie, so we planned to be there for the final part of our holiday. We took the last plane out in the morning and landed at JFK moments before a heavy blizzard forced the airport to close and all remaining flights had to be diverted to Boston.

"I cannot believe how jammy you are, Annie," Charlie said. "It would have to be your plane that makes it for New Year," and I laughed as we checked into the Marriott Marquis.

I put on a black, sexy, backless dress and got ready to celebrate at the exclusive New Year's Eve Ball in the revolving restaurant on the forty-eighth floor. It had the most breathtaking views of New York, which gave me a flashback of Bruce Jon and I smiled to myself.

The complimentary champagne was enough to get me started and I was drunk before I sat down for the dinner at a table full of Japanese business men from Sony. I could hear them talking to Charlie about the new product that they were launching: a tiny digital video camera the size of a matchbox.

I was mortified when I discovered that one of them had taped me with his state-of-the-art matchbox while I was asleep with my head face down in my chocolate cake. Charlie told me that at one moment, as they were having an in-depth discussion about the Super Bowl, I lifted my head and contributed to the conversation by shouting out "meat bowl," burst out laughing and went back to sleep.

I woke up with a second wind and remembered that on a previous New Year's Eve I had watched the big ball fall in Times Square on TV and wanted to experience the atmosphere of that on the street.

So Charlie put me in the lift and went down only to find that all the hotel exits had been locked. A security guard stood at one of the exits and was telling people "for health and safety reasons no-one else is allowed to go out into the streets".

"But surely two more people won't make a difference will it?" I asked.

"Sorry Ma'am, those are my instructions."

"Oh well. Come on then. Let's go back upstairs," I said and we got back in the lift.

When it reached the forty-third floor it stopped and the lights went out. The doors opened and another huge security guard said:

"Everybody, out please. This is the last stop ladies and gentlemen."

"But we need to get back to the Ball on the forty-eighth floor," I protested and showed him my blue wrist band to the exclusive party.

"I'm sorry ma'am but this lift is now closed."

"But how are we going to get there then?"

"The lift will re-open five minutes past midnight and you can go up ma'am."

"Well what's the point of that? We can't go out and we can't go up, so at this rate we are going to be celebrating midnight in the foyer."

"Sorry Ma'am these are the rules, now if you can stand back from the lift and make your way I will appreciate it," he said with a stern look.

We stepped aside and I said to Charlie, "Now what are we going to do?" "Leave it to me. I will get us there," he said looking at a door which said strictly prohibited.

The guard turned his back and we slipped through the door and started running up the metal stairs. A few floors later the stairs ended at a door which, when we opened it, found us on an outside ledge secured with black iron railings forty-seven floors up in the sky, with the wind howling like a ghost.

We heard music faintly in the distance and Charlie spotted a spiral staircase leading to another door. We climbed the stairs, went through the door and found ourselves in a kitchen just as we heard 10, 9, 8, 7. We ran in the direction of the sound of the countdown, to the complete surprise of three chefs that were standing there, ran through the swing doors and found ourselves back at the party at the precise moment when the band leader called out "Happy New Year!"

Poppers exploded to the deafening sound of horns and drums and, as balloons and sparkly confetti fell from the ceiling, Charlie and I burst out laughing and fell to the floor in a heap in hysterics.

"Happy New Year, darling," he said.

"Meatbowl," I said and collapsed on the floor laughing.

CHAPTER 38

The Contract

I returned from New York to find a letter on my desk from the National Council inviting Acropolis Alpha to attend an interview before a panel of officials on 20 March. The letter went on to say that an official would be attending our offices within the next week to discuss a pilot scheme.

I rushed into the directors' office and told them that the company had been shortlisted for interview and to diarise their attendance.

They looked at each other in shock and simultaneously sat back in their chairs.

"Why do you look so shocked? You should be pleased," I said.

They looked like fish out of water gasping for air. The thought of them attending an interview at the National Council was terrifying to them. The worry on their faces was overwhelming and it was not a good time to crack a joke but I couldn't resist it:

"Well, anyway, I can't go on the 20th because I am away that day so you will have to go on your own but don't worry, I'll brief you fully."

I kept a straight face as Kostas slapped his forehead with his hand and Bambos took out a flannel from his drawer and wiped his sweating brow. There was dead silence for ages until I couldn't hold it in anymore and burst out laughing:

"I'm just kidding you. Of course I'm going to be there."

The relief on their faces as I turned around to leave the room was a picture.

"Leave it to me," I said grinning. "I'll prepare for the interview."

"You cheeky cow. You nearly gave me a heart attack," said Kostas.

The meeting for the pilot scheme was scheduled for the week ahead at our offices and neither of the directors wanted to attend. They both asked me on numerous occasions whether they were needed and at their third attempt I told them off.

"Of course you have to be there. You are the directors of the company for God's sake. It's etiquette."

"What is etiquette?" asked Kostas.

"Just make sure you are both here," I said.

The day before the meeting, Kostas told all the staff to wear their best clothes and to remove all clutter and rubbish from their desks. He warned them to come in early in the morning, get their job sheets and leave before 9am, so as not to expose the chaotic disorganised Cypriot madness that occurred each morning.

Anyone would have thought that the Queen was coming. Both directors wore their best suits and by 10am you could hear a pin drop.

I briefed them and explained that it was a good opportunity for us to give a good impression before the big meeting in March. "Look at it as a trial run," but I could see that they were extremely nervous and just then a rather large lady with short, black hair, wearing a brown trouser suit and carrying an attaché case arrived, and introduced herself to the receptionist as Vanessa Statton. When I heard her name I got up and went to greet her.

"Hi, Vanessa. I'm Annie."

"Oh, hello Annie, it's good to meet you," she smiled. "It's nice to put a face to the name."

After taking her drink order I escorted her the short distance to the directors' office, where they both stood anxiously waiting.

I introduced them and we all sat down. Vanessa and I sat opposite the directors, who looked at me all gormless.

It didn't look as though either of them were going to give an introduction, so I opened the proceedings, telling her a bit about Acropolis Alpha and how it had started off as a small local estate agency and developed into local B&B public sector housing, which put us in good stead for the new National Council contract.

Vanessa then said that she was a director of a voluntary consortium and that she was involved in a pilot scheme funded by the government and, as she went on to explain how it worked, I could see that Kostas and Bambos had already switched off.

They were completely out of their depth and their faces were a picture of confusion. Their gormless expressions with their mouths wide open were one of the funniest things I had ever seen and I tried not to look at either of them to stop myself from laughing.

At no point throughout the meeting did the directors say a word, so I had to keep asking Vanessa questions to distract her away from their gormless stares and speechlessness. She was in the middle of telling us about her background when Kostas got up from his desk and walked out without so much as an "Excuse me."

Vanessa looked at me in astonishment. I looked at Bambos who was equally flabbergasted and I had to quickly think of something to say to make light of the extremely awkward situation.

"Do you usually have this effect on men?" I said with a grin. Luckily Vanessa burst out laughing.

"Yes, I do actually!" she replied.

"Don't worry," I said, "so do I."

We both laughed and so did Bambos with great relief, as he wiped his brow again with his flannel.

Luckily I had been following her spiel and reminded Vanessa where she left off. She resumed her speech and I was wondering what on earth had happened to Kostas.

A few minutes had gone by and there was no sign of him, so I ruled out that maybe he had gone to the toilet.

About fifteen minutes later, the door burst open and he walked back in and slammed the door.

"Sorry about that," he said.

In his hand I could see a Tesco's carrier bag folded over like a purse. He walked over to his chair, sat down and, to my horror, as Vanessa continued to speak, he opened up the carrier bag took out some photographs and started to look at them one by one, oblivious to the fact that we were having a very important PR meeting which could affect the whole future success of his company.

I could feel myself getting agitated as I tried to keep eye contact with Vanessa.

I was seething inside and each time Vanessa turned to look towards Bambos I tried to give Kostas a dirty look to catch his attention but he continued to look at the photos.

Bambos coughed loudly in his direction, at which point Kostas looked up all startled, first at Bambos and then at me and, after spotting my dirty look, he opened his desk drawer and slid all the photos inside.

He closed the drawer and put his hands together on top of the desk, grinned at Vanessa and nodded as though he had been following the conversation all along.

Within a few minutes, I could see that his concentration was drifting again, as he started to stare around the room and blatantly kept looking at his watch.

I gave him another dirty look as if to say, "Don't you dare get up again or I will kill you!" He completely understood what I meant and he looked at Vanessa as if he was really interested in what she was saying.

He started to tap his fingers on his desk and, attempting to be discreet, he slowly reached out to his briefcase that was on the floor beside his feet, opened it part way and squeezed a newspaper out through the gap. He thought that it was hidden on his lap but I could see it clearly. He had it open on the horse racing pages and he was studying the form of the horses. Another dirty look in his direction from me made him fold the newspaper in half and, just as Vanessa was listing the things that she required from us, he picked up the phone, dialled the receptionist and whispered: "Tell Fanos number six at Kempton."

I was fuming as I was sure we had lost the contract by now.

Vanessa continued and at one point she happened to mention that she was Italian and Kostas' ears pricked up.

This was the only part of the meeting that he had actually clocked. He proceeded to tell her that he loved Italians, and their furniture was the best, and their football was the best, and how much he admired Gianfranco Zola and that he was the best, and that everything Italian was the best.

Bambos and I were cringing but what finally did it was when he then tried to bribe her into going to the Four Seasons Hotel in exchange for awarding us the contract, at which point Bambos butted in and changed the subject completely by asking Vanessa if she wanted a mint tea.

I muttered under my breath to Kostas: "*Katishi sou* (God help you) when she leaves," and he looked at me with a perplexed look on his face as if to say, "What's the problem?"

Finally the meeting was over and we all stood up and I thanked her for coming. She shook hands with all of us and I quickly escorted her out of the building.

"Have you gone mad?" asked Bambos to Kostas

"But what have I done?" Kostas replied.

"What have you done?" I said "How could you leave the meeting to go and get photos, then bet on a horse in front of her and to top it all off you try to bribe a government official. One thing is for sure, I can't take you to the National Council interview as that is one sure way of losing the contract."

As I left, I heard Kostas say "I didn't want to go to the interview anyway," and he took out his photos from the drawer and went around showing everyone the retirement home he was building in Cyprus.

CHAPTER 39

The Panel

It was 20 March 2001 – the day of the interview.

We travelled by tube to Euston and I was happy with the team I had put together for the interview; three experienced people, one each from the voluntary, public and private sectors and was confident that we had every aspect covered.

I was reluctant to take Bambos but as a director of the company he was expected to be there.

I was used to answering questions under extreme pressure in courtroom environments, so a panel did not faze me and I relished the challenge.

When we arrived at the building we were escorted to the interview room by an official and as we walked through the narrow corridors, I saw Bambos take out a towel from his briefcase and wipe his brow, but did not get the opportunity to tell him to put it away as it looked ridiculous for a grown man to be carrying a huge bath towel with a map of Cyprus on it.

The panel consisted of seven people sitting behind a long table. I had been expecting four, possibly five, but never seven and even I was a little taken aback.

The chairman had a ginger beard and scruffy ginger hair. He said his name was Richard and I smiled at him as he introduced the rest of the panel. After the introductions were made, we got down to business.

The Chair went through the agenda and told us that they

had read the tender and they needed to clarify some points. On that note the questioning began.

One by one we were bombarded as the questions came in thick and fast from procedural to operational, and one by one, we dealt with them constructively and professionally, not encroaching on each other's territory of expertise.

I had just finished telling the panel about our investors, and Bambos leaned over and whispered in my ear, "tell them about our investors."

I whispered back, "I just did. Aren't you listening?"

"*Nai*? Ha!" he chuckled.

I could tell by the nods of approval and smiles on their faces that the panel were impressed. One of them even stopped writing and closed his notebook. I took that to mean that he had heard enough and was already convinced.

Bambos whispered to me again, "*Nomiso aresen tous*!" ("I think they like us!") and kicked me under the table.

I looked Richard straight in the eye and he winked back.

By this time the atmosphere was a bit more relaxed. Some of the officials were smiling and others were sitting back on their chairs.

The Chair finally said that there were no more questions, at which point, one of the officials stood up and said, "If you will excuse us, my colleagues and I have to go now but we will leave you with Richard to complete the formalities. It was a pleasure to meet you all."

I exchanged email addresses and phone numbers with Richard and the interview concluded.

I felt very proud of myself. I was confident that I had performed well and felt that I had put the company in an excellent position to win the contract.

As soon as Bambos stepped out of the building, out came the beach towel to wipe his brow as if he had been the one that had been grilled. He had not said a thing throughout the whole interview and hadn't even followed the proceedings. He just sat there gormlessly whispering the occasional irrelevant comment in my ear as if he was making constructive suggestions.

We arrived back at the office, mentally exhausted, where Kostas was waiting for us.

"Well, what happened?" Kostas asked.

"It went really well," I said but before I could say anything else Bambos interrupted saying: "I told them we were Acropolis Alpha and that we are the best letting agency in London. I told them that we have thousands of houses and they said that we were the best provider and we are definitely getting the contract."

I was flabbergasted and looked at him in disbelief.

"You said no such thing and they never said we have got the contract either. Stop exaggerating," but he just shrugged me off and continued to take all the credit.

Then his phone rang and he said:

"Oh hello, Niko. Yes, I told the National Council that I am Bambos Bambou and I told them we are Acropolis Alpha and that we are the best property company in London and in England and they really liked me and they said that we were the best and ..." He was tapping his chest with his fist like Tarzan.

I walked out of the room and let him carry on giving it large to whoever this Niko was.

I had to wait another few weeks for the decision so Alexis and I took the children to Spain.

George was eleven and he learned to swim during that holiday, so was in his element. He couldn't wait to tell his grandparents that he could now swim without armbands.

As our plane landed at Heathrow I switched on my mobile and there was a message:

"**Annie please call me I need to talk to you. It is really important. Mario. x**"

I ignored the text at first but it played on my mind and out of curiosity that night I texted him "**What's up?**"

Within seconds he called: "Hi Annie."

"Hi," I said very guarded, "what's so important"?

"Annie I have to tell you in person. I can't tell you over the phone."

"Why not?" I asked. "Are the loan sharks bugging my phone?"

"Annie, please can I come over and see you?"

"Good try but no, you bloody well can't. I told you, I'm seeing someone." It went quiet for a moment.

"OK. Well, can I meet you somewhere then?" he pleaded.

"Why?"

"Please, Annie. I really need to tell you in person. Please, as a friend. I promise."

He sounded desperate and in need of help. As much as I could not forgive him for what he did three years earlier, I didn't wish him any harm and was curious.

I agreed to meet him the next day in Aroma patisserie in Palmers Green. I lied to Charlie and told him I was spending the day with George.

As soon as I saw him with that red jacket my heart missed a beat. He was still as gorgeous as ever and his huge beaming smile made me smile back at him. He kissed me on the cheek and we sat down. He ordered two *galatopourekia* (Greek custard pie with syrup), knowing that they were my favourite.

"Go on then," I prompted but I could see he was nervous. "I suppose you are going to tell me that you are gay."

"No," he said abruptly and we both laughed.

"Annie. I have never met a Greek girl like you."

"And of course you would know being out with so many at the same time," I said sarcastically.

"Stop it Annie. You are beautiful, clever, funny and you are kind."

"Now you stop it right there. Where is this going Mario?"

"Please let me finish. You made me so happy when I was with you but I blew it, I know, and I can't ever forgive myself for that. And I know this is going to be a shock to you but I wanted to see you because ..." he stopped.

"Because you what?" I asked and after a pause and a gulping

swallow he said: "Because I love you Annie and I want you to marry me."

I burst out laughing as he sat back on his chair deflated.

"You are unbelievable. You arrogant bastard," I shouted shaking my head. "I would have believed you more if you had told me you were gay." I got up to leave but I saw that he looked distraught and for some strange reason I sat back down.

"Listen Mario. Let me make this clear. I don't love you anymore. I love someone else."

"Annie, please. Can you be my friend at least? I need you in my life. Ever since we split I have had nothing but bad luck. Please?"

"I don't know if I can Mario. I will see."

We did become friends, great friends in fact. He called me regularly to see how I was and he was always there to help out when I needed something.

He found George a football club when I asked for his help and he took him to the trials to make sure that he got into the team. He even baby-sat sometimes and George loved it because he let him stay up late to play on the Nintendo.

I introduced him to women but in true Mario style he continued to date more than one at a time and sometimes found myself stuck in the middle of confrontations and love triangles. Once I even had a drink thrown over me at an Antonis Remos concert by a girl he was seeing. He made her believe that he was having an affair with me just to make her jealous and he left the venue before I had a chance to wring his neck.

Chapter 40

The Set-up

I was at my desk when my mobile rang with an unknown number.

"Hello, Annie Roy," I answered.

A male voice replied. "Hello, Annie. It's Richard."

"Oh, hello Richard. How are you?"

"I'm very well, thank you."

"Have you got any news for me?" I asked.

"Well, off the record, you have been successful and, you have not heard this from me, but it's basically waiting for authorisation from above only."

"Oh my God that's great, I can't believe it. That's such good news. What a relief."

"I knew you would be happy. I wanted to tell you the news myself but please don't tell anyone else yet until it's official. You should receive an official email within the next forty-eight hours. And we have never had this conversation, OK?"

"OK, Richard. I promise and thanks for all your help."

"You're welcome," he said. "But you should be taking the credit, young lady. You were amazing at the interview and you won a lot of admirers that day. No-one impresses my boss and yet he made a point of mentioning how impressed he was with you. You certainly left a lasting impression with all of them, and, of course, with me."

"Oh really? I'm so flattered. My head is getting too big now.

I won't be able to walk out of my door if you carry on like this."

"It's not because of the size of your head that you won't get through the door, young lady ..."

"You cheeky monkey," I exclaimed. "I will ignore that comment. As you say, we have never had this conversation." We both laughed.

"Well, I'd better go," he said. "I'll speak to you again soon."

"Thanks for calling, Richard. Bye."

I rushed into the directors' room.

"I have some news," I said smiling. "Richard just called me, off the record, and said that basically, subject to it being officially stamped from above, we have won the contract!"

"*Sioura?*" ("Are you sure?"), asked Kostas. "What exactly did they say?"

"They said not to say anything until we hear it officially in forty-eight hours. Don't say anything to anyone, OK?"

"Of course not," said Kostas.

"Obviously," said Bambos and no sooner had he said that, he got out his address book, looked up a number and started dialling.

"*Re, Frixo. Epiasamen to contrato. Ne re. pe jintou malakismenou na pai na yamithei, endaxi? Ne re. Miloumen istera*" ("Hey, Frixo. We got the contract so tell that wanker to go fuck himself, OK? We'll speak later.")

I looked at him in astonishment.

"Didn't we just say not to say anything until it's official?"

"It's only Frixo."

"Who the hell is Frixo?"

"Frixo Papas," he said, like I would know who that was. "Don't worry, he won't say anything."

Then Kostas picked up the phone.

"*Re, Andy. Ise gala? Ne, re. Eho efharista nea. Erkethisame to contrato. Irtame proti. Imasten i kalitteri. Xeris di simeni AA?*" ("Hey, Andy. How are you? I have some good news. We've won the contract. We came first. We are the best. Do you know what it means to be AA?").

I had just learned another valuable lesson in business. NEVER say anything to a Greek in confidence. They cannot keep a secret. The word had already spread to Palmers Green. When they came off the phone I tried to put the fear of God in them.

"What are you two doing? What did we just agree? Do you want us to lose the contract before we even get it? You have both just breached National Council confidentiality."

"Oh, Ok" said Kostas.

"I have to go now to plan ahead," I said. "I'll speak to you later."

"OK, Annie. Thank you," said Bambos.

I walked out of their office, looked around and saw them both dialling again. My warning had obviously gone in one ear and out of the other.

The confirmation arrived in the morning and the contract was for five years. I had already discovered during the tender process that Acropolis Alpha had no policies, procedures or recruitment processes in place. It was all about who knew who and friends of friends, nothing to do with experience or qualifications. There was no infrastructure or hierarchy just pure disorganised chaos. Everybody ordered everybody else about, and everyone gossiped all day about who was going out with whom, or how much they won at the Casino and, who had shagged the new receptionist. Sexual harassment was rampant where the males were blatantly using their position against some of the prettier subordinate females who were also blatant in acquiescing to improve their work status and obtain promotions.

It was like running a market stall in a small village in Cyprus. I had to set up the structure and organisation and change the whole system – it was not going to be easy changing people round who had become set in their Cypriot working ways.

I spent days going through the contract, listing the processes that had to be in place and the tools and personnel required to carry it out. I drew up job descriptions for the senior positions, contracts of employment and set up a training programme.

I told the directors that I needed to advertise for staff and they said they would help. "Leave it to us," said Kostas.

I was expecting a quarter-page ad in the *Guardian* or *The Times* but their "help" turned out to be advertising the jobs on LGR London Greek Radio because the owner was a friend and the advertisement was free of charge.

They listed my personal mobile as the contact number without me knowing and I was inundated with hundreds of applications from painters, machinists, drivers, cutters, clothes pressers, to shop assistants, fish and chip shop owners and even hairdressers.

I was bogged down with so many calls that I diverted them to reception and asked the receptionist to ask for people's CVs. Many said that they did not need to send a CV because they were "a friend of Kostas" or "a cousin of Bambos," and refused to speak to anyone apart from them.

"Who are you? I want to speak to Kostas," said a rude man and I gladly passed him on.

I had to be ruthless. I did not care if they were a friend or a relative of the directors or if they owned the biggest cash and carry or factory in London or a hotel in Larnaca. In fact, the more "Do you know who I am?" comments I received, the more determined I was *not* to hire them.

Among the hundreds of broad Greek accents, rude manners, bad attitudes and arrogant chauvinistic statements, I found two excellent applicants, Harry and John, who ended up being my right-hand men.

I spent months flying around the country meeting agents, finding offices, recruiting staff, training them, setting up communications, and providing support, until finally the regional structures were all set up and Acropolis Alpha was now a multinational company.

Everything was coordinated and masterminded by me and my two men in London and within six months the company was housing over three thousand people and I was running a national organisation, managing two hundred staff. Whoever would have thought that the Cypriot Hackney girl would have turned out to be such a high-flying, powerful executive?

I was tired and drained. I had been working long hours for months, having to fit in George, Charlie and my friends whenever I could, which wasn't very often, and put up with Mum's sarcastic comments like "*horkoyira*" ("dirty stop out") and "I thought you had emigrated to *Timbatoo*." She could never say Timbuktu.

Charlie and I were still very much in love but I was keeping a secret from him which was starting to wear me down. I began to realise that, with George getting older, I did not want to have any more children and felt guilty about depriving Charlie of having kids of his own. I knew, in my heart, that there was no future for us and I kept him apart from George so that he wouldn't get attached.

I suspected that Charlie may have been equally in turmoil and it was heartbreaking knowing that I had met a soul mate but knew that one day soon it would have to end.

I was sitting at my desk, thinking about how I should end it, when my mobile rang:

"Anna, *eklithohika exo* (I've locked myself out)" said Mum.

"What? How?"

"I was helping at the church fete and I must have left my keys in the other bag."

"Where's Dad?"

"I dunno. He's gone out with George."

"Well I can't come now, I'm at work. Can't you call Maria?"

"No. She has small babies. I don't want to bother her."

"But you don't mind bothering me? Go to the neighbours and I will be there soon."

"No, I don't want to go to the neighbours. Hurry up. It is raining and I will die of pneumonia if you don't come now?" She hung up.

CHAPTER 41

The Comedy of Errors

Four years into the contractand operationally things were giving me cause for concern. The longer the contract went on, the more flaws were revealed with all the National Council processes.

Inaccurate data and records, in turn, caused financial discrepancies and loss to Acropolis Alpha.

Many times the company had to suffer the financial burden of misinformation and negligence, and the directors had to stomach the loss because they did not want to lose the contract, having already seen the fate of other providers who were dispensed with when they were not willing to conform.

My staff had to take the brunt and pick up the pieces of the National Council blunders – from people getting lost in transit, left unsupported or left stranded at bus stations. It was bad enough that the issue of asylum was very raw and politically controversial but this was scandalous. Every day there would be a crisis caused by the incompetent National Council staff who didn't care. The government set-up was a shambles and mistakes were covered up or glossed over by removing or transferring instigators to other departments before any investigation could be conducted and there was never any accountability.

It was disheartening but I was a professional and had to continue the operations regardless, while keeping the staff motivated. Harry and John created a "classic board" to boost morale, making fun of issues and every time there was a cock-up by the National Council, the staff or the directors, it would be written on the white classic board.

This board became the department's comedy of errors and it was because of this board and the staff's sense of humour that we all remained sane.

Not a day went by when there wasn't a crisis and I had to break the news to the directors that a hunger strike was about to hit the national news. The National Council wanted to evacuate and close down our most lucrative hostel before it caused an embarrassing political scandal at huge financial loss to the company. I prepared myself for all hell to break loose.

"*Psofon. Efka tous exo. As skotohousein*" ("Good riddance, chuck them all out and let them kill each other"), said Kostas.

"*Na pan na kopsoun ton lemon tous, oi kilinjiroi alites*" ("They can go and cut their throats the gypsy peasants"), said Bambos. I gave them a report highlighting the extent of their financial loss.

Bambos read one page and said: "Very good," and then rang the cook to order rabbit for his lunch.

Kostas just put it in his drawer and said he would read it later as he was more interested in betting on the two o'clock at Newmarket. Not that he would have understood it anyway but I realised by their blasé comments that they didn't seem to care much either.

I lost faith in the system and became very disillusioned. All my complaints were hitting brick walls or went un-noticed and I began to be seen as a troublemaker, always reporting National Council incompetence and scams.

Although at times it was disheartening, I had developed a thick skin and would not be swayed or moved on a principle that I considered to be right.

While my staff and I were battling with the National Council, things were happening internally within the company too. Word got around the Cypriot community that easy money was to be had by investing in properties in the North of England. There was a surge of people, mainly friends and acquaintances of the directors, flocking up there at weekends to buy and renovate properties, so that they could jump on the gravy train. I was inundated with calls from "friends" of the directors, asking me to put their properties on the system before they were repaired or certificates were in place. I was a stickler for the rules and would not allow anyone to abuse their position in the company or jeopardise the contract. Overnight I became the bad guy.

Unscrupulous Cypriot landlords attempted to sweet talk me into putting their properties onto the system and when they did not get what they wanted they resorted to lying or threats to get me sacked but I was not swayed by their charms or their threats.

Bolshie, chauvinistic landlords thought that they had the right to throw their weight about and stamp their authority to frighten my young female staff with verbal abuse to get their way.

The biggest culprit was Fanos. His cagey behaviour always made me suspicious of him. He was unqualified and incompetent, but he had a high position in the company by virtue of being Bambos' brother and thought he could do whatever he wanted. He was a fat middle-aged Greek man with a strong Cypriot accent, who walked around the office like he owned the place. He never wanted to talk to me apart from telling me that he "only took orders from the directors, not women".

He was used to trampling over everyone and at first he tried to bully me into doing things his way but the more he tried to stamp his authority on me the more I dug my heels in.

I was not going to let a two-bit, fat, greasy, egotistic, chauvinist bully get his way. It was easier for him, as time went by, to keep me at arm's length. His, know-it-all attitude made him very unpopular not only with most of the staff but also clients, landlords and National Council officials.

He dismissed crucial staff in strategic positions and replaced them with his own people, giving them higher salaries and privileges. He stopped staff overtime and delayed payments to landlords and agents, which all had a negative effect on the contract, as landlords ceased repairs and agents stopped procuring properties that we were contracted to acquire. Staff were resigning and operations were slowly grinding to a halt.

The National Council was demanding explanations from me as to our non-performance. For four years, we were one of the best providers in the country for providing accommodation to house refugees and Fanos managed to single-handedly bring down the performance of the company.

Everyone that he upset used to come to me and I had to calm them down. "Leave him to me," I would say and they had enough faith in me to know that I always did what I said.

For a long time I never rose to his bait but after he bullied one of my girls and brought her to tears, it was time to ruffle his feathers. I sent a builder friend into his office pretending to be a National Council inspector, in order to gain access to his files. I was expecting to find some flaws in his administration which he so tightly protected but instead I unveiled serious dealings of fraud and deception.

It transpired that he was involved in a scam where he was taking backhanders and was authorising supplies under the company name and using the materials to pay for his own properties, as well as doing private jobs on the side.

"Shit. That's heavy," said Andreas the General Manager. "How can someone do that to his own brother and right under his nose too, what scum?"

I felt awful for Bambos but I had to be the one to break the news to him.

After a short silence he said: "But Annie, he is my brother, for God's sake, are you sure?"

"Yes. I'm sorry but I'm sure. Your brother has been bootlegging and receiving backhanders at your company's expense. He has been stealing from you, probably for years. Do you understand that you could lose the contract if this gets out?"

There was silence for a moment as Bambos sobbed. I felt sorry for him as I could see from his despair that the magnitude of his brother's actions had finally sunk in. He composed himself then stormed into Fanos's room in a rage. He grabbed him by the collar and they fought until Fanos was defeated. He shook himself down and ran out of the office leaving an aftermath like a nuclear explosion – silent, subdued and eerie. At that moment, my phone rang:

"Anna, I've locked myself out. That stupid father of yours has gone to the betting office so can you come and let me in?"

"Oh, bloody hell Mum. What, now?"

"Eh, of course now. *Hade.* I'm sitting on the pavement *je mouthkiasen o kolos mou* (my bum's gone mouldy?)"

In the days that followed the sacking there was a sour atmosphere in the air; a small clique was formed in sympathy for Fanos, spreading rumours that I had him sacked because I was a "controlling egotistic bitch".

"Oh, my God," I said to Andreas. "Damned if I do, and damned if I don't," but the remarks didn't bother me as I knew that the majority of the personnel were relieved that Fanos had got what he deserved and it soon became old news.

That night my mobile rang. "Annie, it's Antros," said a voice "I'm sorry to be the one to tell you, but Mario died suddenly this morning of a heart attack."

I couldn't speak from the lump in my throat and the choking back of my tears. From that day on, something changed in me. I seemed to lose all my zest for life. But even in death Mario managed to make me smile when four girls turned up at his funeral all thinking that they were his girlfriend.

Kostas almost finished building his house in Cyprus and was so busy exporting marble, statues and mosaics that he was hardly in the office, but when he was, everyone knew about it. He shouted at staff so that he could be heard imposing his authority while enjoying his new-found fortune and getting thoughts of grandeur beyond his status. He started to name-drop and covered his office with memorabilia and photographs of himself with celebrities, which became a shrine to his new lifestyle. He strutted around the office like a peacock full of self-importance.

"Do you know who I am? I am Kostas Savvas," he was heard to say many times but really he was the office laughing stock and never knew it.

To me, he was Kostas Savvas, the nice man that I had met all those years ago, with that warming smile, who always spoke to me with respect and made me laugh. I was sure that the nice Kostas Savvas, without all the new self-importance, was still there somewhere.

As for Bambos, he was never the same after the sacking. He seemed to give up on the business. He spent most of his time in the Casino and distanced himself from the office. When he did make an appearance his behaviour became irrational and he was constantly angry, snapping at everyone around him, which was totally out of character for him. The contract had taken its toll on all of us.

Both directors got so caught up with their new wealthy image that they lost sight of what was happening around them. Many people manipulated them to try and muscle their way into their lifestyles and due to their kind nature they never hesitated in helping anyone out. They were taken in by people who were making money on their backs but instead of thanking them for helping them they ridiculed them behind their backs. For me it was sad to watch.

The one that caused the most ridicule was when a so-called "friend" persuaded them to invest in a racehorse .

"Anyone who is anyone owns racehorses, look at Alex Ferguson," the "friend" said and that was enough for Kostas to express an interest. Before anyone knew it, they had invested in a horse called Mr Acropolis. They boasted that it was a thoroughbred, from a great stud and its first race was in Epsom. There was an air of excitement on the day of the race and everyone in the office backed it but it came last and the novelty soon wore off when it turned out to be lame and never won a single race.

Then there was the yacht. "I hope it is fibreglass and not wooden?" asked Andreas, who was a qualified engineer.

"Of course it's fibreglass. What do you take me for?" responded Kostas and he shrugged Andreas off, as though he had insulted his intelligence.

It turned out to be wooden and it cost them a fortune to maintain but as long as it fit with the Onassis image they didn't care. They made one bad decision after another but the final straw came when they called me and Andreas into the office and said they had something important to tell us: "*Libon,* (so)," said Bambos, "to replace Fanos and to take our company forward, Kostas and I are pleased to tell you that we will appoint Kostas' son Soteris as Head of Accounts and my cousin Thimos to be Head of Purchasing," and they looked very pleased with themselves.

Andreas choked on his water and I nearly fell off my chair saying, "You can't be serious!"

"Of course, I'm serious. What's your problem?" said Bambos.

"With all due respect" I said "Thimos is a nice guy but he is only a DIY man and not a very good one at that, so what on earth does he know about purchasing? He doesn't even have a good grasp of English. And as for Soteris, he is seventeen years old for goodness sake and is an IT student. His experience is interactive video games, not accountancy. These two departments have a turnover of millions each month so, seriously, if you put these people in those positions we are doomed."

Andreas supported me, saying "Please listen to her, I agree that neither of them are suitable. It's not about employing friends and family, it's about employing suitable people for the job. Haven't you learnt your lesson?"

"Well, we will prove you wrong," said Bambos, whereupon Kostas piped up: "We have made a decision and that's final.

We are the directors. It is our company, not yours" he said.

What else could I say after that? That was the moment that they put the final nail in the coffin and sealed the company's fate.

It wasn't long before Harry came into my office and reported that we were about to be penalised by the National Council for breach of our Key Performance Indicators.

I called an urgent meeting with the heads of departments and directors. There were twelve men and me and, for some inexplicable reason, Kostas wanted to chair the meeting for the first time ever.

Purchasing were blaming accounts for late payments, accounts were blaming the housing officers for bad reporting, and maintenance were blaming purchasing just for the sake of it. It was a complete shambles.

There I was sitting in a room full of men with egos as big as an elephant's and brains as small as ants. They did not let each other speak and they all kept butting in. The directors were shouting at everyone and at each other, everyone was blaming everyone else, phones were ringing, people were walking in and out, and we were going round in circles while I just sat there watching this Cypriot man's board meeting.

I had sat in on hundreds of National Council board meetings, chaired meetings with Tarmac, the biggest property company in the country, conducted trials before judges, and here I was watching a real live circus. All I could think was: "What the fuck am I doing here?"

I found the comments around the table hilarious and were well worthy of the classic board but what had to be the number one classic of all time was when Kostas tried to bring order to the meeting by slamming his fist on the table and shouting out: "By crook and by cook, I'll find out who is responsible and I will sack them from here to Troodos," I had heard it all now and I couldn't control myself any longer. I burst out laughing uncontrollably, like a mad woman in a straight-jacket. I had

had enough of the National Council bureaucracy, the internal politics, the constant bickering and shouting, the gossiping, the male egos, the sexism and the chauvinism.

I was wasting my life away at the expense of my family and killed the meeting dead by shouting at the top of my voice: "I've had it with the lot of you. I'm leaving."

CHAPTER 42

The Farewell

Leaving Acropolis Alpha in 2006 was the best thing I ever did for my sanity and my head was finally at peace.

I didn't make millions but managed to buy a beautiful home in the country. Coincidently my neighbour turned out to be Youlla, whom I had shared a tent with all those years ago in Cyprus. More importantly, I came out with something more valuable than money: respect and self-belief.

Self-belief in that I had a sense of overwhelming self-gratification that I had succeeded in the business world and triumphed over male chauvinism, egoism, pride, greed, jealousy and bullying. For the first time in my life I was very proud of myself.

As for respect, I didn't realise how much I had until colleagues kept coming up at my leaving do and inundating me with praise. " The Cypriot government should employ you as a diplomat to resolve the Cyprus problem. You would soon kick all those men into shape," said Harry.

Andreas pulled me over to the side and said: "I don't think you know this, Annie, but your biggest supporter is Fanos. He said it took a woman to make him see himself for what he really was, a chauvinistic, ignorant, greedy man that stole from his own brother and he is ashamed. You were the only one who stood up to him and you made him take a long hard look at himself and he did not like what he saw. He is a changed man now and he asked me to say 'thank you', if I ever saw you." It made me very emotional.

During the demanding and hectic five years at Acropolis Alpha, I had neglected George and my parents, which I felt guilty about, so was looking forward to spending some quality time with them. George was sixteen and about to take his GCSEs and it felt great being there for him and supporting him, even though he kept saying "Mum, you're doing my head in" every time I asked him to revise.

Mum was busy looking after Vasili's three daughters and, even though it meant I had to hear her sarcastic comments more often, like "Tracey can cook better than you", "Tracey is a great mother, unlike you," I did actually miss her digs which I started to find funny and it was great to see that Mum was finally making it up to poor Tracey.

As for Dad, he wasn't very well what with his cholesterol and his high blood pressure but he continued smoking like a chimney and eating unhealthily and I lost count of the times I told him off.

"The doctors smoke and eat more than I do so leave me alone and let me enjoy my cigarette in peace," he always said.

With lots of time on my hands I made the most of the slow pace that I so badly needed. I drove George to school, had breakfast in my favorite café, Porgies, caught up with my friends and shopped until it was time to pick George up again.

"It's about time you settled into a normal life like everybody else," Mum commented but there was one more thing I had to do before I could settle: end my relationship with Charlie.

I invited him to my house and we sat down as always with our hands and legs entwined. There was silence, with the occasional sigh from both of us. I got the feeling that he somehow was feeling the same and that he was ready for what I was about to tell him.

"Honey, you know what I am about to say don't you?"

He squeezed my hand but didn't say anything. He knew. My eyes started to fill up and as he looked at me I could see his eyes filling up too. I was overwhelmed and weakened.

"Please," I said. "Don't you start. This is hard enough." We both hugged each other hard as he passed me a tissue.

"Honey, I can't do this anymore," I cried. "I love you with all my heart, but I'm hurting and I know you are too."

He hugged me hard and said, "I know. We both know we can't end up together. We are just torturing ourselves. We both get anxious when we are apart and get scared in case the other meets someone else. I wish so much for you to be happy but I get so jealous at the prospect of you meeting someone else. I know you feel the same."

"I do. You know I do!"

"What shall we do Annie?" he asked, choking on his words.

"I don't know, Charlie, I don't know how but I do know that we have to split."

"But how? What do you suggest?" he asked despondently.

"I don't know. What do you suggest?"

"I don't know either."

"Well, I suppose it's a question of whether we can split and have no more contact," I tentatively said.

He gulped as he cried, "No, Annie. I can't do that. There is no way I can do that. I don't want that. I don't want to lose you. I still want you in my life."

"I don't know how we can get over each other if we see each other. It doesn't work. We are both too possessive of each other. It is best to have no contact. You know it is."

"OK" he agreed. "What if we agree not to see each other unless it gets really hard to bear?"

We both chuckled. "I guess we can try that but we know that won't work. We have to be very strong. What about phone calls?" I asked.

"Well, obviously we can't phone each other every day like we have been doing."

"I know, but I don't want to put a limit on it like every other day or something. I wouldn't be able to handle that."

"I wouldn't want that either. What about if we just called each other when we get desperate and try gradually to reduce the calls over time?"

"We can try. Oh my God. I feel sick," I said.

We hugged tightly and I was blinded by my tears.

"What if I meet someone else?" I asked. "Do you want me to tell you?"

"Oh God! I don't know how I will handle that." There was a brief pause and then he said "I guess yes. I would rather know. Have you got someone now?"

"No, I promise I haven't. Have you?"

"No, I promise."

"OK," I said. "Well, I do want to know if you start seeing someone. The last thing I want is to bump into you when you are out with a girl. I would hate you and never forgive you."

"I know, babe. I want the same."

"I'd scratch her eyes out!" I said and we both laughed.

"I would have to dump her there and then," he chuckled. "I would never hurt you."

"I've never been in this position before, where I dump someone who I really love," I said.

There we were, having a civilised discussion about how we were going to break up. Terms and conditions were laid down. Would you believe it? Two people madly in love and letting each other go. Life is sick. We hugged again as if it were the last time.

Letting Charlie go was one of the hardest things I ever had to do but I knew it was the best for both of us.

I cried myself to sleep until I was numb but another layer of thick skin had grown on me. A rhinoceros had nothing on me now.

Just when I thought my heart couldn't take any more God decided to send one of my biggest blows yet.

CHAPTER 43

The Suckling Pig

I desperately needed to get away. George and his football team were scheduled to play some tournaments in Sardinia, so I booked to go with him and the other parents.

Sardinia was baking hot and the first match was in the mountains about an hour's drive away.

The boys sat at the back of the coach, laughing and teasing each other, and the parents were all chatting at the front.

We were a great crowd and I got on exceptionally well with the manager and his wife Miri.

Someone cracked a joke and we were all laughing but I found myself laughing uncontrollably to the extent that I was unable to stop.

Eventually we arrived at the football ground, on top of the mountain. I was exhausted and my ribs hurt from laughing so much on the journey.

The boys went off to get changed into their kits, while the parents were given a quick tour of an ancient relic in a small outbuilding at the side of the mountain.

While we were being shown around, my mobile bleeped and there was a text from Maria:

"**When you get this text, please call me.**"

For a brief moment my heart sank and I had a feeling that something was horribly wrong. Reception was poor and I walked around for ages trying to get a signal. Miri could see how agitated I was and followed me.

"Annie, you look really pale. Are you OK?"

"I'm not sure. I've got a message to call home and I think something must be wrong." I was shaking like a leaf.

Finally I managed to get two bars on my phone and was able to call Maria.

When Maria answered, I could tell from her voice that she was in shock. - "Hello?"

"Maria what is it?"

"Oh, Annie, thank God you called. Dad's on his way to hospital in an ambulance. He couldn't breathe properly. I'm in the car behind the ambulance with Mum."

"Who is in the ambulance with him?" I asked, choking.

Maria's next words reached my ears in slow motion.

"Nobody is with him. They wouldn't let anybody go in the ambulance with him."

I closed my eyes and hid my face with my hand as the tears gushed. I knew in my heart that my dad was dead. I could feel it. I composed myself quickly before preparing Maria for the worst.

"Listen to me Maria. They usually don't let you go in the ambulance when they believe the patient is dead. Maria, please prepare yourself, Dad is dead."

"No, he isn't dead, he's alive," she cried.

"Please call me when you get to the hospital and let me know."

"OK," she cried.

I ended the call and sat on the floor exactly where I stood, in the middle of a dirt track in the Sardinian mountains. I was totally numb. I couldn't speak, I couldn't cry. All I could hear was my own breath as I started to hyperventilate.

"Are you OK?" asked Miri.

"I am waiting for a call about my Dad. He has not been well and had an operation on a blocked artery and had recently been sent home to recuperate."

"He'll be OK, Annie," she said.

"I feel that he is already dead. I know you are going to think I'm mad but I can feel him here with me now and I know that he is at peace. I can feel it. That moment when I was having the laughter fit on the coach, I feel that's when he died. I just know it Miri."

"Let's wait and see," she said.

I stared at the sky and I had an overwhelming feeling of peace and tranquility.

My mobile rang and I saw Maria's name on the display and pressed the answer button. "He's dead, isn't he?"

I could hear her choking, trying to find the words to tell me until Maria managed to mumble, "Yes."

But I already knew and my feelings had somehow shut down.

Like a robot, I spoke to Maria: "What did they say he died of?"

It took her ages to answer: "Heart attack."

"Well, I'm on top of a mountain in the middle of nowhere right now but as soon as I get back down to the hotel, I'll be on the first flight back home."

"OK," she managed to say and hung up.

"He's dead, Miri. I knew it."

"Oh my God, I'm so sorry Annie."

"He's dead and I'm in the middle of fucking nowhere and there's not a damn thing I can do about it."

Miri put her arm around me and I stayed sitting on the floor. Some parents saw me and came over to see what was going on and Miri told them the news.

I just stared at the ground.

"Let's leave her alone for a bit," a voice said. I nodded; that was all I could do. I waited until the trance passed but it took time. I became conscious that I had to get up and deal with the day ahead. The quicker the match was over, the quicker I could get back to the hotel and pack.

All I could think about at that moment was George. Should I tell George? How was I going to tell him and how was he going to take it? Dad had been the closest person to him his whole life. He used to drive him to school every day and pick him up. He was with him all the time. Should I wait until after the game?

The teams were about to start playing in five minutes and I didn't think I could last the whole game without bursting into tears and it would be worse telling him then. So I decided it was best to tell him now in case he heard it from someone else. I got up off the floor and walked towards the club house, where the boys were coming out of the changing rooms in their kits. I did not want to tell him in front of his friends, so I asked Miri if she could call George over.

She went over and beckoned him with her right hand. He came running over to her at once, and Miri told him that I wanted him. He started running towards me.

"What do you want, Mum? I'm about to play."

"Darling, I have to tell you something. And it's best that you hear it from me. I just got a call from Auntie Maria and *papou* died a few minutes ago." I tried to stay strong for him.

He looked at me in silence. He just stared at me, not saying a word. I stepped forward and hugged him. He rested his chin on my shoulder. I had just caused him a great deal of pain and that made me feel as if I had wrenched my own guts out. I pushed him gently away so that I could look at him.

"Listen to me darling. *Papou* loved you very much, you know that. He made no secret that he loved you more than anything and *Papou* always loved watching you play football, so he would want you to go out there and play. Play for him. Go and score him a goal. He will be watching you, OK?" I smiled at him.

He turned and ran back to the pitch where the boys were waiting. I so wished I knew how George was feeling so that I could fix it somehow. I didn't want him to hurt.

I believed at that moment that the best thing would be for him to see me strong and not to break down. Seeing his Mum break down would be harder for him to bear. He had enough dealing with his grandfather's death. I just had to stay strong and I lifted my head up high, took a very deep breath and walked over to the pitch.

I was greeted by the other parents, who all passed on their condolences. This time I was able to thank them and the whistle blew for the start of the game.

Then my mind wandered to the last time I had seen Dad.

It had been the day I was leaving for Sardinia, two days ago, and I had a go at him for smoking a cigarette when he had just come out of hospital. I was angry with him and didn't even say goodbye.

I shook my head in disgust at myself. Why didn't I just say goodbye to him? Why? His last memory of me was me telling him off. Fuck! Why did I do that? I felt bitter regret that was going to haunt me for the rest of my life.

And then I remembered another incident three weeks earlier, when Dad had come to my house to see George. I had been making George a bacon sandwich and I asked Dad if he wanted one too. He said no. "*En thelo, gori mou.*" ("No, my daughter"). I asked again if he was sure and he said, "Yes I'm sure."

So I made the sandwich for George and as he sat down to eat it and I was clearing up, Dad came into the kitchen and said: "OK, *game mou je menan*" ("Make me one, too.").

I went ballistic. "I asked you twice if you wanted one and you said no. Now I have to wash the pan just to make you one."

I went on and on at him as I cleaned the pan and banged the kitchen cupboards, huffing and puffing, just to make him feel bad. I slammed the sandwich down in front of him. He ate it without saying a word.

Why the fuck did I do that? So what if he had changed his mind and wanted a bacon sandwich? Why didn't I just make it for him saying, "No problem, Dad." Why did I have to shout my mouth off at him and make him feel bad? It was only a fucking bacon sandwich for God's sake! Poor Dad! Tears poured from my eyes and I had to walk away from the pitch.

I never forgave myself for those two things. However good I was to him, the amount of times I had helped him, sent him on holidays, paid for his car and his satellite dish, given him money, watched football with him, everything good I had ever done for him while he was alive did not matter, because all I could think about were those two moments when I told him off for the cigarette and the bacon sandwich. That was all that was important. I hated myself.

Eventually I wiped my eyes and walked back to the match. I watched as our boys were being kicked and pushed by the other team. The Italian boys were playing dirty and I could see our team starting to retaliate. The whistle kept blowing and the game was stopping and starting for fouls. The whistle was blown again and I saw George storm over to one Italian boy and push him to the floor. One of the other boys went for George and George pushed him and kicked him to the ground. This was so out of character for George. He was usually so cool.

The other boys all rushed over to pull them apart and they were both sent off by the referee.

George came storming off the pitch, swearing at the boys on the touchline and crying his eyes out. The Italians were pointing at him and laughing at him for being a cry baby. But George was never a cry baby. I went over to him but he shrugged me off and walked away. "Get off me!" I left him alone as he walked to a verge and sat down, his head on his knees, crying.

My heart bled for him. George wasn't crying because he had been sent off. He was crying for his *papou.* His death had finally sunk in.

I saw our manager walk over to his Italian counterpart. They spoke for a few moments and then the Italian looked at me as tears started pouring down my face again. He nodded at me as if acknowledging my pain. He then went over to his players on the touchline and said something to them. They suddenly stopped laughing and looked at me. Then something wonderful happened.

Two of the boys walked over to me and shook my hand. One said in broken English: "We are sorry." As the tears rolled down my cheeks, I thanked them and tried to smile.

Then they walked passed me towards George. One of them tapped him on the shoulder to make him look up. "Sorry about your *papou*." I swear I heard him say *papou.* Maybe it was the same word in Italian. George looked up and nodded at them as one of them reached out his hand and my heart filled with pride as George reached over and shook it. He was so dignified in such a moment of pain and I was so proud of him. Dad would have been very proud too – then I was able to smile.

The game was finally won by the Italians, but however dirty the players had been on the pitch, they were the exact opposite off it. They all shook hands and patted each other on the back, acknowledging each other's efforts with respect. George had got up and walked to the touchline and he was swamped by everyone who wanted to shake his hand. The match was over but the day was not.

The Italian manager came over to tell us that the team was going to take us to their village, where food had been prepared. All I wanted to do was get back to the hotel but now I had to get through the celebrations too.

The other parents were wonderful and helped me get though the day. They kept asking if I was OK and if there was anything they could do to help.

I could see George enjoying himself with his team mates and the Italians were joining in the banter, so I felt some comfort knowing that he was OK. Then I saw something that made me smile … and reminded me of Dad. Whenever we had been expecting guests to visit from afar, Dad would always get really excited and say: "*Na sfaxoumen don shiron*" ("Let's slaughter the pig"). It was one of his catchphrases.

And there, right in front of my eyes, was a suckling pig turning round and round on a spit, and at that moment an overwhelming feeling of happiness rushed through me.

I felt that he was standing close to me, giving me that toothless grin of his, excited at the sight of the roasting pig. To me, it seemed to symbolise him telling me to celebrate, and not to cry and somehow, gave me the strength to do that.

I had to endure a few more hours on the top of that mountain among music and laughter before I could leave for home.

George and I left Sardinia first thing in the morning.

CHAPTER 44

The Red Robin

My brother-in-law picked us up from the airport and took us straight to Mum's house.

Nothing could have prepared me for what I was about to encounter. As the front-door opened, I could hear the overwhelming sound of women crying. It was morbid and deafening and, as George walked along the corridor before me, I saw Mum coming towards him dressed in black, reaching out her arms for him.

"*To moro mou, to moro mou*" ("My baby, my baby"), she cried.

She grabbed him and hugged him, crying loudly as George tried to console her.

My sweet, darling sixteen-year-old son was comforting his grandmother. This was another proud moment for me.

We all walked into the lounge which was crammed with people all dressed in black. It was as if a black cloud had descended on the room. My sister, Mum, auntie Marika, Dad's sister from Cyprus, other aunts, Mum's friends, everywhere I looked there were tearful faces, bellowing and wailing, and all looking relieved to see me. I had to cover my ears. As everyone stood up to greet me, I was overwhelmed with the sadness in the room. I felt that they were all lost souls in need of comfort and I didn't know what to do or say to make things better. I felt a powerful sense of duty as the eldest child to say the right things: I had to say something.

"Don't cry. Dad would not have wanted this. Please stop crying."

The sobs became mere sniffles. Everyone tried to compose themselves and the room became almost silent and eerie. I looked around but could not see my brother. "Where's Vasili?"

Mum said that he was upstairs. I went upstairs and found him in Dad's bedroom, lying face down on the bed, crying.

"Vasili, it's me," I said as I put my arm around him, but he just cried louder.

"I want my dad. I want him back. He's my dad. He can't leave me. I want him back," Vasili cried.

He was distraught and I couldn't bear to hear him talking like that.

"Vasili, he wouldn't want you to cry. He is happy where he is. It was his time."

"No, it wasn't his time. He didn't want to die," he shouted angrily.

"I know, Vasili, but Dad was a broken man. You saw him recently. He could hardly walk and his heart couldn't take it anymore. Dad hated being like that. God spared him from further suffering. That's what Dad would have wanted. So get up, come down and celebrate his life. He would be so sad if he saw you like this."

"No, I don't want to go. I want to stay here." He broke down in tears again so I left him alone to mourn. The lounge was still very solemn. I could hear the occasional deep sigh but the room finally seemed to be at peace.

"Has anyone called an undertaker?" I quietly asked.

"No," said Mum behind her tear-stained tissue. She started to cry again and so did my sister and auntie Marika, which started everyone else off too. I couldn't bear the wails and walked out of the room. I phoned the undertaker and his voice at the end of the phone was the most, calming voice that I had ever heard. He quietly explained what had to be done. I had to be strong for Dad. Nobody else was in a fit state to do anything.

My brother was inconsolable and my sister was a zombie who couldn't speak from shock and Mum was just screaming. I had nobody to console me, no husband, no boyfriend, nobody and I knew that I had to do this all alone. I owed it to Dad.

It was Sunday so I had to wait until Monday to get the death certificate from the registrar and start the funeral arrangements. I wanted to go to the mortuary to see Dad and I asked if anyone wanted to go with me. Everyone shook their heads apart from George, and my brother-in-law offered to take us.

When the door to the chapel of rest was pushed open, I saw my Dad lying there on a bed covered with a white sheet up to his neck. He looked just the same as he always did with his red rosy cheeks and a beaming smile. I put my hand on his face, it felt cold and I bent down and kissed his forehead. I had not expected him to be smiling but it was unmistakeable. Even George said "*Papou* is smiling, Mum."

I knew that whatever had greeted him when he died, it had made him smile. And from that moment on I felt no sadness. I just felt at peace knowing that he was in a good place.

I visited him every day while he was in the mortuary and I spoke to him, believing that he could hear me. Not from the actual body on the bed, but I could feel his presence in the room. "Hello, Dad," I used to say as I brushed his hair away from his forehead. "How are you today?" His smile was there throughout the entire time. I tried to convince Vasili and Maria to visit him too, believing that they would find peace when they saw him smiling, but they were both disturbed at the thought. They wanted to remember him as he was.

I had to register the death and get the death certificate to release his body to the funeral parlour. I chose the best mahogany coffin, with a picture of the Last Supper engraved on the sides.

Finally, I had to go to the cemetery to pick the plot where he would be laid to rest. I had to make these difficult and heartbreaking decisions on my own as the rest of my family were in no fit state to participate in the arrangements.

The days leading upto the funeral were traumatic. Family came over from Cyprus and Mum's house was like Piccadilly Circus, with everyone coming to pay their respects, and the phone did not stop ringing.

Mum made herself busy by baking and mopping every day. She could not sit still. It was probably her way of coping.

Maria pulled me to the side and told me that Mum had been rude to Dad's sister from Cyprus and that I should have a word with Mum because she couldn't bear it any more. Then Vasili told me that he really hated Mum because she was not mourning Dad's death: "She is shouting at everyone and losing her temper and she stressing me out. I've had enough of her." he said.

I told him it was just her way of dealing with it, but in view of what Maria had said, I decided to have a word with Mum.

They followed me into the kitchen where Mum was frantically making coffees for her latest guests, who were sitting in the garden.

Mum was slowly losing her patience with everyone getting in her way. She was like a time bomb about to explode. I told her to calm down because she was stressing everyone else out. She suddenly threw the large Greek coffee pot into the sink, spilling the burning hot coffee all over the kitchen floor:

"*Thkaole!* (Get out of my house)," she bellowed at me. "I don't want you here. You are just like your father. I don't want you here, get out. You are not my daughter."

There was shocked silence in the room as she became even more hysterical and continued to swear at me at the top of her voice.

She had to be restrained by Uncle Nicholas otherwise she would have physically lashed out at me. He led her forcibly into the quietness of the empty lounge away from everyone.

Vasilis and Maria followed her as I waited in the kitchen, digesting what she had just said to me in front of all those people.

How dare she? I had had enough of her tantrums and rudeness and everyone pussy footing around her and I stormed into the lounge.

"How dare you shout at me? It's bad enough that I have had

to make all the arrangements by myself to save you lot from the hurt and the heartache, and you have the audacity to humiliate me in front of our guests, take out your frustration on *me* and tell me I am not your daughter? If it weren't for you, Dad would still be alive. It's your foul mouth and constant nagging that gave him the heart attack that killed him. Why don't you just shut the fuck up and stop stressing everyone out. Look at those two." I pointed at Vasili and Maria. "Look what you have done to them. Look at the state of them. They can't stand you at the moment either. Tell her Vasili."

I wanted him to tell her what he'd told me but he looked at me with his bulging bloodshot eyes and said "Don't have a go at Mum." He put a tissue to his mouth to try and muffle his sobs. I stared at him with daggers but he would not look at me.

So I turned to Maria. "Go on. You tell her what you told me earlier." Maria stared at the floor, tears pouring from her eyes. "I can't cope with all this," was all she managed to squeak.

I was frozen in my tracks. My brother and sister, these two spineless forty-something's had put me up to have a go at Mum because she was stressing them out and instead of backing me up, while I was fighting their corner, they just sat there like two pathetic children and took Mum's side, making me look like the bad guy.

I stared at all three of them, one by one, as they all carried on looking at the floor. I picked up my bag, turned around and walked straight out of the front door, slamming it shut.

I sat in my quiet, peaceful house all alone. This was the loneliest I had ever felt. Lonelier than that day in Cardiff when I was fourteen and nobody stuck up for me for wanting to be an actress and laughed at me instead. Lonelier than when Jack left me and nobody consoled me, instead they slagged me off for going out all the time and wearing short skirts. Now here I was again, the day before my Dad's funeral and after everything I had just gone through to sort out the arrangements, trying to be strong for everyone and getting no support, not even a thank you, I was once again the family punch-bag and scapegoat.

I sat and cried. I should have been crying for Dad, instead I was feeling sorry for myself and getting angry at my spineless family. My sixteen-year-old son had more gumption than all of them put together. But I was not going to allow them to ruin my Dad's day.

Four hours went by and nobody came to see if I was OK. I knew my brother and sister wouldn't have the guts to face me. Instead they sent my sister-in-law, Tracey, to bring the plates of food for the wake next day, which was to be in my house. She had been sent to test the water and check my mood before the others arrived.

I ignored everyone and went to my room while they brought all the food and drinks in. I had decided to give my Dad the send-off he deserved and didn't care about anybody except myself and my son.

The funeral went as well as could be expected. I kept my composure throughout and made sure that everything went to plan. I was in the first car with George, Maria, Vasili and Mum, but I didn't care that they were upset or crying. It was their problem.

I was not going to be the one to console them. They could console themselves in the way they knew best. I was celebrating Dad's life and if they didn't like it they could lump it as far as I was concerned.

Agios Demetrios Church in Edmonton was packed when we arrived. The first face I saw in the crowd was Charlie's. I got out of the car and stood alone, while the others were being consoled. I didn't care about their feelings and emotions. I was there for Dad. I had a job to do and was going to finish it by myself if that's what it took.

George stood up in front of a packed church and read a testimony to his *papou* that he had written himself and there was not a dry eye in the house. It was one of the proudest moments of my life. He was only sixteen and he was my hero yet again.

When it was over, I stood ceremoniously in line as all the congregation greeted us one by one to pass on their condolences once more. I did my bit and stood there until it was all over.

The sun was shining as Dad was buried in the plot I had chosen at Southgate Cemetery and among dozens of howling mourners I did not shed a single tear.

I smiled as a little red robin came and perched on top of a tombstone nearby. It caught my eye because it was flapping its wings just as I looked in its direction. It was Dad come to watch his own funeral. He had probably come along to check out who was there and it made me smile. I was sure that he would have loved the dark mahogany coffin with the Last Supper carved on the side – as it was the top of the range.

Maria threw into the grave a photo of all the grandchildren and Vasili threw in a pack of cards and a cigarette, while being held up by Mum. I chuckled as I remembered his words back at the house "Don't worry Mum, I will look after you". Who was he kidding? She ended up looking after him as usual.

One relative who I didn't know fainted and another wanted to throw herself into the grave. They were both whisked away from the graveside by the undertaker, who then started to eat the Halloumi and drink the Commandaria sherry that was laid out for the mourners.

The sun continued to shine as we had the wake in the garden. It was busy yet peaceful and Dad would have loved it. Food was in abundance and the sherry was going down a treat. Haris and Angel kept telling me how wonderful it was and that Dad would have been very proud. The robin, of course, was there and heard it all – it was my little secret. The sun was beginning to set and the last of the guests started to leave.

Mum and Maria helped me clear up but not much was said. Mum's outburst was swept under the carpet, like it always was, and I had to stomach it as usual, like I always did, because my family thought I was strong and could take anything. Little did they know that this would be the last time that I was going to be their punch-bag because my heart had finally turned to stone and they had helped to cause it.

CHAPTER 45

The Fix

I believe that everybody, at one time or another during their lifetime, has a crisis period which affects their lives forever. For me, that period was 2006.

I lost my Dad, my soul mate and one of my best friends all in that year and everything changed. I even lost Haris that year too. George had to see his father face-to-face for the first time when we went to Haris' funeral and I had expected some kind of moving reunion from Jack after all the years he hadn't seen his son. But apart from the occasional glance, he just ignored George, like he never existed, while he paraded the current female victim at the end of his arm. If I had not been at a funeral I would have punched him in the month. My heart bled for George that day, but his father's actions made George finally realise what a low life his father really was.

The events of 2006 made me reflect on my life and the people in it. I ruthlessly dropped all the hangers-on and users who I had accumulated over the years and who had drained my energy. People who I had helped and motivated, but who were never there for me when I needed them. They were there, instantly, during the good times but disappeared in a flash during the bad. One thing was for sure, if my trust and tolerance levels were low before, they were now worse than ever.

I became bitter and angry, an Iron Lady who didn't give a shit about anything or anyone anymore apart from me and George.

I told people what I thought of them to their face and didn't care whether I hurt them or not.

I confronted bullies and stopped loud-mouthed people in their tracks with my sharp tongue, while at the same time got angry with weak, pathetic people who frustrated me and brutally ridiculed their weaknesses. I no longer saw the good in people and became judgemental. I forced my opinions onto people and became verbally aggressive to anyone I felt was bullshitting or sat on the fence. I finished their sentences or rudely interrupted them and wouldn't let anyone get a word in edgeways. I particularly despised cheating spouses and loathed two-faced people and manipulative users or stirrers.

I would be enraged with passion if I thought there was an injustice going on and found myself arguing at shop checkouts, and shouted in waiting rooms over the slightest of things and even snapped at people just for phoning me.

My family and friends were on tenter hooks, all pussy footing around me in case I flipped my lid and this prissiness would annoy me too and made me lash out even more.

I developed daily migraines to the extent that I thought my head was going to explode. I was a bear with a sore head and the pain was killing me. I had become immune to all domestic painkillers and went to the doctor to prescribe me something stronger.

As soon as he asked me what was wrong, I broke down crying in front of him and couldn't stop. He tried to console me unsuccessfully and by the end of the session he said: "Miss Ross, I have diagnosed that you clearly have severe depression."

"Me? How can I have depression? That's ridiculous."

I was stunned into silence as he went through the symptoms of depression and I had every one of them. "You have two choices," he said, "I could either prescribe you with anti-depressants or refer you for psychiatric treatment." I guess that most people would have been mortified to hear the news that they would be referred for psychiatric treatment but I was delighted.

I registered myself at the Priory and was looking forward to peace and quiet and a well-earned rest in the country mansion set in twenty acres of beautiful parkland.

The psychiatrist who assessed me confirmed that I had severe depression but was in denial. "I'm not depressed," I said, "I'm just worn out and I want people to just leave me alone."

"Very well," she said, "I have booked you in for therapy classes three times a week starting Monday." I didn't notice until I went back to my car and looked in the mirror, that I had a large twig stuck in my hair. It must have been dislodged from the honeysuckle outside my front door when I left the house that morning. I burst out laughing and was surprised that the psychiatrist hadn't mentioned it to me. No wonder she thought it was severe!

My classes were chosen by my therapist and I had no say in the matter. My first class was Behavioural Activation and I didn't know what that meant.

The classroom was small with nine high-backed armchairs placed in a small circle and it overlooked the gardens. One by one, the chairs were all taken and I noticed that there was very little eye contact. Most of the people were looking down at the floor when the therapist walked in.

"Hello, everyone. I see that there are some new faces today. For the benefit of everyone, can we go round the room and introduce ourselves?"

I noticed that the woman opposite was wearing a pair of slippers and I could feel myself wanting to laugh. I was dreading having one of my laughing fits but managed to control myself.

I hadn't caught anybody's name as I was busy fighting back the laughter, wondering what the hell I was doing there.

"For the benefit of the newcomers," said the therapist, "can someone tell us what behavioural activation means, please?"

There was no answer.

"Anybody?" she asked, but there was still no answer.

Everyone was staring at the floor or out of the window. This was going to be a bundle of laughs I thought.

"OK," said the therapist. "Behavioural Activation is tackling any unhelpful behaviours that may be keeping your depression or anxiety going."

"I'm sorry, I don't understand," I said.

"What don't you understand?"

"What do you mean by 'unhelpful behaviours'?" I had only been there for five minutes and already I was interrogating the therapist.

"It will become clear in a while. If you want, I can come back to it later."

"Oh, Ok. Sorry," I said.

The therapist then said: "I am going to go round the room and ask those of you who were here last week, to tell the group what you did that was positive and how it helped you forget about your depression at that moment in time." She asked the guy sitting next to her to go first.

He was a short, middle-aged, bald man with glasses, wearing a thick woolly jumper with a scarf around his neck. It was the middle of summer and he must have been boiling.

"Well," he said in a very slow, squeaky voice "I managed to polish one wing of my car and I found that very therapeutic. I am going to build myself up to polish another part of the car this week."

I raised my eyebrows as I wondered whether he was having a laugh.

Hearing his pathetic voice, a grown man telling us that he was looking forward to finding the strength to polish his car, was making me angry.

I felt like slapping him round the face, shaking him hard and saying, "Pull yourself together, man!" but I restrained myself.

"Well done, Paul," said the therapist.

"Well done?" I thought. What was she talking about? She should have slapped him, not patted him on the back for polishing one wing of his car. She then moved on to the woman in the slippers.

"Well, I managed to telephone a friend," said the woman.

"And how did that make you feel?" asked the therapist.

"Good. It made me feel really good, actually."

I frowned as I listened to the conversation in disbelief. Had I heard correctly? This woman had made a phone call? And that means what exactly? I wasn't getting it. I made fifty calls a day sometimes. How is that relevant to depression? I just had to say something:

"Excuse me, but I just don't get it."

"What don't you get?" said the therapist.

"Any of it. I think I must be in the wrong class."

The therapist checked the register and said, "No. I have you down for this class Annie."

"Well, I'm sorry but I'm not at the same level as these people."

"What do you mean?"

"I make fifty phone calls a day and if I had to polish my car I would polish all of it in one go. I don't get it!"

"OK, Annie. You have to be a bit more patient and I think you will find that by the end of the session, it will all fall into place."

"OK, but at the moment I'm confused and I'm not getting it."

Everyone was now looking at me and as I looked at them, one by one, their eyes went back down to the floor. The therapist skipped a couple of people who were obviously new like me and came to the woman sitting next to me.

"Janet, what behaviour did you change or do which helped you take your mind off your depression?"

Janet spoke in a very low voice. I could hardly hear her even though I was sitting right next to her. "I played with the children!" she said "and I was so proud of myself, actually."

I was waiting for the rest.

"That's good news, Janet," said the therapist.

I couldn't for the life of me work out why that was so good. Don't people normally play with their children? Was I missing something here?

I must be in a room full of idiots I thought. I sat back in my chair but, instead of feeling relaxed, I was getting wound up.

I thought they were all pathetic. Surely they must have all been putting this zombie act on. Then I had an urge to start laughing again and spent the rest of the lesson biting my top lip to hide my grin.

At the end of the class the therapist asked me if I had understood the concept that behaviour like telephoning, cleaning, writing, eating and playing with children affect depression and anxiety, and these activities help people to get back on track.

"I guess I understand the concept, but I still don't think I am at the same level as these people. I can clean, write, make phone calls without any problem so I shouldn't be here. It's making me more depressed, in fact. I thought these classes are meant to stop anxiety, not build it up. Listening to these people is depressing. Me, watching you pat them on the back instead of kicking them up the backside is also depressing me. What are you trying to do? Keep them down and make them depressed?"

"OK," she said, sounding quite agitated. "Maybe you shouldn't be here. You might benefit more from an assertiveness class or anger management classes."

"Yes, I think I agree because this is not helping me. It's annoying me. No offence to anyone here but I don't have a problem with doing any of these things. What I need is peace and quiet."

My timetable was changed and I found myself in a class to build my self-esteem. Like I needed to build up my self-esteem!

I questioned why my psychiatrist had decided to put me in this class but perhaps she knew best, I thought. It became apparent to the therapist halfway through the first class that I should not be there, either.

I ended up by boosting everyone else's self-esteem by giving them all a good kick up the backside. I was telling them off for being so negative and feeling sorry for themselves.

The therapist asked me if I wanted to conduct the class and I didn't know if she was being serious or sarcastic.

I told her that nobody respected wimps or wishy-washy people. She asked me to respect other people's feelings and not to be so judgemental.

We ended up having an argument in front of the whole class.

"I get the impression that the people here are being drugged up to the hilt to keep their morale low just so that the Priory could make more money from their medical insurance."

She got angry with me and said: "You are ruining the class for everybody else." So I told her maybe she should attend Anger Management herself.

At this point she cut the session short and told everyone that she would see them next week. One of the patients just looked at me as if to say, now look what you've done.

I looked at her and said, "Most normal people would be happy to get an early lunch." But she gave me a dirty look.

"Oops," I thought to myself and grinned.

After lunch, I half expected to be called to the registration room to get a ticking off but nothing happened.

My next class was Assertiveness and I was actually looking forward to this one.

I started off quite calm until the therapist said "Shouting and losing your temper is not being assertive. Putting your point across calmly and constructively is being assertive." "Being a bully," she added, "is not being assertive."

"Well, I'm Greek so shouting and losing my temper is being assertive where I come from. Your rules should take into account cultural differences."

I persuaded the therapist to change the topic of discussion from, "assertiveness in the workplace" to "whether cultural differences affect assertiveness". I was proud that I had managed to get the subject of the day changed to suit me. "How's that for being assertive?" I asked her.

It became an interesting discussion between me and an Asian

guy against the rest of the class who were English. They had difficulty in understanding why the two of us were shouting passionately for the cause, while they were all calm and collected, proving my point that cultural differences did affect assertiveness.

It turned out to be very constructive for some patients because after the class finished, one girl came up to me and said "You remind me of my controlling father, and now understand that just because he shouts at me, it doesn't mean that he doesn't love me. I know now that maybe he just has a lot on his plate and needs time to relax."

Another lady came up to me and said "In the past I thought that my older brother was condescending and unreliable, but now I think that maybe I've been too demanding of him. I have to learn to do some things for myself and relieve my brother of some responsibilities."

Well, who would have thought it? Everyone was learning from my experiences and benefiting from me being in the Priory, apart from me. Who was going to help me? I was even used in the Anger Management class as an example of how *not* to react to provocation.

My group therapy continued for only a few more weeks until the psychiatrist finally admitted that it was not doing me any good.

"I told you that from the start." I said...

"Suffice it to say, my therapist, my doctor or my psychiatrist never did get to the bottom of my psyche. My psychiatrist reported that I had an unusual form of anxiety which required only specialist counselling and so here I am with you Dr Michael," said Annie.

"Wow. I see. That's one hell of a story Annie. No wonder you ended up here. I'm surprised you didn't end up here sooner."

"That's all well and good but you promised me, when I first came to you, that you would fix me. I went back to my roots like you asked me to, and have described to you, in detail, all my experiences, and told you about the many people that have come and gone in my life but, I still don't know who I am."

"But Annie. Don't you see? You don't need fixing. You are already fixed," said Doctor Michael

"How can I be fixed? I'm all screwed up. I've always lived a double life – a Greek one at home and an English one in public. I'm bitter and angry at being an Anglo Cypriot girl and not fitting in to this world that I'm in."

"You just can't see it can you? For an intelligent woman I am surprised you haven't clocked on sooner?

"What do you mean?"

"Annie, everything that happens, always happens for a reason and the people that come into your life always have a purpose. You just haven't realised the significance of what has happened to you that's all. So let me enlighten you: you were born to poor immigrant parents so that you can appreciate possessions, the value of money and other people's cultures. Laurie made you wise and cultured. Meeting Jack gave you belief that you are equal to others irrespective of their wealth and status, and breaking up with him showed you that pain will always be overcome with time. Angel gave you dignity and class, and Kiri and Tina gave you liberation. It was here that you truly began to live. As much as you thought she hindered you, your mother actually kept you grounded and gave you stability. Mario made you wise-up to men, and Sheila and Frosso made you wary of friends. Thekla broadened your horizons and meeting the rock star and the sheik gave you faith and taught you to never to look a gift horse in the mouth. Charlie showed you how true love should really feel and breaking up with him gave you your biggest asset, strength. Acropolis, as you already figured, gave you confidence and self belief. George has made you whole and, in death, your father has given you peace."

"Gosh, I suppose I never looked at it that way before" said Annie. "So you see Annie, you are not screwed up at all, you are complete in fact. You have been blessed with all the tools of life, you just didn't notice them, that's all. This may be your calling. God has made you experience every emotion in life so that you can counsel people who are not as emotionally fortunate as you."

"Hmm, okay, well there might be some element of truth in what you say, Doctor," said Annie, "but the way I see it, is that I was that Cypriot girl alone at the window, all those years ago, and all these years later, irrespective of who has come and gone in my life and the experiences that I have gained, I am still that same lone girl. Nothing has changed. So I have to disagree with you and stand by what I said earlier: I am Greek and I am built that way and there is not a damn thing I can do about it!"

"Trust you to disagree with the Doctor. I suppose it wouldn't be you if you didn't argue, it's in your nature," said Doctor Michael.

"There you see? That's my point exactly. It's because I'm Greek. I keep telling you."

"Anyway, before we end up in an argument again," said Doctor Michael, "I think this is a convenient place to stop, don't you think? Let's leave it there for today. In our next session I want you to tell me all about your sexual encounters and experiences which, I noticed, you cleverly left out this time."

"Mmm, that should be interesting," said Annie.

As Annie got into her car to leave, her phone rang:

"Anna, I'm locked out. Come and let me in."

"For fuck's sake, Mum, not again!"